LOGIC:
A COMPUTER APPROACH

LOGIC:
A COMPUTER APPROACH

Morton L. Schagrin
*State University of New York
at Fredonia*

William J. Rapaport
*State University of New York
at Buffalo*

Randall R. Dipert
*State University of New York
at Fredonia*

McGraw-Hill Book Company
*New York   St. Louis   San Francisco   Auckland
Bogotá   Hamburg   Johannesburg   London   Madrid
Mexico   Montreal   New Delhi   Panama   Paris
São Paulo   Singapore   Sydney   Tokyo   Toronto*

LOGIC: A COMPUTER APPROACH

1 2 3 4 5 6 7 8 9 0 DOCDOC 8 9 8 7 6 5

ISBN 0-07-055131-6

This book was set in Helvetica
by J. M. Post Graphics, Corp.
The editors were Emily G. Barrosse
and James R. Belser; the designer was Robin Hessel;
the production supervisor was Charles Hess.
The drawings were done
by Volt Information Sciences, Inc.
The cover was designed by Eric Elias;
cover art by David Channon;
R. R. Donnelley & Sons Company was printer and binder.

Library of Congress Cataloging in Publication Data

Schagrin, Morton L.
Logic : a computer approach.

Bibliography: p.
Includes index.
1. Logic—Data processing.   2. Algorithms.
3. Electronic digital computers—Programming.
I. Rapaport, William J.   II. Dipert, Randall R.
III. Title.
BC138.S32   1985   160'.28'54   84-19430
ISBN 0-07-055131-6

CONTENTS

To the Student   **xiii**

To the Teacher   **xv**

Chapter 1
The Nature of Logic   **1**

Deductive Logic   2
Arguments   3
     Premise and Conclusion Indicators   4
     Validity and Soundness   6
Truth Values   7
Summary   9
Exercises   10

Chapter 2
Logic, Computers, and Algorithms   **13**

Mechanical Reasoning   14
Computers and Reasoning   16
How Computers Work   17
     Computer Languages   18
     Machine Languages   19
     Higher-Level Computer Languages   19
Algorithms   20
     Mechanical Procedures   21
Flowcharts   22
A Program Design Language   27

CONTENTS

Operation Statements	28
Control Statements	29
Summary	32
Exercises	33

Chapter 3
Sentential Logic:
The Connectives 'Not', 'And', and 'Or'   **37**

Negation	38
The Truth Function FNEG	40
Truth Tables and Algorithms for FNEG	42
Double Negation	43
Atomic and Molecular Sentences	45
Conjunction	45
The Truth Function FCNJ	47
Disjunction	52
The Truth Function FDSJ	53
Inclusive and Exclusive Disjunction	55
Sentences with Multiple Connectives	56
Other Connectives	57
Summary	58
Exercises	59
Suggestions for Computer Implementation	64

Chapter 4
Sentential Logic:
The Connective 'If . . . Then . . .'
and Additional Connectives   **67**

The Conditional	68
The Truth Function FCND	70
Symbolizing Conditionals	72
Only if	74
Necessary and Sufficient Conditions	75
The Biconditional	76
Exclusive Disjunction	77
Unless	79
NOR	81
NAND	82
The Two-Place Truth-Functional Connectives	82
Summary	83
Exercises	83

CONTENTS

**Chapter 5
Sentential Logic:
Algorithms for Calculating Truth Values
and Determining Well-Formedness**   **87**

An Informal Method for Calculating Truth Values   88
    Observations about the Informal Method   89
    Innermost Subformulas   90
The Algorithm: TRUTH-VALUE CALCULATOR   91
    Refining Step 5(d): Finding the Innermost Subformulas   92
    Refining Step 5(e): Replacing Innermost Subformulas with Truth Values   93
Formulas and Sentences   95
    An Algorithm for Determining Well-Formedness   96
Summary   98
Exercises   98
Suggestions for Computer Implementation   101

**Chapter 6
Sentential Logic:
Algorithms for Truth Tables
and Determining Validity**   **105**

General Truth Tables   107
The Algorithm: TRUTH-TABLE GENERATOR   108
Determining Validity   109
The Algorithm: VALIDITY/INVALIDITY DETERMINER   112
Alternative Methods   113
WANG'S ALGORITHM   114
Summary   125
Exercises   125
Suggestions for Computer Implementation   129

**Chapter 7
Sentential Logic:
Logical Equivalence, Normal Forms,
and Polish Notation**   **133**

Tautologies and Arguments   134
    Arguments and Corresponding Conditionals   135
Logical Equivalence   136
Normal Forms   138
Consistency and Satisfiability   141
Polish Notation   144

CONTENTS

Summary	147
Exercises	148

Chapter 8
Sentential Logic:
A Natural Deduction System — **153**

A Simple Formal System: The Game of Stars and Slashes	154
Formal Systems	157
A Natural Deduction System	157
Conjunction Introduction	158
The Format of a Derivation	160
Conjunction Elimination	161
Demonstrating the Validity of an Argument with a Derivation	163
Subproofs and Negation Introduction	165
Subproofs	166
Negation Introduction	167
SEND and RETURN	168
Using Subproofs	169
Using ~INTRO	170
Negation Elimination	171
Comment Lines in a Derivation	172
Completeness	175
Summary	176
Exercises	176

Chapter 9
Sentential Logic:
Additional Rules of Inference — **179**

Conditional Introduction and Elimination	180
Disjunction Introduction and Elimination	185
Truth Preservation	189
Biconditional Introduction and Elimination	189
Rules of Replacement	191
Modus Tollens	196
Summary	198
Exercises	198

CONTENTS

Chapter 10
Sentential Logic:
An Algorithm for Checking Proofs   **203**

Lines of a Proof   204
The Algorithm: Proof-Checker   205
    The Procedure CHECK-LINE-STRUCTURE   206
    The Procedure CHECK-SENTENCE-STRUCTURE   208
    The Procedure CHECK-RULE   208
    The Procedure CHECK-SUBPROOF   213
Applications and Modifications of Proof-Checker   216
Summary   219
Exercises   219
Suggestions for Computer Implementation   220

Chapter 11
Sentential Logic:
A Method for Producing Proofs   **223**

General Strategies for Constructing Proofs   224
    Analogous Problems   224
    Forward-Looking and Backward-Looking Strategies   226
Tree-Searching Strategies   229
The Method: PROOF-GIVER   232
Applications of PROOF-GIVER   237
Limitations of PROOF-GIVER   240
Summary   245
Exercises   245
Suggestions for Computer Implementation   246

Chapter 12
Predicate Logic:
Quantification   **251**

Individuals and Properties   252
    Individual Constants   252
    Variables   253
Quantifiers   254
    Well-Formed Formulas   255
    Scope   255
    Free and Bound Variables   256
    An Algorithm for Sentences   256
Truth Values of Quantified Sentences   258

Quantifying Molecular Formulas   258
    Existential Quantifiers   259
    Universal Quantifiers   260

Dossiers and Models   263
    Representative Individuals   263
    Models   264
    Determining whether a Sentence Is TRUE in a Model   266
    Limitations of Models   270

Relations   270

Symbolizing   273

Summary   276

Exercises   277

Suggestions for Computer Implementation   279

Chapter 13
Predicate Logic:
Quantifier Inference Rules   **281**

Universal Quantifier Rules   282
    Universal Elimination   283
    Universal Introduction   284

Existential Quantifier Rules   286
    Existential Introduction   286
    Existential Elimination   287

Some Examples   289

Quantifier Negation Rule   290

Invalid Arguments   295

Summary   296

Exercises   297

Chapter 14
Predicate Logic:
Determining Validity and Proving Theorems   **301**

Decidability   302

Models   302

Church's Thesis   304

Mechanical Theorem Proving   305
    Resolution   306
    The Proof Method   310

Summary   311

CONTENTS

Appendix A
Applications of Sentential Logic
to Circuit Design and Arithmetic   313

Electric Circuits   314
Logic Gates   315
Combining Logic Gates   318
Translating between Logic and Circuits   320
Simplifying Circuits   321
Circuits for Adding   323

Appendix B
Turing Machines   327

Turing's Analysis of Computation   328
Turing Machines   330
Turing-Machine Programs   331
    Negation   331
    Conjunction   333
    Palindromes   334
Church's Thesis   338

Bibliography   341
Index   343

TO THE STUDENT

Learning by Learning to Explain

One of the best tests of whether you really know something is whether you can explain it clearly to someone else. In other words, one of the best ways to learn is by learning to explain. Of course, relatively few of us ever have the chance to put this into practice.

However, with the introduction of small, relatively inexpensive personal and home computers, almost anyone can now have a "student" on whom to practice "explaining" how to do certain things. Computers are ideal students for learning how to do certain things—at least, things that deal with the manipulation of symbols. They don't tolerate unclarities or contradictions, they have enormous and highly accurate memories, and they are patient. They don't ever embarrass or make fun of their "teacher," and—unlike cases in the real world of education—it is no great tragedy if they fail to "learn" to do what we hoped to teach them.

The one disadvantage of present-day computers as "students" is that they are not as flexible as human students would be in understanding what we say to them. The "explanation" must be given as a *program*: a sequence of instructions written in a highly precise computer programming language (such as BASIC or Pascal).

The teaching of symbolic logic is ideally suited for the use of computers as "experimental students." This is so because all the elementary principles of logic (such as truth functions and ways of showing the validity and invalidity of arguments) and even many of its more advanced techniques (such as strategies for proving theorems) are admirably suited for the use of a computer. The learning of these techniques involves learning to handle information and symbols in certain ways—exactly what computers are best at doing.

Using Computers When Reading This Text

Since you, the reader of this text, are to play an *active* role in a real or imaginary interaction with an ideal student (the computer), you must learn something about how computers, xiii these ideal students, "think." Understanding how to "talk" to computers is a topic that is explicitly discussed in Chapter 2 and is dealt with in numerous examples.

The chief tool in understanding how to "talk" to computers is what we call a "program design language." This is not an actual computer language; rather, it is a language that has many features in common with actual computer languages (such as BASIC and Pascal) and that has some features which promote clear thinking about instructions to be given to computers. Any instructions written in our program design language could easily be translated into an actual computer language. It is a "program design" language in the sense that we can use it to give a *sketch* of what the actual program would eventually look like.

Thus if a computer is available—a large one, or even a very small one—and if you know a real computer programming language, you will be able to *apply* the instructions we state in our program design language. All that has to be done is to translate the instructions into whatever actual instructions your computer will accept.

Actually running programs on a computer would make reading this text fun and would probably also make you more aware of some of the finer points in the theory of logic and the applications of these principles. *But using a computer is by no means necessary for understanding the content of this book—or even for having fun with it.* Thus if you do not have a computer to use, you need not feel left out. One very easy way to test some instructions, to see if they work, is to pretend that *you* (or a friend) are the computer and then do exactly what your instructions say to do.

What You Will Know about Computers after Reading This Text

If you complete this text, you will know a great deal about computers and their applications. Even if you consider yourself an "expert" on computers, you will find a new field for the application of what you know: the field of symbolic logic. For the novice who knows little or nothing about computers or logic, the text is self-sufficient. You should be able to learn all you need to know about computers for completing this book by carefully reading Chapter 2 and by thinking about what has been said. *Actively thinking* is part of *reading with understanding* that is often underestimated. To stimulate thinking, it is strongly recommended that you try one or more of the exercises at the end of each chapter.

Of course, if you know nothing about computers when you begin reading this text and you understand every sentence and example in it, you still will not be fully prepared to walk up to any computer and begin operating it. But we venture to say that you will find it much easier to do so after having completed this book. You will also find it easier to understand the basic principles behind any programming language. And, most important, you will have a sound knowledge of one of the key ideas of computer science: the idea of an *algorithm*—crystal-clear instructions for explaining how to do something.

Morton L. Schagrin
William J. Rapaport
Randall R. Dipert

TO THE TEACHER

This text uses concepts from computer science to cover all the traditional topics in an introductory deductive logic course: the nature of logic, sentential logic, truth tables, natural deduction, and predicate logic. Although there are many fine introductory logic texts, none of them approaches the study of logic from a point of view arising out of the insights of computer science, nor do any texts easily relate to the widespread availability of computers. The use of this text should not present any difficulties for an instructor familiar with any of the usual introductory textbooks in symbolic logic. Nevertheless, several remarks are in order.

Some of the more powerful techniques introduced in a traditional logic course, such as constructing truth tables, are, in fact, rather tedious procedures to carry out. They require many steps, usually use a lot of time and paper, and are very sensitive to small, easy-to-make errors. Many teachers of logic have probably wished to be able to teach and test the basic *principles* behind such methods rather than their time-consuming implementations. But teaching, learning, and testing in traditional logic courses have often centered on the details of *applying* such methods because, among other things, of the lack of a suitable framework for talking about exactly what one is doing when, say, one constructs a truth table.

Computers, and the increasing sensitivity to specifying how information and symbols are manipulated by them, provide an escape from this dilemma and an opportunity to return to *principles* of logic. We can let the computer do the "dirty work" while we concentrate our attention on grasping the major ideas and learning how to "explain" these ideas to a computer in such a way that *it* can apply them. All that is necessary is to have some understanding of how computers work and how to "explain" to them what to do. (These topics are addressed in Chapter 2.)

The use of computers proposed in this book is thus quite different from many educational uses to which computers have recently been put, e.g., in learning foreign languages or even in learning logic. In these applications, computers are used like electronic flash cards or like "programmed" texts—guiding us through the subject matter, tutoring us along the way, gently correcting our mistakes, and giving us useful information at appropriate times.

TO THE TEACHER

In these traditional uses of computers in education, the computer has the "active" role: *It* "explains" something to *us*. In the way we use computers and computer-inspired methods in this book, *we* "explain" to the *computer* what is to be done. It is, thus, the student who has the active role in the learning process, not the computer. (This is discussed at greater length in "To the Student.")

For these reasons among others, the central computer science notion stressed throughout the text is that of an *algorithm:* the means by which "explanations" are given to the computer. While we do not cover every possible topic of interest in logic, we do cover those that lend themselves to the algorithmic approach. Many students in computer science have difficulty with this concept; here, it can be learned within the context of a logic course. Thus while our main purpose in writing the book is to teach *logic,* we also address some of the problems and issues of *computer literacy,* and so, in addition to its intended use in introductory logic courses in philosophy or mathematics, the text is also especially appropriate for a logic course that serves as a prerequisite for entry into a computer science program, or as a supplementary text in computer science courses.

The algorithms in the text *can* be programmed on a small home computer (we have done so in BASIC on a VIC-20); yet access to a computer is *not* required. Furthermore, the algorithms in the text are not necessarily the most elegant that can be constructed. Our intention was to present easily understandable algorithms, not necessarily clever ones. We hope that readers will be motivated to construct simpler and faster algorithms, for this can be done only if the reader understands the logical issues that we are trying to teach.

Chapter 1 is an introduction to the nature of logic and to the notions of argument, validity, and soundness, employing some of the techniques of informal logic.

Chapter 2 contains a discussion of the nature and history of computers and the impact of logic on their development. It presents the notion of an algorithm and the top-down design–stepwise refinement method of constructing one, as well as a "program design language" that does not require the reader to know any specific programming language. The language of flowcharts is also introduced.

Chapters 3 and 4 present algorithms for computing the truth functions for negation, conjunction, disjunction, material conditional, biconditional, exclusive disjunction, NOR, and NAND. The treatment of sentential connectives and their associated truth functions gives more explicit attention to the *functional* nature of these connectives than is customary in other introductory logic texts, thus broaching the relationship between (recursive) functions and algorithms. Our rules of formation do not allow the dropping of outer parentheses. E.g., a conjunction will always be expressed as (A & B) and never as A & B. The reason for this is that certain later algorithms—such as the one for determining whether a formula is well-formed—would be considerably more complicated if outer parentheses could be dropped.

Chapter 5 contains an algorithm, TRUTH-VALUE CALCULATOR, for computing the truth values of molecular sentences and an algorithm for determining the well-formedness of a sentence.

Chapter 6 contains an algorithm, TRUTH-TABLE GENERATOR, that "nests" TRUTH-VALUE CALCULATOR in a count-loop in order to generate truth tables. The use of truth tables is quite standard, although it is unusual to clearly state an algorithm for generating them. The chapter also contains an algorithm, VALIDITY/INVALIDITY DETERMINER, that uses the output of TRUTH-TABLE GENERATOR to determine the validity or invalidity of arguments in sentential logic. (Although each algorithm should be followed precisely, in the cases where one algorithm uses a previously introduced one as a "subroutine," the instructor can relax the requirement that the details of the subalgorithm be followed to the letter.) Most introductory logic textbooks usually include a "shorter truth-table method" by which an argument is shown to be valid or invalid without the need for the full truth table. Quite often, however, certain strategies and tricks are needed to employ the shortened methods with any success. We replace these usually incomplete methods with a version of WANG'S ALGORITHM, which is not only extremely clever but also useful in introducing the computer-science idea of a "stack." As part of this algorithm, there is also a "subroutine" for identifying the main connective of a sentence.

Chapter 7 presents algorithms for transforming a sentence into conjunctive normal form and into Polish notation, as well as discussions of tautologies, logical equivalence, arguments and corresponding conditional sentences, consistency, and satisfiability.

Chapters 8 and 9 present a new natural deduction system for sentential logic, one that relies on the similarities between, on the one hand, proofs and subproofs in logic and, on the other, programs and subprograms in computer science (including parameter passing and the scope of global and local variables). It should be noted that no prior knowledge of the computer science notions is needed to use or to understand the natural deduction system. Rather, it is our hope that a familiarity with the deduction system will make the computer science concepts clearer.

In Chapters 8 and 9, and in other places where we manipulate sentences as strings, we always use single quotes. Elsewhere, sentence letters alone and (single) quoted molecular formulas denote sentences.

The astute reader will notice that we go to extraordinary lengths in Chapters 8 and 9, and again in Chapters 12 and 13, to control the information that may flow into and out of a subproof. These considerations arise in the context of our SEND and RETURN rules. To some, these measures might seem to lengthen derivations and to involve us in unnecessary complications. However, we believe that these techniques are, in fact, very well-justified. One reason for them is given in the text: They closely parallel the proper use of global and local variables in elegant computer programs.

Another reason has a far more secure foundation in logical theory. The extension of a natural deduction system to deal with certain issues in modal logic, and with issues of relevance and entailment, requires exactly this degree of care with information flowing into and out of subproofs. The lack of care with which most natural deduction systems deal with this information makes their users insensitive to these issues, and renders the systems themselves incapable of being easily modified to deal with anything but the most well-trod paths in the philosophy of logic (namely, "standard" logics). Although we shall not extend our system in these directions, we wish to have a system that is, in principle, capable of being so extended.

One of the first logicians to promote the use of natural deduction systems that carefully (and with full consciousness, import information into subproofs and export it out) was Frederic Fitch in his 1952 *Symbolic Logic*. It is his pioneering efforts that we follow. Sound logical practice thus mirrors—and predates—sound programming practice.

Chapters 10 and 11 present two of the most significant features of the text: the algorithm PROOF-CHECKER and the mechanical procedure PROOF-GIVER. The former enables a student to check a proof in the text's natural deduction system for validity; the latter helps the student construct proofs in the text's system. Thus one of the hardest

TO THE TEACHER

topics for a student to learn in an introductory logic course is covered by purely mechanical methods.

Chapters 12 and 13 cover the syntax and semantics of predicate logic and extend the natural deduction system to cover the universal and existential quantifiers.

Chapter 14 discusses the limitations on the algorithmic approach to predicate logic in the context of Church's theorem and Church's thesis, and it discusses mechanical methods of theorem proving. It presents an algorithm for using resolution (another technique for determining validity, much used in computer science) and extends PROOF-GIVER to predicate logic.

Appendix A covers the application of sentential logic to circuits and computer arithmetic, and Appendix B covers Turing machines.

Exercises at the ends of the chapters test the students' comprehension of the basic material, as well as extend the material. There are frequent suggestions for computer implementation of the algorithms; these can be used by instructors who wish to emphasize the computational aspects of logic or by students with access to hardware who are interested in doing independent work.

Most of the material can be covered in a one-semester course. A typical course might consist of Chapters 1 through 12, with selections from Chapters 13 and 14 as time or preferences permit. Chapters 1 and 2 can be covered in the reverse order, or both could be covered together. In Chapter 6, WANG'S ALGORITHM is optional. Instead of covering all of Chapter 7, an instructor might prefer to use selections from among its topics; this can be done easily, since most of the sections are independent of each other. Chapter 8 contains a complete natural deduction system for sentential logic using only negation and conjunction. Thus Chapter 9, while strongly recommended, could be omitted in view of the completeness of the system in Chapter 8. Chapters 10 and 11 can be covered in any order, and it is quite possible to introduce the algorithms in these chapters during the presentation of the material in Chapters 8 and 9. The appendixes are independent of each other; Appendix A could be covered following Chapter 4, while Appendix B could be covered following Chapter 2 or Chapter 14.

We are grateful to Dawn Beke, who encouraged us to begin; to Kaye Pace, Anne Murphy, and Jim Dodd, who encouraged us to continue; to Leslie Burkholder (Carnegie-Mellon University), who class-tested an earlier version and made many useful suggestions; to our reviewers, who caught several major errors and made many valuable comments. We also want to acknowledge our debts to our teachers of logic and computer science at the University of Michigan, Chicago, Rochester, California at Berkeley, at Indiana University, and the State University of New York at Buffalo. Finally, many thanks to our students (who gleefully caught typos) for their excitement (and surprise) at seeing connections between logic and computers.

Most texts, like most computer programs, have undetected bugs. We urge readers who find them, or who have any suggestions for improvement, to contact us.

Morton L. Schagrin
William J. Rapaport
Randall R. Dipert

CHAPTER 1

THE NATURE OF LOGIC

Logic, in its broadest sense, is the study of correct reasoning. It produces and examines methods for identifying good reasoning, as well as bad reasoning, in all places: in our own thought, in the writings of others, and in the conversations of our friends. Logic provides rules for determining how we *should* move from one belief to another. Seen in this way, logic gives us the standards for determining which beliefs are acceptable on the basis of other beliefs. Logic is thus sometimes described as the study of the "laws of thought." This is true if by it we mean a study of the laws of correct thought or reasoning. Logic is a study not of how people do reason but of an ideal way of reasoning.

To produce the standards of "correct reasoning" in all fields—everyday life, psychology, history, physics, and mathematics—would obviously be a very tall order. In different areas, and in different circumstances, there are varying standards of "correct reasoning." In mathematics, we often have very rigid rules for what counts as a correct calculation, proof, or demonstration. But determining whether to take our umbrella with us, on the basis of present weather conditions and current predictions, is necessarily a far less rigid procedure. Here, it might be acceptable to reason: "It is overcast, and the clouds are dark; therefore, it will rain, and I should take my umbrella."

Consider this sentence:

1. Some apples are red.

From this sentence, and the knowledge that (2) All apples are fruit, we might correctly reason:

3. Some fruit is red.

It would be erroneous, however, to conclude that:

4. All fruit is red.

To infer (3) from (1) and (2) is always correct reasoning—as we shall see—while to infer (4) from (1) and (2) is not.

Deductive Logic

There is a core of reasoning that is accepted by all sciences and disciplines under all circumstances. This core is given the name *deductive logic*. In deductive logic, we are interested in studying reasoning that *never* strays from true beliefs to false ones.

If a piece of reasoning is acceptable according to the standards of deductive logic, then we can be sure that it is correct reasoning in all circumstances. On the other hand, if this reasoning does not come up to the standards of deductive logic, we cannot automatically dismiss it as bad reasoning. Such nondeductive reasoning might be acceptable in some sciences or under some circumstances.

Deductive logic—the standards of reasoning acceptable to all disciplines in all circumstances—forms the topic of this book. As we shall explore in later chapters, the study of deductive logic has extensive connections with computers and with methods used in computer science. For example, elements of deductive logic are extensively used in the programming of computers, and computers can easily be used to solve problems in deductive logic.

If there is any discipline that has historically used only deductive logic as a standard of correct reasoning, with no extensions or additions, it is mathematics. In other words, the standards of reasoning aimed for in mathematics closely resemble the standards of deductive logic. This is not to say that mathematics is "the same as" deductive logic: Logic is the study of how to identify correct reasoning, whereas mathematics rarely studies the methods it uses, and it is often more concerned with the products of mathematical reasoning.

The development of modern logic owes much to the various attempts to make mathematics rigorous. But what constitutes "rigor"? The history of modern attempts to characterize rigor can be traced to such seventeenth-century Rationalist philosophers as Descartes and Leibniz, who championed the notion of reasoning as a step-by-step process, with all the steps being made explicit, none being hidden:

THE NATURE OF LOGIC

We shall comply with it [the method for finding out the truth] exactly if we reduce involved and obscure propositions step by step to those that are simpler, and then starting with the intuitive apprehension of all those that are absolutely simple, attempt to ascend to the knowledge of all others by precisely similar steps. [Descartes, *Rules for the Direction of the Mind,* Rule V (1628).]

Such a method was what mathematicians studying the foundations of their discipline required; since logic was precisely the study of such steps, logic and mathematics have become almost inseparable (in theory if not in practice).

Arguments

A notion fundamental to logic is that of an "argument"—not in the sense of fights or quarrels, but in the sense in which people speak of a lawyer "arguing" a case. Typically, a lawyer might try to convince a judge or jury that, say, the defendant is not guilty. The way the lawyer does this is by presenting evidence to support the claim of innocence, i.e., reasons why the judge or jury should believe in the defendant's innocence. Note carefully that we have distinguished between persuasion by reasons and persuasion by any means whatever. Some successful persuasion might take the form of jokes, emotional appeals, an appealing turn of phrase, or a friendly face. This more general form of persuasion is usually given the name *rhetoric*. Logic considers more narrow forms of persuasion—forms which would appeal only to an ideal rational person (or to a sophisticated computer). These forms include what we describe as reasons, evidence, and argument—and not smiles, jokes, or emotional appeals. Abstracting from a particular case, we can define an *argument* as a set of sentences, some of which are identified as reasons for one of the others.

For example, a lawyer might try to convince the jury that the defendant could not have committed a murder in New York on the night of January 29, because the defendant was in Los Angeles from the 27th through the 31st. The lawyer could cite as evidence the testimony of two highly reputable witnesses who were with the defendant the entire time. The lawyer's case might consist of the following sentences:

1. Witness A was with the defendant in Los Angeles from January 27 through January 30.
2. Witness B was with the defendant in Los Angeles from January 28 through January 31.
   Therefore,
3. The defendant was in Los Angeles from January 27 through January 31.
   Therefore,
4. The defendant was not in New York on January 29—the night of the murder.

In this example, sentences (1) to (3) are offered as reasons for believing sentence (4).

Actually, the lawyer's case consists of two distinct arguments: Sentences (1) and (2) are offered as reasons for sentence (3), and sentence (3) is offered as a reason for sentence (4). In each argument, there is a set of sentences, some of which are reasons for the remaining one. That remaining sentence is the claim that is being argued for; it is called the *conclusion* of the argument. (Do not confuse the conclusion of an argument with the conclusion of an essay; the latter is typically only a summary of what has been said in the main body of the essay.) Each of the reasons or bits of evidence for the conclusion is called a *premise.*

Often, a number of premises are unstated. Sometimes they are so obvious that they need not be stated (for example, the lawyer's case did not state that Los Angeles is so far from New York that it would have been impossible for the defendant to have gotten there and back without the disappearance being discovered by the witnesses). When evaluating an argument, it is sometimes important to include all the unstated premises. In some cases, these missing premises might not be obvious (for example, suppose a foreign lawyer ignorant of U.S. geography were reading about our case), or they might even be false (the lawyer might be trying to mislead the jury). None of the examples in this book will have missing premises.

Premise and Conclusion Indicators

The very first step in evaluating an argument is to identify the conclusion and find all the premises. To identify the premises and conclusion, it often helps to look for certain key words that indicate whether a sentence is a premise or a conclusion.

Premise indicators. The sentence following each one of these expressions is usually a premise:

> For
> Since
> Because
> In view of the fact that
> As is shown by the fact that
> Assuming that
> Granted that
> Given the fact that
> The reason is that
> Is implied by
> Is entailed by
> Follows from the fact that

Conclusion Indicators. The sentence following each one of these expressions is usually a conclusion:

> Therefore
> Thus

Hence
So
Then
Consequently
Accordingly
That's why
It follows that
Which implies that
This entails that
This proves that
Which means that
From which we can deduce that
As a result, we may infer that

Using these indicators as evidence of a sentence's being a premise or a conclusion, we can now apply them to an actual argument. Consider the following argument, in ordinary English:

The reduction of the level of inflation can apparently be accomplished only by temporarily increasing the amount of unemployment. So, all possible options will be unpopular—since both inflation and unemployment are unpopular.

In this argument, we can detect one conclusion indicator, 'so', and one premise indicator, 'since'. The conclusion of this argument appears to be:

All possible options will be unpopular.

One of the premises is:

Both inflation and unemployment are unpopular.

The other premise—which does not contain a premise indicator—is the first sentence; it is fairly obviously given as evidence for the conclusion.

The natural way to test these guesses (since our indicators only provide us with good first attempts) is to rewrite the argument in very clear premise-conclusion form. If the result seems to preserve the "intent" of the original argument, it is probably a correct analysis of the premises and conclusion. For example:

1. Reducing the level of inflation increases the amount of unemployment.
2. Both inflation and unemployment are unpopular.
   Therefore,
3. All possible options are unpopular.

This does seem to be a correct reconstruction of the intent of the original argument.

CHAPTER 1

Validity and Soundness

Suppose we have an argument. How do we know if it's a *good* argument? Should we believe the conclusion if we believe the premises? In other words, are the premises good reasons for the conclusion?

One important test of a good argument is to determine whether the premises are true. False premises do not provide us with good reasons for accepting a conclusion. Often, however, it is difficult to know whether the premises are true or false. Yet regardless of whether the premises are true or false, there is another test that can always be performed: In deductive reasoning, the conclusion must *necessarily follow* from the premises. That is, the relationship between the premises and the conclusion must be such that if the premises were true, then the conclusion would be true also.

Before this latter test is described more precisely, it might be helpful to consider another way of looking at arguments. Instead of asking when an argument is good, we could ask when it's bad. There are two ways an argument can go wrong: It can be logically incorrect, or it can be factually incorrect. An argument is *logically incorrect* if the conclusion does not necessarily follow from the premises, and an argument is *factually incorrect* if one or more of the premises are false.

You might think that there's a third way: The conclusion could be false. But there are only two ways that could happen. Either the argument was logically incorrect, in which case the conclusion did not follow from the true premises, or the argument was factually incorrect. If the argument were both logically and factually correct, then the conclusion would *necessarily* follow from the premises, and so it could not have been false.

Since we sometimes do not know whether the premises are true or false, the test for logical correctness often becomes the more useful test. The technical name for logical correctness is *validity*. We can define it as follows:

> To say that an argument is *valid* means that it is impossible for the conclusion to be false while the premises are all true.

Notice that this definition does not say or imply that the premises of a valid argument *are* true—that's a matter of factual correctness, not logical correctness. Nor does it say that the conclusion is true. All that the definition says is that the conclusion would have to be true if the premises were true. We shall sometimes speak of a "valid conclusion," meaning a conclusion of a valid argument.

An argument that is not valid is said to be *invalid*. Thus an argument is invalid if it is possible for the conclusion to be false while the premises are true.

The best kind of argument, of course, is one that passes both tests—an argument that is both logically and factually correct. Such arguments are said to be "sound." Thus we define a *sound* argument as one that is valid and has all true premises. And, as we have seen, there are two ways for an argument to be unsound: either by being invalid or by having at least one false premise (or both!).

THE NATURE OF LOGIC

What follows are several arguments that demonstrate some of the possible combinations of true or false premises and conclusions, described according to whether they are valid or invalid, sound or unsound. Try to see why each one is valid or invalid, as the case may be.

1. VALID and SOUND
   All dogs are mammals.   (true)
   Lassie is a dog.   (true)
   Therefore,
   Lassie is a mammal.   (true)
2. INVALID and UNSOUND
   All Volkswagens are vehicles.   (true)
   The President's limousine is a vehicle.   (true)
   Therefore,
   The President's limousine is a Volkswagen.   (false)
3. VALID but UNSOUND
   All cats are dogs.   (false)
   All dogs are mammals.   (true)
   Therefore,
   All cats are mammals.   (true)
4. INVALID and UNSOUND
   All recent Presidents have lived in the White House.   (true)
   Ronald Reagan has lived in the White House.   (true)
   Therefore,
   Ronald Reagan is a recent President.   (true)

Truth Values

Sentences, as well as propositions, statements, and assertions, are frequently described as being the kinds of things that are true or false. The truth or falsity of a sentence is called the *truth value* of the sentence.

Determining the truth value of a sentence is equivalent to answering the question of whether the sentence is true or false. Some sentences have the interesting property of always being true, such as this sentence:

$$1 = 1$$

Some sentences are always false, such as

$$1 \neq 1$$

And the truth values of some sentences depend on the way things are, so to speak, such as:

The President of the United States is over 60 years old.

—which depends on who is President.

Up to this point, we have talked rather nebulously about the "truth values" of sentences as being either true or false. These truth values are perhaps most intuitively thought of as properties of sentences, much as tallness is a property of the Empire State Building. We must be careful not to confuse the truth value of a sentence with the sentence itself. The truth value of the sentence 'The earth is flat' is identical to the truth value *false,* but the sentence itself is not identical to the truth value *false.* Falsity is a property of this sentence; it is not identical to it.

Several important computer programming languages preserve the uniqueness of truth and falsity and have special words, usually simply 'TRUE' and 'FALSE', to indicate them. We shall also maintain this distinction and use these capitalized expressions to refer to the truth values of sentences. These two values, TRUE and FALSE, are often called "Boolean values," after the nineteenth-century British logician George Boole. Expressions having one of these values—usually, sentences—are often called "Boolean variables."

One important logician, Gottlob Frege (1848–1925), went so far as to claim that the truth values of sentences are unique and abstract things called The True and The False. This level of abstraction is, however, not always necessary, and for a variety of reasons—primarily "technical" rather than philosophical ones—logicians and computer scientists often find it useful to treat the truth values of sentences (TRUE or FALSE) as if they were numbers. The most usual identification is of the number 1 with TRUE and 0 with FALSE.

This identification is not to say that FALSE is really the same as 0 or that TRUE is really the same thing as the number 1. In fact, we could if we wished reverse this assignment and treat falsity as 1 and truth as 0! But most logicians associate 0 with falsity and 1 with truth. Their reasons for doing so vary but are primarily connected with easily remembering which is which. Some might say that a false sentence is "worthless," that nothing is greater than the truth, that truth is greater than falsity, or that truth is unity. None of these sayings are very clear, nor are they worth pursuing; but perhaps ideas like these have helped logicians and students remember which is which. (There are also some deeper reasons for identifying 0 with falsity and 1 with truth. They have to do with the behavior of 0 and 1 in ordinary arithmetic, as we shall see.)

It is increasingly common in computer science, and obviously useful in avoiding confusion, to use terms such as 'TRUE' and 'FALSE' rather than arithmetical substitutes such as '1' and '0'. In this text, we shall use both 'TRUE' and 'FALSE' as well as arithmetical equivalents, depending on the circumstances.

It is extremely useful to be able to distinguish clearly the truth value of a sentence from the sentence itself. To help ourselves do this, we shall introduce some notation. We shall use the capital letters (possibly with numerals):

A, B, C, . . . , O, A1, B1, . . . O1, A2, . . .

to designate particular sentences, and we shall use

V(<some sentence>)

to designate the truth value of a sentence. For example,

C = 'The earth is flat.'
V(C) = FALSE

In other words, 'V(C)' designates the truth value of sentence C. When we discuss arbitrary or nonspecified sentences, we shall use boldface capital letters from later in the alphabet:

P, Q, R, . . . , Z

Here are some concrete examples using this notation:

A = 'Logic is fun.'
B = 'All birds fly.'
V('There exists an odd number.') = TRUE
V('The earth is flat.') = FALSE
V(B) = FALSE
Consider a sentence **P** such that V(**P**) = TRUE.
For every sentence **Q** either V(**Q**) = TRUE or V(**Q**) = FALSE.

Summary

Logic is the study of correct reasoning. One branch of logic, *deductive logic,* studies reasoning that never moves from TRUE sentences to FALSE ones.

A basic unit in logic is an *argument,* which is a set of sentences, one of which (the *conclusion*) is claimed to follow from the others (the *premises*). There are two important attributes that a good deductive argument has. First, all its premises are TRUE. When this is so, we say that the argument is *factually correct.* Second, when an argument is such that *if* the premises *were* all TRUE then the conclusion *would* also be TRUE, we say that the argument is *logically correct.* Another word for logical correctness is *validity.* An argument that is both factually correct and logically correct is said to be *sound.*

We shall use the capital letters A, B, C, . . . , O to designate particular sentences, and we shall use the boldface capital letters **P, Q, R, . . . , Z** to designate arbitrary sentences. Every sentence has one *truth value,* either TRUE or FALSE. We shall sometimes represent TRUE and FALSE with the numbers 1 and 0, respectively. We shall indicate the truth value of a sentence, **P,** by writing V(**P**).

Exercises

A. Identify the premise and conclusion indicator words, the premises, and the conclusions in the following arguments.
   1. Computers cannot be intelligent, because they are not human.
   2. Robots could not be persons, since they don't have minds, and having a mind is a necessary condition for being a person.
   3. God does not exist. If he did exist, he would not allow suffering to exist. But there is suffering.
   4. Intelligent life might exist elsewhere in the universe. Yet we might never be sure of this fact, because this intelligent life might be too distant from us ever to be discovered.
   5. Deficit spending by a government always produces inflation. The reason for this is that deficits increase the money supply without increasing the number of goods. And this is just what inflation is—a money supply increasing more rapidly than the supply of goods.
   6. "Thinking is a function of man's immortal soul. God has given an immortal soul to every man and woman, but not to any other animal or to machines. Hence no animal or machine can think." (Turing, 1950, in Anderson, 1964, p. 14.)
   7. "There are a number of results of mathematical logic which can be used to show that there are limitations to the powers of discrete state machines [i.e., computers]. The best known of these results is known as Gödel's theorem, showing that, in any sufficiently powerful logical system, statements can be formulated which can neither be proved nor disproved within the system, unless possibly the system itself is inconsistent. [But humans can know whether these statements are true or false.] . . . This is the mathematical result; it is argued that it proves a disability of machines to which the human intellect is not subject." (Turing, 1950, in Anderson, 1964, p. 16.)
   8. "The nervous system is certainly not a discrete state machine. A small error in the information about the size of a nervous impulse impinging on a neuron, may make a large difference to the size of the outgoing impulse. It may be argued that, this being so, one cannot expect to be able to mimic the behavior of the nervous system with a discrete state machine." (Turing, 1950, in Anderson, 1964, p.22.)
   9. "Now the common philosophical argument is that minds and mental states are so extremely unlike bodies and bodily states that it is inconceivable that the two should be causally connected. It is certainly true that, if minds and mental events are just what they seem to be to introspection and nothing more, and if bodies and bodily events are just what enlightened common sense thinks them to be and nothing more, the two *are* extremely unlike. And this fact is supposed to show that, however closely correlated certain pairs of events in mind and body respectively may be, they cannot be causally connected." (Broad, 1962, p. 97.)

B. Make up a simple argument in English that has:
   1. A TRUE conclusion but that you believe is invalid.
   2. A FALSE conclusion but that you believe is valid.

THE NATURE OF LOGIC

C. Fill in the blanks in the following chart using:

T for TRUE	I for "invalid"
F for FALSE	S for "sound"
V for "valid"	U for "unsound"
? for "There is not enough information."	

For example:

I Premises are T = All TRUE, F = At Least one FALSE	II Argument is Valid or Invalid	III Argument is Sound or Unsound	IV Conclusion is TRUE or FALSE
1. T	V	S	☐
2. F	V	☐	☐

Answers to Examples

1. The conclusion of a *valid* argument with TRUE premises (i.e., a *sound* argument) must be TRUE, so the blank in column IV should be a T.
2. A *valid* argument with a FALSE premise is *unsound,* so the blank in column III should be filled in with a U. Since such an argument could have either a TRUE conclusion or a FALSE one, the blank in column IV should be?

	Premises	Argument		Conclusion
3.	F	☐	U	☐
4.	F	I	☐	☐
5.	T	I	☐	☐
6.	T	☐	U	☐
7.	☐	V	U	F
8.	☐	V	☐	F
9.	☐	V	☐	T
10.	☐	☐	S	T
11.	☐	I	☐	T
12.	☐	☐	U	T
13.	☐	I	☐	F
14.	☐	☐	U	F
15.	F	☐	☐	F
16.	F	☐	☐	T
17.	T	☐	☐	T
18.	T	V	☐	☐
19.	☐	☐	S	☐
20.	T	☐	☐	☐
21.	☐	V	☐	☐
22.	☐	☐	U	☐
23.	☐	☐	☐	F
24.	T	☐	☐	F

D. Some sections of prose, as we have already noted, contain *several* arguments. In the two sentence groups following the example, count the number of distinct arguments, and use the sentence numbers to indicate the premises and conclusions of the distinct arguments. Example:

1. Computers are made out of nonliving material.
2. Only living material is capable of having feelings.
3. So computers do not have feelings.
4. But having feelings is necessary for thinking in the broad sense.
5. Therefore, computers do not even think in the broad sense.

Answer:
    Number of arguments: 2
    Structure of the first argument:
      Premises: 1, 2
      Conclusion: 3
    Structure of the second argument:
      Premises: 3, 4
      Conclusion: 5

Group a

1. Geometry is a branch of mathematics.
2. Therefore, mathematics includes more subject matter than geometry.
3. Mathematics is a branch of logic.
4. So logic includes still more subject matter than mathematics.
5. Furthermore, logic must therefore include far more subject matter than geometry.

Group b

1. All prime numbers are odd.
2. So, no even numbers are prime.
3. Some odd numbers are divisible by 3.
4. So, not all odd numbers are prime.

LOGIC, COMPUTERS, AND ALGORITHMS

The historical connections between logic and computers run long and deep. It is now easy to think of the history of computers only in terms of the increasing speed and efficiency they acquired at performing mathematical computations. Looking back, we tend to see only the progression of calculating tools such as the abacus, slide rules, adding machines, pocket calculators, and computers, all of which seem to have been designed primarily to perform mathematical calculations.

But historically, this picture of computers as mathematical calculators is not entirely complete. Some of the first designs for computing machines were intended not to perform mathematical calculations but to perform the essentially logical task of determining correct deductive reasoning. That is, a number of early computers were designed to generate the logically valid conclusions from premises, or to "test" reasoning to determine whether or not it was valid.

CHAPTER 2

Mechanical Reasoning

The application of machines to the determination of correct reasoning was a very natural development. First, the evolution of symbolic methods of writing logical problems allowed the posing of such problems: Without having ways of clearly and concisely symbolizing reasoning, in the form of "symbolic" logic, the communication of such problems to machines would have been impossible. Similarly, the development of mathematics and the communication of mathematical problems to computers would have been impossible without concise, systematic ways of symbolizing mathematical problems—using arabic numerals and such symbols as '+' and '−', for example.

Second, the question of what constitutes sound reasoning is an age-old and vitally important question in philosophy and other disciplines. With a revival of the study of this question in the seventeenth century (by Descartes, Leibniz, and others) and some tentative speculations about what good reasoning consisted of, the question naturally arose as to whether machines could be constructed to "reason," or at least whether they could determine the validity of reasoning produced by humans. Machines that could evaluate the correctness of human reasoning—even if they could not creatively reason themselves—would be of considerable use in mathematics and other fields. They could check long or complicated reasoning for validity. Because of these two factors, the history of computers is full of attempts to build machines that could reason or that could test reasoning.

One of the most fanciful and amazing attempts to make reasoning a "mechanical" matter is to be found in the work of the Spanish mystic and priest Ramon Lull, who lived in the thirteenth century. Nothing in the life of this fantastic figure was dull—except perhaps his numerous and voluminous books. (For more material on Lull's life and work, the reader is urged to read the first chapter of Martin Gardner's *Logic Machines and Diagrams*.) Lull is usually regarded as one of the earliest writers to attempt to construct a notation for solving logical problems—as well as perhaps the first to attempt to build a mechanical device to solve logical problems. The machines he constructed to perform the task were composed of concentric dials; by turning one of the dials, one obtained various combinations of symbols. (The dials perhaps most resembled what we see today in "wheels" to combine soil, location, or other parameters in order to determine when best to plant certain seeds.)

The German philosopher, mathematician, and diplomat Gottfried Wilhelm Leibniz (1646–1716) was very impressed by Lull's ideas. Leibniz was a thinker with grand plans for improving the way we reason. He proposed, for example, the use of a universal "logical" language. This language would be designed so that every sentence would show clearly its logical content, much as equations in mathematics are universally understood, and display logical relationships among sentences clearly and unambiguously.

Coupled with Leibniz's plans for a universal logical language were proposals to discover the *methods* according to which good reasoning proceeds. These methods would be gathered together in what Leibniz called a *calculus ratiocinator* (a "calculus of reasoning"). Using this calculus of reasoning, thinkers could reason and come to the same conclusions in a virtually mechanical way, just as two accountants always eventually agree on the result of an addition. Leibniz even suggested that machines could then be used to take some of the drudgery out of long or complicated chains of reasoning.

LOGIC, COMPUTERS, AND ALGORITHMS

(Leibniz did not build this reasoning machine, but he did build, in 1673, a mechanical calculator for doing arithmetical computations.) Leibniz himself did not make much progress with his twin goals of a universal logical language and a "calculus of reasoning." But his ambitious goals served for centuries as an inspiration to philosophers, mathematicians, and, more recently, computer scientists.

The first working "logic machine" can perhaps be credited to the eighteenth-century British writer, politician, and tinkerer Charles Stanhope (1753–1816). Stanhope invented a mechanical contraption that he called a "Demonstrator." Like most early logic computers, it was operated by moving knobs or levers to set certain premises "true." One then read from indicators exactly which conclusions logically followed from these premises. (One could also use the Demonstrator to determine conclusions made probable by the premises.)

A far more complex logic machine was invented by the British economist and logician William Stanley Jevons (1835–1882). Jevons's computer was popularly known as the "logical piano" because of its input keyboard. Jevons, living almost a century after Stanhope, had the advantage of being able to use a sophisticated system of logical notation created by George Boole in the 1830s and 1840s (now known, in its modified form, as "Boolean algebra"). Jevons's logical piano, although representing a considerable advancement over Stanhope's Demonstrator, was nevertheless restricted in several key respects: it could handle so-called "particular" statements of the form 'Some A's are B's' (such as 'Some evergreens are pines') only with great difficulty and could not deal with arguments referring to more than four distinct classes.

Our discussion up to this point has separated the idea of a *logic* machine—a machine to solve logical problems—from a calculating machine to perform additions, multiplications, and so on. We have thus not considered some of the often quite sophisticated machines designed strictly for arithmetical calculations (such as an adding machine invented by the French philosopher Blaise Pascal). One machine, however, deserves mention in spite of the fact that it was designed primarily for solving arithmetical problems: the "analytical engine" of Charles Babbage, an Englishman who developed his ideas in the 1830s and 1840s. Babbage's analytical engine was never completed in his lifetime. (It was partially completed after his death by his son.) What is remarkable about Babbage's engine, however, is that its overall design had certain similarities to modern computers. Like modern computers, the analytical engine was to be an "all-purpose" computer, capable of performing whatever task its operator wished it to; it was "programmable" by cards, it had a "memory," and it could make decisions about what operation to perform next.

Babbage did not receive much support for his ideas from the British intellectual community, but he found a tireless defender in Lady Ada Lovelace—the beautiful and illegitimate daughter of the English Romantic poet Lord Byron. A recently developed computer language, Ada, has been named after this famous defender of the power and future of computers.

The late nineteenth century saw the improvement of mechanical logic computers like Jevons's, as well as designs for the first electric logic machines. It also saw the entrance of American ingenuity, with machines and designs by the philosopher Charles S. Peirce (1839–1914) and by his student Allan Marquand (1853–1924). But the development of sophisticated computers to solve general logical problems awaited the rapid evolution of electronic switching circuitry after World War II. The background of this history is the well-known, and amazingly rapid, evolution of switches from mechanical devices to electric ones (such as relays), then to electronic ones (such as vacuum tubes), and finally to compact electronic devices (such as transistors and chips).

While the forces behind all these modern developments were undoubtedly motivated by efforts to speed up arithmetical calculations and data processing (as opposed to the essentially logical goals of identifying correct reasoning), a deep interest has remained in "logical" uses of computers. Indeed, it rapidly became apparent that aspects of the design of electronic computers were virtually the same as certain types of logical analysis. Modern computers operate by controlling the flow of electric signals in various parts of their circuitry. The question of whether an electric signal is on or off parallels the question of whether a sentence is TRUE or FALSE—since here, too, there are only two possible values. The exploration of the close relationships between the on-off control of electric signals and the TRUE-FALSE operations of logic falls within a branch of engineering called "switching theory," which was extensively studied in 1937 and 1938 by Claude Shannon. (Appendix A treats this subject at greater length.)

In the 1950s and after, computer scientists moved quickly into the area that had originally interested earlier philosophers and logicians: determining whether arguments were deductively valid and, if they were, giving proofs. In fact, one of the first programs in the field of artificial intelligence was the Logic Theorist, which was capable of proving theorems in sentential logic. (For more information on this and other recent programs, see Slagle, 1971, and Rich, 1983.)

Any modern computer—a large, or mainframe, computer or even a microcomputer— can be programmed, in most cases, to determine whether an argument is valid. It can also be programmed to show *why* the conclusion validly follows from the premises. In addition, a computer can be programmed to check whether a proof you have produced obeys the accepted rules of inference. But for extremely interesting reasons (discussed in Chapter 14 and in Appendix B), it appears that computers cannot generally decide whether a given conclusion does or does not validly follow from given premises. At the end of many of the chapters of this book, we give some practical advice on how to go about transforming what we say into an actual computer program.

Computers and Reasoning

Do existing computers think? Is it possible for computers to think? These are difficult and inevitably asked questions to which we cannot do full justice here. They are dealt with in the area of computer science called Artificial Intelligence and in an overlapping area of philosophy, the philosophy of mind.

A question related to—and some even say identical to—the question of whether computers can think is the question of whether they can imitate some of the behavior we typically identify as being the product of "thinking." The behavior that could tempt us to say that computers can think might be responding appropriately to ordinary questions ("What time is it?" "How are you today?") or carrying on a conversation.

Another type of behavior that might tempt us to say that a computer can think is some evidence of "reasoning." Behavior we take as evidence of reasoning includes:

1. Deciding correctly whether an argument is, or is not, valid.
2. Deducing from a sentence other sentences that follow validly from it.
3. Producing a derivation showing that an argument is valid—if indeed it is.

In this book, we shall address the question of how to instruct a computer to perform these activities and shall thus examine some respects in which computers might be said to be capable of reasoning.

The question of whether computers are capable of thought (or of emotion) is a difficult and controversial one. But part of what we consider to be "thought" is reasoning, and reasoning might be just the kind of activity computers *can* do—as we shall see in coming chapters.

For a more complete discussion of these fascinating questions, the reader is urged to consult any of the following books on Artificial Intelligence:

Alan Ross Anderson (ed.), *Minds and Machines* (Englewood Cliffs, N.J.: Prentice-Hall, 1964).
Margaret Boden, *Artificial Intelligence and Natural Man* (New York: Basic Books, 1977).
Daniel C. Dennett, *Brainstorms: Philosophical Essays on Mind and Psychology* (Montgomery, Vt.: Bradford Books, 1978).
Hubert Dreyfus, *What Computers Can't Do: The Limits of Artificial Intelligence,* rev. ed. (New York: Harper and Row, 1979).
John Haugeland (ed.), *Mind Design: Philosophy, Psychology, Artificial Intelligence* (Cambridge, Mass.: M.I.T. Press, 1981).
Douglas R. Hofstadter, *Gödel, Escher, Bach: An Eternal Golden Braid* (New York: Basic Books, 1979).
Pamela McCorduck, *Machines Who Think: A Personal Inquiry into the History and Prospects of Artificial Intelligence* (San Francisco: W. H. Freeman, 1979).
Bertram Raphael, *The Thinking Computer: Mind Inside Matter* (San Francisco: W. H. Freeman, 1976).
Elaine Rich, *Artificial Intelligence* (New York: McGraw-Hill, 1983).
Joseph Weizenbaum, *Computer Power and Human Reason: From Judgment to Calculation* (San Francisco: W. H. Freeman, 1976).
Patrick Henry Winston, *Artificial Intelligence* (Reading, Mass.: Addison-Wesley, 1977).

How Computers Work

The modern electronic digital computer (see Figure 2-1) was devised to perform calculations and process information with incredible speed. The calculations a computer can perform range from the simple addition of two numbers to a sequence of hundreds of operations, such as multiplication, taking square roots, and finding the sines of angles. As we are all aware from the bills and "personalized" notices we receive in the mail, computers are also adept at storing, manipulating, and selecting information contained in what may be millions of records. This second set of tasks computers perform is often called data processing, or information processing.

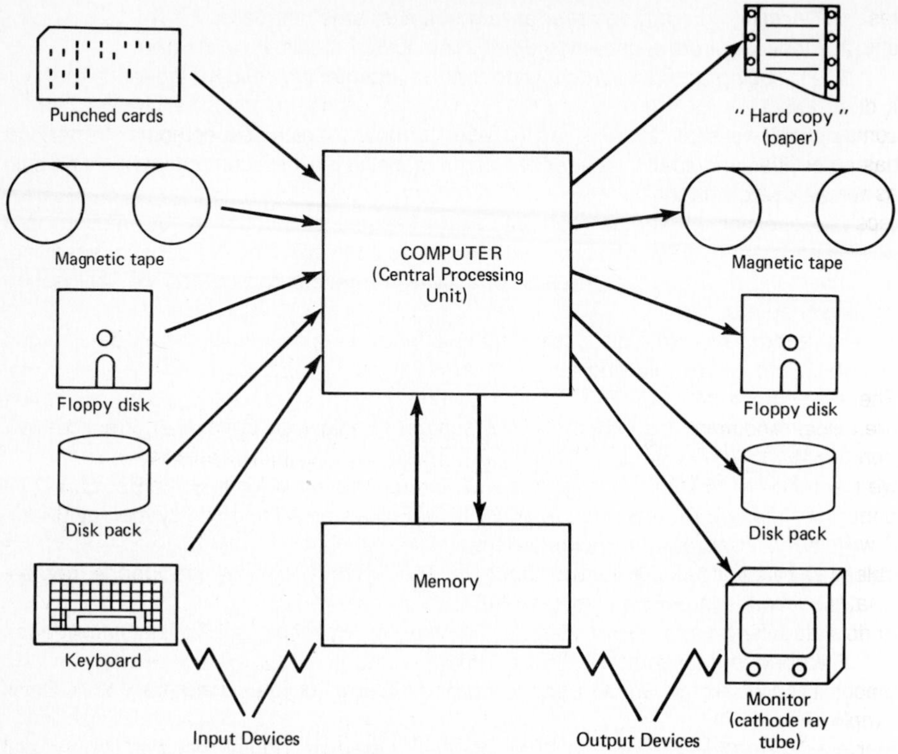

Figure 2-1   The structure of a typical computer system.

Computer Languages

It is practically a cliché that computers have no "imagination"; without proper instructions, they cannot perform the calculations or operations we would like them to. Thus the main activity of human beings who work with computers is to provide these instructions.

Once we are connected electronically to the computer, what do we say (or type)? This stage of communication with computers is fascinating, but complex. If we want the computer to perform some operation for us, we must tell it what to do in great detail. The computer would in most cases understand very little of what we mean when we talk to each other in ordinary English.

If we were to type "Add these numbers: 5 and 8," a computer would almost certainly not know what to do—unless it had been prepared for just this kind of sentence. It would probably respond with an "error" message or fail to do anything. So our next observation is that computers (at present) will not understand just any sentence of English, even if the sentence were clear to any human being who knew English. Instead, computers are prepared by their designers to understand only small, and frequently odd-sounding, portions of English. These are the so-called "computer languages." In many cases, they

LOGIC, COMPUTERS, AND ALGORITHMS

resemble English to some degree but use only a small portion of the words and con-structions an English speaker would know.

What a computer will do when instructed in a computer language is often surprising. It does *exactly* what the instruction tells it to do—nothing more and nothing less. A computer will not stop doing what you have told it to do because what you told it to do has no end or no point or couldn't reasonably have been what you meant it to do. But, as we all know, human beings sometimes ignore, correct, or change instructions they receive.

Machine Languages

The most cumbersome of the languages in which we can communicate with computers are called "machine languages." They direct the computer to perform exactly the elec-tronic operations it would actually have to perform to come up with a result. In particular, we must specify in maximum—and usually excruciating—detail exactly what has to be done to perform an operation. For example, consider the addition of decimal numbers. If we were communicating with the computer in machine language, we would not be able to say anything like "Add the integers 18 and 37." The computer would not recognize what "addition" is, it would not know what an "integer" is, and it would have no idea what to do with the symbols '18' and '37'.

Preparing our instructions for a computer—what is usually called a "program"—in machine language, we would have to describe how to add two integers. This sounds simple enough. But remember, the computer knows nothing about addition. Some glim-mer of what we would have to tell the computer to do might arise if we begin to recall how we add. We put numbers in neat columns, like so:

18
37

Then we begin at the right. . . . Suddenly, our description of this "simple" operation would get complicated indeed.

Higher-Level Computer Languages

To explain in machine language how to add two numbers requires a very long expla-nation. You can perhaps begin to see that if we had to tell each other, or tell computers, exactly what to do in this kind of detail every time we wanted a calculation performed, life would be very unpleasant and all too short. We humans solved this problem long ago. We came up with a word that describes this procedure in a kind of shorthand. That word is "addition." Related to it is the command "Add . . . !" which tells us to perform the procedure we just began to examine a moment ago. Rather than saying:

Put numbers *n* and *m* in columns, with the last digits of each number lined up with each other. . . .

we instead say to one another:

Add *n* and *m*.

We all know what this means, and many of us are reasonably proficient at performing the procedure that is abbreviated by this incredibly useful shorthand.

Computer scientists have developed ways of communicating with computers that avoid the intimidating detail we would otherwise have to use in order to communicate with computers in machine language. These are the *higher-level languages*. These higher-level languages perform a trick human beings long ago hit upon: certain words or symbols are used to abbreviate rather complicated but frequently used procedures. Almost all higher-level computer languages have abbreviations for the most commonly used arithmetical operations, such as addition, multiplication, and division, as well as for other operations.

There are now a large number of computer languages available. (We shall use "computer language" from now on to refer to higher-level languages.) All perform the same function of abbreviating certain often-used procedures, which are cued by certain symbols (∗, /, +, $, %, etc.) or words (called "reserved words") that resemble their ordinary-language counterparts (DIV, IF, NOT, etc.). These languages differ a great deal from one another, usually because each is designed for ease of writing certain types of programs.

Algorithms

The key to communicating with computers—whatever language one chooses—is the notion of an algorithm: a detailed, step-by-step description of a process a computer or a person would use to solve a problem or perform a task. To get a better idea of what an algorithm is, consider this seemingly simple instruction:

Cook frozen peas.

This general instruction can be refined into a sequence of more specific instructions: Boil some water in a pot, add the peas, cover the pot, and simmer for a few minutes. But how much water? How many peas? How hot is "simmer"? How many minutes? Different cooks will answer these questions differently.

Similarly, different musicians following the same score will perform the same piece of music in different ways—often producing very different results. The missing precision and detail in the recipe or the score—the instructions—must be supplied by the cook or the performer. A sequence of instructions that is completely precise in all details would not allow the performer to deviate from the procedure. Such a sequence of instructions for performing a task is a *mechanical procedure.*

LOGIC, COMPUTERS, AND ALGORITHMS

Mechanical Procedures

A special type of mechanical procedure is an algorithm. An *algorithm* is a detailed, step-by-step, finite sequence of instructions for performing a task that satisfies the following two properties: (1) given any required information, the task must be completable in a finite number of steps with finite resources, and (2) it must be completely mechanical and unambiguous, in the sense that no creativity or extra information need be used by whoever or whatever carries out the instructions.

Sometimes, problems that seem very complex or that seem to require some kind of interpretive judgment can be expressed in surprisingly simple algorithms. On the other hand, tasks that are so simple that we perform them every day without careful thought can be enormously difficult to express algorithmically. As we have seen, the single instruction "Add n and m" is an instruction that isn't explicit enough if the person or machine that is supposed to carry it out doesn't know what 'add' means. To produce a more explicit algorithm for adding, we need to provide instructions that are more precise and more detailed. Such an algorithm would consist of a detailed sequence of instructions that someone with no creativity and no understanding of "addition" could follow to produce the correct sum. Finding out what to tell the computer to do will often consist of first examining how *we* make such calculations. It will consist of making explicit what has long ago become second nature to most of us: the process by which we add numbers.

One very useful way of creating an algorithm is called the "top-down" approach, and we shall use it often. To employ this method, one first sketches in broad strokes and in their proper order the steps that seem to be necessary for performing the task. One then returns to these steps and makes them sufficiently precise and detailed so that whoever (or whatever) is following the instructions will know what to do at each step. This phase of designing an algorithm is called "stepwise refinement."

As a first step in a top-down analysis, we could refine the single instruction "Add n and m" into four instructions:

1. Write down n.
2. Write down m.
3. Calculate their sum.
4. Write down that sum.

This is our "broad" view of what needs to be done. Such a broad view of what needs to be done is called the "main procedure." Each step of a main procedure frequently needs to be made more explicit. Each of these main steps, when spelled out in detail, becomes a subprocedure.

Instruction 1 is precise enough, but 2 can be further refined:

2.1. Write the ones digit of m directly beneath the ones digit of n.
2.2. Write the tens digit of m directly beneath the tens digit of n.

and so on.

Instruction 3, of course, is the crucial one. It can be refined as follows:

    3.1. Look up the sum of the ones digits in a table (which contains such facts as
        $0 + 0 = 0, 0 + 1 = 1, \ldots, 2 + 3 = 5, \ldots, 9 + 9 = 18$).
    3.2. Write down the ones digit of that sum beneath the ones digits of n and m.
    3.3. If there is a tens digit of that sum, then write it down above the tens digit of n.
    3.4. Find the sum of the digits in the next column to the left.

and so on. Instruction 3.4 needs to be refined too, since the table referred to in 3.1 presumably only gives sums of two numbers, and if step 3.3 must be performed, there will be three numbers in the tens column.

    Step 3.3 is an example of a decision that must be made in following the algorithm, but it is not the sort of decision that requires creativity or extra information—it is completely specified.

Flowcharts

The algorithm above was written in English. A *program* is a way to communicate an algorithm to whoever or whatever will carry it out. For humans, giving the instructions in English (or some other natural language) is probably best. But for a computer, a program in a computer language (such as BASIC or Pascal) must be used.

    Before a program is actually written, the algorithm can be presented in "flowchart language." A *flowchart* is a graphic presentation of an algorithm. A flowchart is a "graph" consisting of points connected by arrows. The points, or "nodes," represent steps of the algorithm, and the arrows represent the order in which the steps are to be performed. (This is sometimes called the "flow of control," whence the name "flowchart.")

    Two especially important nodes in a flowchart are a "start" point and—if the procedure is ever to terminate—a "stop" point. The most common portrayal of these points in a flowchart is with the words 'START' and 'STOP' enclosed in rounded shapes:

Figure 2-2 START and STOP nodes.

    Other important nodes in a flowchart are "operations": points at which we give instructions for something to be done, such as an addition. These instructions are surrounded by rectangles. Figure 2-3 shows examples of operation nodes.

LOGIC, COMPUTERS, AND ALGORITHMS

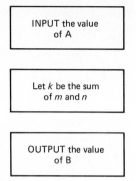

Figure 2-3   Operation nodes.

(With some systems of drawing flowcharts, certain operations are contrasted through the use of different shapes—especially for "input" and "output" operations. We shall keep things simple, however, and use one shape for all operations.)

Finally, there are "test," or "decision," nodes, which contain sentences that are either TRUE or FALSE (or, sometimes, questions that have yes or no answers). These tests are surrounded by diamonds and have two routes flowing out of them: their TRUE (or "yes") branch and their FALSE (or "no") branch. Figure 2-4 shows examples of test nodes.

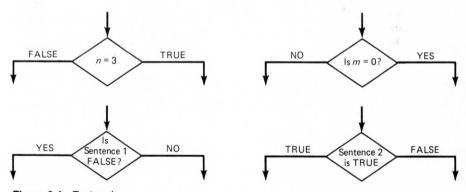

Figure 2-4   Test nodes.

Because there are two routes leaving test nodes, the flow of control through the flowchart is said to "branch" at these points. Such branches are important not because they make any calculation or take any important observable action but because they determine which of two alternative steps comes next.

A flowchart consists of a START node and STOP nodes and a number of operation rectangles and test diamonds in between, all connected with lines that have a direction indicated by an arrow. The simplest possible such flowchart is one that does absolutely nothing other than start and stop:

Figure 2-5   The simplest possible flowchart.

Consider this slightly more glamorous flowchart:

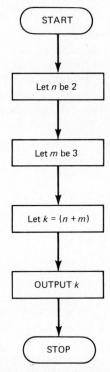

Figure 2-6   A flowchart for adding 2 and 3.

This procedure adds 2 to 3 and displays '5'. Note that the flowchart assumes that we have a procedure for adding two numbers; it does not describe how to do this. It is common in flowcharts, as it is in English and in computer languages, to assume that such simple arithmetical procedures are already available.

Two very common operation rectangles contain 'INPUT . . .', where the instruction gets some information from the operator or from a place where information is stored, and 'OUTPUT . . .', where the instruction communicates some information.

In the example just given, the procedure eventually communicates the value that is the result of adding 2 to 3. We could modify the previous procedure so that it takes any two numbers and communicates their sum. Consider:

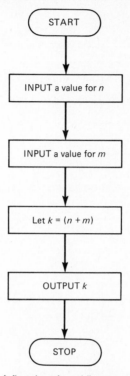

Figure 2-7   A flowchart for adding any two numbers.

Now the procedure will "ask" the operator for information whenever we have an input operation. This procedure will do so twice. If we program a computer to follow this flowchart, the computer will stop at the first 'INPUT . . .', waiting for information about what value the variable n should receive. When given a value, it will then proceed to the third step, "asking" us what the value of m should be. It will then, without further tutoring, compute the value of k—the sum of n and m—and communicate the result.

There is a possible flaw in the procedure we have just given. Let us assume that we are at a computer terminal. The computer that is following this algorithm is connected to our terminal and pauses to ask us what the value of variable n should be. The entire procedure is written to expect a *number*, of course. But our terminal has letters too, and we decide to input the expression 'This is'. The computer then pauses to ask us what the value of m should be. Still playing our pranks, we type 'fun'. Now the computer reaches the fourth step: it must calculate the sum of 'This is' and 'fun'. But what is the (arithmetical) sum of 'This is' and 'fun'? The question does not have a clear answer. If we were to try this on a real computer programmed to follow the flowchart, various things could happen. The computer might stop altogether, or it might give an "error" message, or it might even output some unusual expression that it "thinks" is the sum of the two expressions. No damage would have been done to the computer, for it is almost impossible to break computers by doing such things.

To improve the procedure and to prevent pranksters from misusing it, we can modify it as follows:

Figure 2-8 A flowchart for adding any two numbers, with error messages.

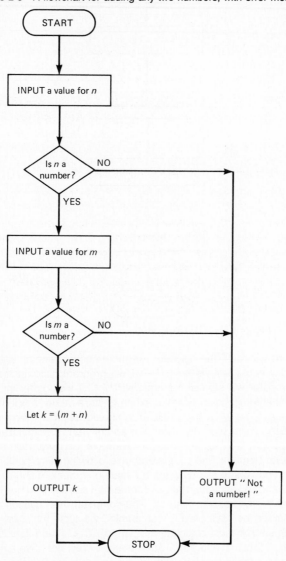

If *n* or *m* is not given a numerical value, a computer following the flowchart now informs us of this fact by outputting 'Not a number!' and halts. If both *n* and *m* are numbers, the appropriate sum is output. Note the way we used our tests (in diamonds) to handle undesired possibilities; tests can, of course, be used to handle differing desired possibilities as well.

At this point, you should have some idea of what an algorithm is and of how a flowchart can be used to present one. The question of whether a flowchart does indeed present an algorithm is a difficult one. By intuition, we can say that a flowchart does not present an algorithm if there is a possible flow of control through the flowchart that does not ever reach a STOP node.

Although we cannot here give all the rules for determining when a flowchart presents an algorithm, we can give four guidelines for proper flowcharts:

1. Any operation rectangle must have one and only one path leading away from it.
2. Every test diamond must have two and only two paths leading away from it, one labeled TRUE (or "yes") and the other labeled FALSE (or "no").
3. All nodes (with the exception of START and STOP) must have at least two lines connecting them to other nodes.
4. The paths connecting nodes are "one-way streets." The flow of control from one node to another can only go in in one direction.

The language of flowcharts unfortunately has its limitations. When the task to be performed is complex, requiring a lengthy algorithm, the flowchart presentation of this algorithm might cover many pages and be nearly unreadable. Flowcharts are useful and enlightening only when they are relatively simple. Another problem with flowcharts is that they do not closely resemble what is often the "final product" of our work with algorithms, namely a computer program. A computer program is a sequence of instructions without the boxes, branches, and arrows of flowcharts connecting them.

A Program Design Language

An alternative to using flowchart language to portray an algorithm is using a "program design language." An algorithm presented in program design language looks much more like a computer program would. We shall, in fact, use this approach when an algorithm is at all complex or lengthy. Using a program design language (rather than a flowchart) to portray an algorithm will allow the reader easily to convert the algorithm into a computer program or into a perfectly understandable sequence of instructions in ordinary English.

The program design language we shall use in this book has the following features:

1. Every algorithm will be portrayed through the use of a numbered sequence of instructions.

2. The form of these instructions will be restricted to a handful of basic patterns.
3. Subsidiary or dependent operations will be indented.
4. Large sections of the algorithm for performing some clear but subsidiary task will be separated and labeled.

This last feature is often called "modular design," and it is the essence of what is considered good programming style. In practice, modular design requires us first to perform a top-down analysis of the task and then to divide our algorithm into subprocedures, each of which singles out some distinct and clearly identified task. We shall use names in capital letters to label our algorithms in program design language, as well as to label the subprocedures that make them up.

Our program design language will allow just two basic kinds of instructions: *operation* statements (or "operations" for short) and *control* statements. An operation statement indicates an operation or action the person or computer following the algorithm is to perform. Control statements are instructions concerning how often, under what conditions, or in what order operations are to be performed. They "control" the performance of operations.

An important part of many control statements is the test, or condition. A *condition* is a sentence that is either TRUE or FALSE. It can never be an instruction itself. For instance, '4 > 2' is a TRUE sentence and thus could be a condition. One could not order, or direct, anyone to make 4 greater than 2, so it is not an operation. What follows the condition in a conditional control statement is an instruction (or a sequence of instructions).

Consider the following example of a control statement:

IF the amount in your checking account is less than $20.00,
    THEN pay a service fee of $1.00.

The control portion of this instruction is the control pattern: IF <condition>. In this example, the condition is 'the amount in your checking account is less than $20.00'. The instruction portion contains a single operation: pay a service fee of $1.00. That is, the condition of an instruction tells us when to do something, and the operation portion tells us what to do.

Operation Statements

Ideally, the operations contained in an algorithm should be very simple ones. Certainly they should be ones that the person or computer following the algorithm could reasonably, and without further instruction, be expected to understand. More complex operations should be described by listing a sequence of several simpler operations. Because computers—other than robots—do not do much besides asking for, and giving, information to human users, two common operations are:

INPUT . . .

and

OUTPUT . . .

The first instruction, INPUT . . . , tells the person or computer following the algorithm to obtain some information from its environment; it looks in its own records or asks the user to give it some information. The second instruction, OUTPUT . . . , tells the follower of the algorithm to write, or in some other way communicate, some information. Because these two operations require the user of the algorithm to react with some "outside" environment—that is, with a world outside the computer—they are often called "external" operations or, even more descriptively, "input-output" operations.

There are operations, however, that the algorithm uses for its own purposes. These might be called "internal" operations. Chief among these is the operation of assigning certain information to a name. This information can then be recalled later in the algorithm by using that name. This operation is frequently called an "assignment," and the name given to the information is most frequently called a *variable*. Examples of assignment statements are:

Let n be 5.
Set n to the old value of n plus 1.
Let THISSTRING be the string 'Logic is simple'.

Each of these instructions "assigns" certain information to an expression (here, to the letter 'n' and to the word 'THISSTRING'). This information can be a number, a truth value, or a sequence of characters (called a "string"). It is common in computer programming languages to restrict the type of information that can be assigned to kinds of variables. The categories of information are called the "data type" of the information (and of the variable). We shall not worry in this book about the kind of information associated with names and shall instead let any name refer to any type of information. We shall also have no restrictions on what expression can serve as a variable, but we shall often pick a name, such as 'THISSTRING', that helps us to remember what information is stored there. The form of the assignment statement will be rather free, including such expressions as 'Let . . .', 'Set . . . to . . .', and 'Call . . .'.

Control Statements

The control statements in an algorithm are just as important as the operation statements, for knowing when to do something, and how often, is just as important as knowing what to do.

One important feature of our program design language is this: Unless otherwise indicated, instructions are to be performed in the order in which they occur. For example, if we had the algorithm

1. Let *n* have the value 5.
2. Let the new value of *n* be 1 plus its old value.
3. OUTPUT the value of *n*.
4. STOP.

its application would be as follows. After step 1, '*n*' refers to this information: 5. After step 2, '*n*' has the value of its former value, 5, plus 1—that is, 6. Finally, the value of *n* is output, and at this point in the algorithm, '*n*' refers to this information: 6. So this algorithm has the final, observable result of simply outputting '6'.

Another very useful control statement in an algorithm is (as we mentioned) the *conditional instruction:*

IF <some condition>
   THEN <instruction>

Here is an example of an algorithm that uses a conditional instruction:

1. Let *n* have the value 7.
2. Let *m* have the value 5 + 2.
3. IF the value of *n* is the same as the value of *m*,
      THEN (a) OUTPUT "*n* and *m* have the same value."
4. STOP.

Since the condition in step 3 is in fact TRUE (once the first two operations have been performed), the operation indicated by step 3(a) would be performed. The sentence '*n* and *m* have the same value' would be written or displayed. If the condition had been FALSE, the sentence would not be displayed.

Other useful control statements are:

FOR <some sequence of values>
   <instructions>
WHILE <some condition>
   <instructions>
GO TO <some step in the algorithm>
STOP

The first type of control statement, usually called a FOR-loop, says that the indicated instructions are to be repeated as many times as the sequence of values indicates. Here is an example of an application of the FOR-loop:

1. INPUT a sentence.
2. FOR every character in the sentence
      (a) IF the character is 'e'
            THEN OUTPUT "Letter 'e'."
3. STOP.

If the sentence we had input to the algorithm at step 1 were

This is a sentence.

then in step 2 of the algorithm each character in this sentence would be examined (letters, spaces, and punctuation). Every time we encountered the letter 'e', step 2(a) would direct us to output the phrase "Letter 'e'." The procedure would move to the last step (3) only after every character in the sentence had been examined. In other words, step 2(a) is repeated as many times as there are characters in the input sentence. Only then does control move to step 3.

A WHILE statement tells us to repeat the indented instructions as long as a certain condition remains TRUE. When the condition becomes FALSE, we move to the next nonindented instruction. Both the FOR statement and the WHILE statement tell us, in differing ways, how many times to repeat (indented) instructions.

A GO TO statement tells us to go to some other step in the algorithm. Since it is reasonably common to have each step in an algorithm labeled in some way, a frequent form of the GO TO statement is, for example, 'GO TO step 4'. GO TO statements are widely frowned upon by enlightened algorithm writers because of the confusion they produce: when reading an algorithm, we must jump back and forth from one place to another. Consequently, we shall use them rarely. (Their use can be eliminated altogether, but in several of our informally described algorithms, it is simpler and clearer to use GO TO's than to avoid them.)

The most obvious control statement is STOP, which tells us that we have completed the algorithm.

Consider this algorithm presented in our program design language:

1. INPUT the value n.
2. INPUT the value m.
3. IF n is not a number, or m is not a number,
     THEN (a) OUTPUT "Input values not both numbers."
          (b) STOP.
4. IF m is 0
     THEN (a) OUTPUT "Division by 0 is impossible."
          (b) STOP.
5. Let k be n/m.
6. OUTPUT k.
7. STOP.

This algorithm was designed for the task of simply dividing one number by another. It was also designed to avoid difficulties caused by not having numerical values assigned to the names 'n' and 'm' (step 3) and by division by 0 (step 4). Several features about the algorithm are important to note.

First, when the algorithm is applied, it must be followed step-by-step, jumping over indented steps if a condition is FALSE, until a STOP is encountered. One does exactly what each step says. If a statement is a conditional one and the condition is TRUE, one performs the indicated (indented) instructions. If a statement is a conditional one and

CHAPTER 2

the condition is FALSE, one does not perform the indicated instructions. Instead, one simply goes on to the next step that is not further indented. (In the jargon of algorithms, this is often called "falling through" to the next step.)

Second, it often happens that if a condition is TRUE, several operations should be performed. When we have more than one operation dependent on a condition being TRUE, these operations will always be indented from the condition itself. We have this arrangement in steps 3 and 4.

Summary

Computers can be used to solve "logical" questions (such as "Is this argument valid?"), or they can be used to give proofs that demonstrate why an argument is valid. A notion important for directing computers to answer these logical questions is the idea of an *algorithm:* a sequence of instructions for performing a task such that given any required information, the task can be completed in a finite number of steps; in addition, the instructions are completely mechanical and unambiguous, in the sense that no creativity or extra information needs to be used by whoever or whatever carries out the instructions. A computer program is the presentation of an algorithm in a way that allows a specific computer to follow it properly.

We shall present algorithms in one of two ways: in a *flowchart* or in a *program design language.* An algorithm presented in our program design language will visually more closely resemble an actual computer program than does one presented in flowchart form.

Either in flowchart form or in program design language, every instruction in an algorithm is of one of the following kinds:

Operation Statements
1. External
   a. INPUT
   b. OUTPUT
2. Internal
   a. Assignments: Let <variable> be assigned <information>

Control Statements
1. Unconditional control
   a. STOP
   b. GO TO
2. Conditional control
   a. IF <condition>
         THEN <instructions>
   b. FOR <sequence of values>
         <instructions>
   c. WHILE <condition>
         <instructions>

LOGIC, COMPUTERS, AND ALGORITHMS

Exercises

A. An important test for determining whether computers can "think" was proposed by the British mathematician and computer scientist Alan Turing and is known as the *Turing test* (see Turing, 1950 in Anderson, 1964). A simplified version of the test he proposed is as follows. Suppose you are seated at a terminal or some other communication device. You have no idea who or what is at the other end. You begin a "conversation" on the terminal, asking questions, receiving answers to these questions, receiving and answering questions about yourself, about your beliefs, and about the world. You might play games, ask for advice, and do all the other things we do when we communicate with other human beings.

If you have every reason to believe that you are communicating with a human being, then whatever is at the other end—even if it's a computer—must be admitted to be *thinking*. In other words, we should count as having the ability to think whatever can converse as a thinking human being can.

Answer the following questions concerning the Turing test:

1. Is it possible that we could be communicating with another thinking human being yet not be able to determine that this human being was indeed *thinking*? One possibility: The person at the other end can't type. Yet this surely does not necessarily mean that he or she cannot think. What are other possible reasons why a thinking human being might not give us, or be able to give us, evidence of his or her thinking?
2. In the light of the first question, consider these two statements:
   a. If a person or computer passes the Turing test, then he or she or it can think.
   b. If a person or computer fails the Turing test, then he or she or it cannot think.

   Are both statements reasonable? (The computer program ELIZA is supposed to be a counterexample to statement (a); see Weizenbaum, 1976.)
3. Imagine yourself at a terminal administering the Turing test to someone (or something). Construct three questions (and their answers) that you think would be sufficient to determine if the test taker could think. *Hint:* At least one question should require *reasoning* and not just knowledge.

B. The following algorithm written in our program design language is for administering and grading a short quiz on state capitals.

1. LET A be 0.
2. Answer TRUE or FALSE: "The capital of California is Sacramento."
3. LET V(CA) be your response.
4. Answer TRUE or FALSE: "The capital of Ohio is Toledo."
5. LET V(OH) be your response.
6. Answer TRUE or FALSE: "The capital of New York is Albany."
7. LET V(NY) be your response.
8. IF V(CA) = TRUE
   THEN LET A be the former value of A plus one.

9. IF V(OH) is not TRUE
   THEN LET A be the former value of A plus one.
10. IF V(NY) is not FALSE
   THEN LET A be the former value of A plus one.
11. IF A = 3
   THEN OUTPUT "Perfect Score."
12. IF A = 2
   THEN OUTPUT "Better luck next time."
13. IF A < 2
   THEN OUTPUT "Terrible!"
14. STOP.
   a. Take the quiz. What are your answers at steps 3, 5, and 7? What would the procedure do after step 10?
   b. If you had answered the questions perfectly, what would the procedure have output?
   c. Suppose your answers at steps 3, 5, and 7 had been:
      TRUE
      I DON'T KNOW
      FALSE
      What would be the value of A at step 4? after step 8? after step 9? after step 10? What evaluation of the answers would the procedure have output?
   d. Answer the same questions in (c), but suppose the input responses had been:
      FALSE
      I FORGET
      THIS IS A STUPID TEST
   e. Redesign steps 9 and 10 so that the test is always scored correctly.

C. Consider the following algorithm for administering and grading a quiz on the planets.
   1. Answer: "What is the planet just beyond the earth?"
   2. LET P4 be your answer.
   3. Answer: "What is the closest planet to the sun?"
   4. LET P1 be your answer.
   5. Answer: "What is the farthest planet from the sun?"
   6. LET P9 be your answer.
   7. Answer: "What is the largest planet?"
   8. LET P5 be your answer.
   9. LET A have the value 100.
   10. IF P5 is not 'JUPITER'
      THEN LET A be 25 less than its former value.
   11. IF P9 is not 'PLUTO'
      THEN LET A be 25 less than its former value.
   12. IF P1 is 'MERCURY'
      THEN GO TO step 14.
   13. LET A be 25 less than its former value.
   14. IF P4 is 'MARS'
      THEN GO TO step 16.

15. LET A be 25 less than its former value.
16. OUTPUT "Your grade is: ."
17. OUTPUT A.
18. STOP.

   a. If your answers at steps 2, 4, 6, and 8 were MERCURY, MERCURY, PLUTO, and JUPITER, respectively, what would your score be?

   b. If your answers at steps 2, 4, 6, and 8 were VENUS, SATURN, PLUTO, and JUPITER, respectively, what would the value of A be after step 10? after step 11? after step 13?

D. The refinement of step 2 of the "algorithm" for adding given in the text on page 21 is incomplete: it doesn't tell you when to stop. Revise this step so that someone following the algorithm will know when to stop.

E. Write a brief algorithm for performing some simple task. Have another student attempt to follow the algorithm, and report back on whether he or she was able to follow your algorithm without using any creativity or imagination.

F. Symbolic logic usually deals with expressions that are mixtures of letters ('A', 'B', . . .) and other symbols, such as), (, v, and ~. Consider the following tasks for which an algorithm can be written.

   1. A question that sometimes arises is the question of *how often* a symbol occurs in a string of symbols. For example, it is easy to see that in the string
      ASFAHDA$%123
   the letter 'A' occurs three times. Write an algorithm for determining how often, in an input string, the letter 'A' occurs.

   2. Another question that arises about strings (and which we shall later use) is the question of *how many distinct* symbols occur in a string. For example, in the string
      ASDF%$121AD$%1
   there occur eight distinct symbols: A, S, D, F, %, $, 1, and 2. Write an algorithm for inputting a string and outputting the number of distinct symbols in that string.

G. Consider the following alleged algorithm for buying milk:

   1. Go to the supermarket.
   2. IF they have milk,
      THEN buy some.
   3. IF they do not have milk,
      THEN (a) Go to another supermarket.
          (b) GO TO step 2.
   4. Go home.
   5. STOP.

Answer the following questions:

   a. Draw a flowchart for this "algorithm."

   b. What happens if there are an indefinite number of supermarkets, and none have milk?

   c. Revise the algorithm to deal with the contingency in (b).

   d. Draw a flowchart for your revised algorithm.

SENTENTIAL LOGIC:
The Connectives 'Not', 'And', and 'Or'

One of the most important and basic branches of logic is the logic of sentences, also called *sentential logic.* Sentential logic examines arguments by looking at parts no finer or more detailed than *declarative sentences.*

We shall regard a sentence as a linear sequence, or string, of symbols that expresses a proposition. Two or more distinct sentences can express the same proposition. Consider the following strings:

The earth is round.
Round is the earth.
Die Erde ist rund.

Each line contains a string of symbols (in this case, letters, spaces, and periods). The first sentence, for example, is composed of the sequence of symbols 'T', 'h', 'e', ' ' (space), 'e', and so forth.

The three lines above are in fact three distinct strings: the symbols are arranged in a different order in each line, and the last line—in German—even lacks a letter that the other two have. They all, however, express roughly the same thought or proposition. Some strings are apparently not sentences: they do not clearly express propositions in any language we know. Examples of strings that do not express propositions (and hence are not sentences) are:

Egl%! Oglrn.%
Glub af noc.

CHAPTER 3

As an example to work with, consider the proposition that Richard mailed Alison a book. We would normally express this proposition in English by the sentence:

1. Richard mailed Alison a book.

There are grammatical rules for transforming this sentence into other English sentences that express the same proposition. For example, the sentence

2. Richard mailed a book to Alison.

expresses the same proposition as sentence (1). Note that (1) and (2) are different sentences, since they are different strings of symbols.

Negation

Now, it could be false that Richard mailed Alison a book. There are many ways for this proposition to fail to be true:

It may not have been *Richard* who mailed a book.
He may not have mailed it *yet.*
He may not have *mailed* it but rather delivered it personally.
It may not have been *Alison* to whom Richard sent a book.
And it may not have been a *book* that he mailed.

Any combination of these facts would also make the original proposition false. Each of the examples in this list could be expressed with different phrasing. But since, for the purposes of sentential logic, we are only interested in the truth or falsity of propositions, we shall be satisfied with the very general and nonspecific proposition *that it is not the case that Richard mailed Alison a book.* This is called the "denial" of the original proposition, and it can be expressed in English by this sentence: It is not the case that Richard mailed Alison a book.

We see, then, that if we wish to construct a sentence in English expressing a denial of a proposition, we can simply take a sentence expressing the original proposition and prefix that particular string of symbols with the string 'It is not the case that'. The resulting sentence is the *negation* of the original sentence.

To avoid writing sentences over and over again, and to simplify the visual presentation of what we have just discussed, we shall follow our convention from Chapter 1 and use the boldface capital letters **'P', 'Q', 'R', . . . ,'Z'** to designate any possible strings that are sentences. So, we can now say that the standard way to form a negation of a sentence **P** is to write:

It is not the case that **P.**

'NOT', 'AND', 'OR'

We can simplify matters further by letting the string 'It is not the case that' be replaced by a single symbol: $\sim$. Thus we represent a negation of a sentence **P** as:

$\sim$**P**

Some concrete examples are shown in Table 3-1.

Propositions are either true or false. A sentence has the truth value TRUE if the proposition it expresses is true, and a sentence has the truth value FALSE if the proposition it expresses is false. As we discussed in Chapter 1, we shall use the capitalized words 'TRUE' and 'FALSE' to designate the two possible truth values of sentences. It is useful to have different, but related, symbols for sentences and for their truth values. We shall continue our practice of using upper-case letters to indicate sentences and of using the 'V( )' notation to represent the truth value of a sentence. For example:

C = 'The earth is flat.'
V(C) = FALSE

How would we describe, in general, when the negation of a sentence is TRUE? When, for example, is the following sentence TRUE?

It is not the case that Richard mailed Alison a book.

This answer should come to mind: The negation of a sentence is TRUE just when the sentence itself is FALSE. In the present case,

It is not the case that Richard mailed Alison a book.

is TRUE just when

Richard mailed Alison a book.

is FALSE. In addition, the negation of a sentence is FALSE just when the original sentence is TRUE. We see, then, that the truth value of a negation depends just on the truth value of the original sentence.

TABLE 3-1. Negations of Sentences.

Sentence	Colloquial Negation	Standard Negation	Symbolic Negation
Fido barks.	Fido doesn't bark.	It is not the case that Fido barks.	$\sim$(Fido barks.)
John is singing.	John isn't singing.	It is not the case that John is singing.	$\sim$(John is singing.)
$2 + 2 = 4$	$2 + 2 \neq 4$	It is not the case that $2 + 2 = 4$	$\sim(2 + 2 = 4)$
$7 < 10$	7 is not less than 10.	It is not the case that $7 < 10$.	$\sim(7 < 10)$

CHAPTER 3

The Truth Function FNEG

The dependency relationship between a sentence and its negation can be expressed more precisely and clearly by saying that the truth value of the negation of a sentence is a "function" of the truth value of the original sentence. A *function* produces just one unique output for a given input (or inputs). Negation is called a "truth function" because it outputs a truth value (the truth value of the negation) from an input that is the truth value of the original sentence.

As an example of a function, the distance covered by a moving object depends on its speed and the length of time it has been moving at that speed. We describe this situation by saying that distance is a function of speed and time. Similarly, the value of a simple arithmetic sum $(m + n)$ depends on the values of the numbers—called "summands"—being added.

Mathematicians and scientists have developed a well-known notation for expressing these dependency, or functional, relationships. We might write, for example,

Distance = FDIS(Speed, Time)

to express that the distance covered by a moving object is a function of both its speed and the time it has been traveling at that speed. Similarly, we might write

Sum = FSUM(Summand 1, Summand 2)

to express the obvious fact that the value of a sum is a function of both of the numbers being added.

We have used names for these functions that begin with 'F': FDIS and FSUM. This helps us to remember when something is a function. The remaining letters distinguish one function from another, but they should also be chosen to help us remember what the function is for. In these two cases, FDIS and FSUM seem to be obvious choices for the distance-covered function and the sum function.

In describing truth functions, such as negation, we shall also follow these conventions. The names of truth functions will begin with 'F', and the letters that follow will be ones that help us remember what the function is for. We shall let FNEG be the name of the negation function. So when we write

$V(\sim\mathbf{P}) = \mathrm{FNEG}(V(\mathbf{P}))$

we are simply saying that the truth value of a negation, $\sim\mathbf{P}$, is a function (FNEG) of the truth value of $\mathbf{P}$.

There are two ways of characterizing functions. First, we can list all the possible inputs and corresponding outputs of a function. When we do so, we are characterizing a function *extensionally*. For example, the following tables partly characterize the functions FDIS and FSUM extensionally:

'NOT', 'AND', 'OR'

Inputs		Output
Speed, mi/h	Time, h	FDIS (Speed, Time)
10	1	10
1	10	10
20	3	60

and so on

Inputs		Output
m	n	FSUM (m, n)
0	0	0
1	0	1
3	2	5

and so on

It is easy to see that this way of characterizing a function is often very clumsy. In the above two examples, the lists would go on indefinitely before the functions were ever completely described.

Another way of characterizing a function is *intensionally:* we give an algorithm for calculating the output of a function from its inputs. The algorithm gives us a method—a recipe—for generating the output of a function from its inputs. The algorithm is said to *compute* the function when its inputs and outputs agree with those of the function. (This is not to say that the algorithm is identical to the function.) For example, an algorithm for FSUM is

1. INPUT m.
2. INPUT n.
3. OUTPUT $m + n$.
4. STOP.

and an algorithm for FDIS is

1. INPUT speed.
2. INPUT time.
3. OUTPUT speed $\times$ time.
4. STOP.

The method of giving an algorithm that computes a function is often easier than listing all the possible inputs and outputs. In fact, giving an algorithm is often the only way to characterize a function completely. A function is characterized when its output is specified for any of the possible inputs it might take. Naturally, there can be several different algorithms that compute the same function.

CHAPTER 3

Truth Tables and Algorithms for FNEG

We can in fact characterize the truth function FNEG with almost equal ease by making an input-output listing or by giving an algorithm. This is so because while numerical variables can take an indefinite number of values—1, 2, 3, . . .—truth values can only be one of two values: TRUE and FALSE.

The complete extensional characterization of the FNEG function is as follows:

Input	Output
V(**P**)	FNEG(V(**P**))
FALSE	TRUE
TRUE	FALSE

An extensional characterization of a truth function, like the one above, is a *truth table.* In writing truth tables, we shall always list the inputs on the left of the vertical line and the output on the right (though we shall not always use the labels "Input" and "Output").

We can also characterize the FNEG function by giving an algorithm that produces the same results displayed by the truth table. Informally, we can say that FNEG "reverses" the truth value of its input. But this is probably uselessly informal, because the idea of "reversing" a truth value, while intuitively clear, is not a concept rigorously employed by people or computers.

We can, moreover, draw a flowchart that presents an algorithm for computing the FNEG function for some arbitrary truth value of a sentence **P** taken as input.

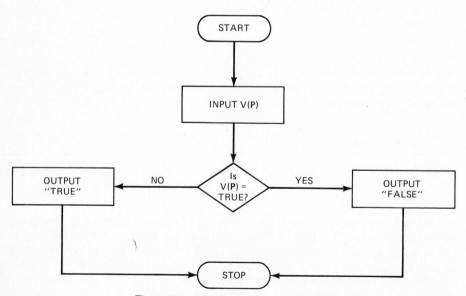

Figure 3-1 Flowchart for computing FNEG.

Or we can use an algorithm written in our program design language to characterize the FNEG function:

```
1. INPUT V(P).
2. IF V(P) = TRUE
      THEN OUTPUT "FALSE."
3. IF V(P) = FALSE
      THEN OUTPUT "TRUE."
4. STOP.
```

Up to this point, we have talked about the truth values of sentences as being either TRUE or FALSE. If we recall our earlier mention of associating the number 1 with TRUE and 0 with FALSE, we can see that a very compact algorithm for characterizing the FNEG function is possible. We should first note that if we use the numbers 0 and 1, the truth table for FNEG is

V(P)	FNEG(V(P))
0	1
1	0

Since we are working with numbers now, if we wish to find an algorithm for FNEG, we might look for simple arithmetical operations that behave like this.

Here is one simple arithmetical algorithm that does the trick:

```
1. INPUT V(P).
2. OUTPUT 1 − V(P).
3. STOP.
```

We can show very simply that this arithmetical operation behaves exactly the way FNEG is supposed to behave. If V(P) = 1 (that is, if P is TRUE), then 1 − V(P) = 0. If V(P) = 0 (that is, if P is FALSE), then 1 − V(P) = 1. In other words, the algorithm consisting of only the simple operation 1 − V(P) does the job of "reversing" the truth values, exactly as FNEG is supposed to.

Double Negation

We have seen that there is a functional relationship between a negated sentence and the original sentence: the truth value of the negation depends entirely on the truth value of the original sentence. That is:

$$V(\sim P) = FNEG(V(P))$$

We might wonder about the relationship between a sentence that is *twice* negated and the original sentence. For example, consider this sentence:

It is not the case that it isn't raining.

What is the relationship of the truth value of this sentence to the sentence 'It is raining'? If we let A = 'It is raining', then the symbolization of 'It is not the case that it isn't raining' is:

$$\sim\sim A$$

Since the truth value of a singly negated sentence is related to the truth value of the original sentence by FNEG, a double negation (like '$\sim\sim A$') must be related to the original by two applications of FNEG. In other words,

$$V(\sim\sim A) = FNEG(FNEG(A))$$

It so happens that the truth value of '$\sim\sim A$' is the same as the truth value of A. In sentential logic, in other words, two "negatives" make a "positive." Informally, this is easy to see, since each application of FNEG reverses the truth value. Two applications of FNEG would reverse the truth value twice, bringing us back to the original truth value. We could obviously continue the pattern:

$$
\begin{aligned}
V(\sim\mathbf{P}) \quad &= FNEG(V(\mathbf{P})) \\
V(\sim\sim\mathbf{P}) \quad &= FNEG(FNEG(V(\mathbf{P}))) \quad &= V(\mathbf{P}) \\
V(\sim\sim\sim\mathbf{P}) &= FNEG(FNEG(FNEG(V(\mathbf{P})))) = V(\sim\mathbf{P})
\end{aligned}
$$

and so on.

We can make several observations about this process. First, the output of a truth function can be the input of another truth function. This possibility allows us to chain truth functions together, as in FNEG(FNEG(FNEG . . .)).

Second, no matter how complex a sentence is, the truth value of that sentence is a function of the truth values of the sentences that are its "truth-functional parts." Sometimes, this functional relationship is expressed by a single truth function. For example, the relationship of $V(\sim\mathbf{P})$ to $V(\mathbf{P})$ is just:

$$V(\sim\mathbf{P}) = FNEG(V(\mathbf{P}))$$

But other times, the functional relationship might be expressed by more than one use of a truth function. For example, the relationship of $V(\sim\sim\mathbf{P})$ to $V(\mathbf{P})$ is:

$$V(\sim\sim\mathbf{P}) = FNEG(FNEG(V(\mathbf{P})))$$

That is, the truth value of a twice-negated sentence is obtained by applying FNEG twice to the truth value of the sentence, $\mathbf{P}$. More generally, in expressing the functional relationship of the truth value of a complex sentence to the truth values of its parts, there will occur one application of a truth function for every occurrence of a sentence "connective." Besides negation, we shall consider two other sentence connectives in this chapter: conjunction and disjunction.

Atomic and Molecular Sentences

Some sentences seem to be quite simple, sometimes containing only a single word for the subject and a second word for the verb (for example, 'Fido barks'). But merely counting the words in a sentence will not always reveal whether the sentence is simple or more complicated. A clue to one way of dealing with this question can be found by examining negated sentences. These sentences, for instance:

It is not the case that **Q**.
~**Q**

are strings of symbols explicitly containing a simpler sentence within the whole string—in this case, **Q**. So, an initial characterization of a *simple sentence* is that it is a sentence that does not contain any simpler sentences. Molecular sentences, on the other hand, contain one or more simpler sentences. In sentential logic, we shall only consider compound sentences that are composed of sentences linked together by truth-functional *connectives*.

To represent the simplest sentences, it is convenient to reserve the initial letters of the alphabet (possibly with numerals):

A, B, C, . . . , O, A1, B1, . . . , A2, . . .

We call these *atomic* sentences. Any sentences built up out of atomic sentences by means of truth-functional connectives will be called *molecular* sentences.

With the distinction between atomic and molecular sentences in mind, let us begin to explore the many different ways in which molecular sentences can be formed from atomic ones or from simpler molecular ones.

Conjunction

We begin with one of the simplest and most common types of molecular sentences. The sentence

Tom is happy and I'm in love.

is a *conjunction* of two simpler sentences, each of which is called a *conjunct*. The first conjunct is the atomic sentence

Tom is happy.

and the second conjunct is

I'm in love.

In this example, both conjuncts happen to be atomic sentences; we shall see later that this need not be the case.

There are a few other ways in English to construct conjunctions. Instead of using the word 'and', we might have written:

Tom is happy but I'm in love.

This sentence is also a conjunction. In our standard representation of conjunctions, it will be represented by 'Tom is happy and I'm in love'. (The two English sentences do not mean exactly the same thing; the use of 'but' usually indicates that what follows is somehow the more important or contrasting conjunct. For example, I might say 'Tom is happy but I'm in love' if I thought that my condition—being in love—was a better or more important one that Tom's being happy.)

Even a semicolon can be used to construct a conjunction:

Tom is happy; I'm in love.

(English teachers properly complain, by the way, when you use a comma here instead of a semicolon.) Finally, some other variants of conjunction in English are

While Tom is merely happy, I'm in love.

and

Although Tom is happy, I'm in love.

Just as we used a special symbol for negation, we shall also use a special symbol for conjunction. We have a great deal of freedom in this choice, although perhaps the symbol that is used most often is the ampersand, &, which occurs on all typewriters. Some logicians use a period, others use the symbol $\wedge$ and still others use different symbols for conjunction. For convenience we shall use only &. Our choice of letters for sentences is also quite free—so long as we assign distinct letters to distinct sentences.

A proper symbolization of our initial example, 'Tom is happy and I'm in love', is:

(A & B)

Here

A = 'Tom is happy.'
B = 'I'm in love.'

and the special symbol & stands for the 'and' that connects them. We shall say that & is a *two-place connective* because it connects two sentences to form a new, molecular sentence.

The Truth Function FCNJ

How would we describe when the truth value of a conjunction is TRUE? When, for example, is the conjunction

Tom is happy and I'm in love.

TRUE? When is it FALSE? The general answer to this question is:

A conjunction is TRUE just when both conjuncts are TRUE.

In the case at hand, 'Tom is happy and I'm in love' is TRUE just when 'Tom is happy' is TRUE and 'I'm in love' is also TRUE.

If both conjuncts are TRUE, then the conjunction is TRUE. If even one conjunct is FALSE, then the conjunction is FALSE. The truth value of a conjunction is a function of the truth values of its parts (its conjuncts). Since the relationship between the truth value of a conjunction and the truth values of its parts is again a functional one, we can talk about this new truth function exactly as we talked about the negation truth function before.

Let us call this function FCNJ. The truth value of a conjunction of two sentences **P** and **Q** is the result of applying the function FCNJ to the truth values of the conjuncts. In symbols,

$$V(\mathbf{P} \ \& \ \mathbf{Q}) \ = \ FCNJ(V(\mathbf{P}), \ V(\mathbf{Q}))$$

But how does this conjunction function behave? We know that $FCNJ(V(\mathbf{P}), V(\mathbf{Q}))$ equals TRUE if **P** and **Q** both have the value TRUE. And it equals FALSE if either **P** or **Q** has the value FALSE, or if both **P** and **Q** have the value FALSE. In other words:

```
FCNJ(FALSE, FALSE) = FALSE
FCNJ(FALSE, TRUE)  = FALSE
FCNJ(TRUE, FALSE)  = FALSE
FCNJ(TRUE, TRUE)   = TRUE
```

This is a complete extensional characterization of the conjunction function.

We can also display this information in a truth table:

V(**P**)	V(**Q**)	V(**P** & **Q**)
FALSE	FALSE	FALSE
FALSE	TRUE	FALSE
TRUE	FALSE	FALSE
TRUE	TRUE	TRUE

CHAPTER 3

The conjunction function, FCNJ, can also be computed by an algorithm, such as the one portrayed by the following flowchart.

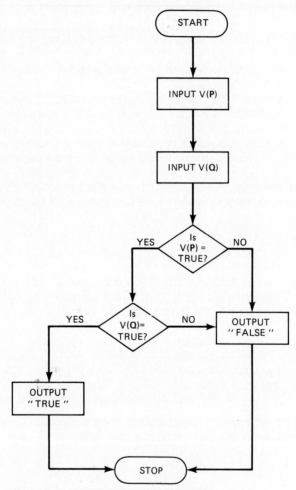

Figure 3-2 Flowchart for computing FCNJ.

'NOT', 'AND', 'OR'

Many other algorithms also compute FCNJ, for instance:

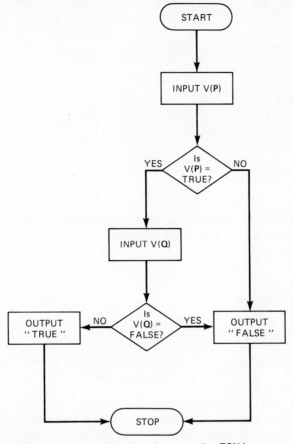

Figure 3-3 Another flowchart for computing FCNJ.

It is also possible to give an algorithm for FCNJ in our program design language:

1. INPUT V(**P**).
2. INPUT V(**Q**).
3. IF V(**P**) = TRUE
      THEN IF V(**Q**) = TRUE
                  THEN GO TO Step 6.
4. OUTPUT "FALSE."
5. STOP.
6. OUTPUT "TRUE."
7. STOP.

Many other correct algorithms for FCNJ can also be written in our program design language. For example, the following algorithm for FCNJ is also correct (note that it does not use a GO TO instruction):

```
1. INPUT V(P).
2. INPUT V(Q).
3. IF V(P) = TRUE
      THEN IF V(Q) = TRUE
                  THEN (a) OUTPUT "TRUE."
                       (b) STOP.
4. OUTPUT "FALSE."
5. STOP.
```

Another algorithm is possible if we return to associating 1 with TRUE and 0 with FALSE. To see this, we first rewrite the extensional characterization of FCNJ, using 1 and 0. We obtain

$$FCNJ(0, 0) = 0$$
$$FCNJ(0, 1) = 0$$
$$FCNJ(1, 0) = 0$$
$$FCNJ(1, 1) = 1$$

That is, FCNJ is 1 only when both of its inputs are 1, and it is 0 otherwise. Since we are working with numbers now, we might ask ourselves which *arithmetical* functions behave like this for values of 0 and 1.

There are in fact many simple arithmetic functions that "mimic" FCNJ, given the values of the conjuncts as inputs. We are going to adopt a particular algorithm that may not be familiar to you but is easy to follow. We take the value of FCNJ(V(P), V(Q)) to be the *lesser* of the values V(P) and V(Q). This is usually written as the *minimum* function:

$$MIN(V(P), V(Q))$$

For example,

$$MIN(2, 5) = 2$$
$$MIN(5, 2) = 2$$
$$MIN(5, 5) = 5$$

So the algorithm is:

```
1. INPUT V(P).
2. INPUT V(Q).
3. OUTPUT MIN(V(P), V(Q)).
4. STOP.
```

'NOT', 'AND', 'OR'

The relevant inputs for MIN are given below:

MIN(0, 0) = 0
MIN(0, 1) = 0
MIN(1, 0) = 0
MIN(1, 1) = 1

Since the MIN function works exactly the way the FCNJ function should, we can conveniently use the MIN function to compute the FCNJ function.

When employing one of these procedures, we would probably want to generalize the initial steps slightly so that we could (1) determine that the compound sentence we are evaluating is a conjunction and (2) write a procedure that identifies and then asks for the truth values of the appropriate atomic sentences. We shall give the full procedure in a later chapter.

If we are dealing with a conjunction of two atomic sentences, we can refer immediately to a characterization of FCNJ to find the value of the conjunction. But how do we deal with a conjunction of conjunctions? Or what if some of our sentences are negations? Take, for instance, a conjunction of the form

((**P** & **Q**) & **R**)

Its two conjuncts are (**P** & **Q**) and **R**. The first of these conjuncts is itself a conjunction, (**P** & **Q**), while the second conjunct appears to be atomic, **R**. An English sentence with this logical structure is:

Both Tom and Mary will be coming to the party, as well as Bill.

To evaluate the truth value of such a conjunction, we naturally need to know the truth values of the two conjuncts: (**P** & **Q**) and **R**. But to determine the truth value of (**P** & **Q**), we must first know the truth values both of **P** and of **Q**. So, to find the truth value of ((**P** & **Q**) & **R**), we must first find the truth value of the conjunction (**P** & **Q**) and then find the truth value of the conjunction of that sentence with **R**. The relationship of the truth value of ((**P** & **Q**) & **R**) to the truth values of **P**, **Q**, and **R**, as described above, is:

V(**P** & **Q**)   = FCNJ(V(**P**), V(**Q**))
V((**P** & **Q**) & **R**) = FCNJ(V(**P** & **Q**)   , V(**R**))
                    = FCNJ(FCNJ(V(**P**), V(**Q**)) , V(**R**))

Consider another example:

(~**P** & **Q**)

An English sentence with this logical structure is 'I'm not a Democrat, but Bill is'. To find the truth value of this sentence—which is also a conjunction—we first find the truth value of ~**P** and then find the truth value of the conjunction of that with the truth value of **Q** [which is V(**Q**)]. The result is:

V(~**P** & **Q**) = FCNJ(FNEG(V(**P**)), V(**Q**))

Finally, look at this example:

~(**P** & **Q**)

This is the negation of the entire conjunction (**P** & **Q**). An English example is 'It is not the case that Napoleon was both a genius and mad'. To find the truth value of such a sentence, we first find the truth value of the conjunction and then the truth value of the negation of that:

V(~(**P** & **Q**)) = FNEG(FCNJ(V(**P**), V(**Q**)))

The previous two examples should alert us to the importance of parentheses and to the fact that we shall have to analyze the logical structure of sentences carefully.

Let us state carefully some of the kinds of strings that are sentences, paying more attention to the use of parentheses. Here, we assume that sentences are not actual sentences in English but rather their representations by single letters and certain combinations of single letters.

Rules

1. A string consisting of one of the single letters (possibly with a numeral),
    'A', 'B', . . . , 'O', 'A1', 'A2', 'A3', . . . is a sentence.
2. If a string **P** is a sentence,
    then its negation, ~**P**, is a sentence.
3. If strings **P** and **Q** are sentences,
    then their conjunction, (**P** & **Q**), is a sentence.

So far, these are the only sentences we have. Rules 2 and 3 have clear parallels in English. The English parallel to rule 2 would say that given any sentence (for example, 'All apples are fruit'), its negation ('It is not the case that all apples are fruit') is also a sentence. The English parallel to rule 3 would say that given any two sentences, we can form a new conjunctive sentence using them—for instance, by placing the word 'and' between them.

Disjunction

We shall examine another common, two-place sentence connective in this chapter, the one usually expressed in English by the word 'or'. A sentence composed of two other sentences connected by 'or' is a *disjunction*. The two sentences which make up a disjunction are called its *disjuncts*. To create a disjunction in English, take any two sentences and write 'or' between them.

As before, we shall employ a special symbol for this connective. For disjunction, we shall use a wedge (v). Thus if the sentences

1. Interest rates level off.
2. The price of gold rises.

are represented by 'A' and 'B', respectively, then

(A v B)

represents 'Interest rates level off or the price of gold rises'.

Disjunctions are FALSE just in those situations where both disjuncts are FALSE. They are TRUE if even one disjunct is TRUE. Disjunctions are thus relatively more generous than conjunctions: they are TRUE in comparatively more situations than conjunctions. To take a concrete example, the sentence 'Interest rates level off or the price of gold rises' is FALSE only when inflation fails to level off and when the price of gold does not rise. That is, the disjunction is FALSE only when both disjuncts are FALSE—and it is TRUE otherwise. Using our notation,

V(A v B) = FALSE only if V(A) = FALSE and V(B) = FALSE

In the cases where V(A) = TRUE or V(B) = TRUE or both, then V(A v B) = TRUE.

The Truth Function FDSJ

Associated with the sentence connective v is another truth function, which we shall call FDSJ. The function FDSJ takes as inputs the truth values of the two disjuncts and outputs the truth value of the entire disjunction. Its extensional characterization is:

```
FDSJ(FALSE, FALSE)  = FALSE
FDSJ(FALSE, TRUE)   = TRUE
FDSJ(TRUE, FALSE)   = TRUE
FDSJ(TRUE, TRUE)    = TRUE
```

Or, displayed as a truth table:

V(**P**)	V(**Q**)	FDSJ(V(**P**), V(**Q**))
FALSE	FALSE	FALSE
FALSE	TRUE	TRUE
TRUE	FALSE	TRUE
TRUE	TRUE	TRUE

Again, we can also compute this truth function by giving an algorithm. In flowchart language, an algorithm that computes FDSJ is:

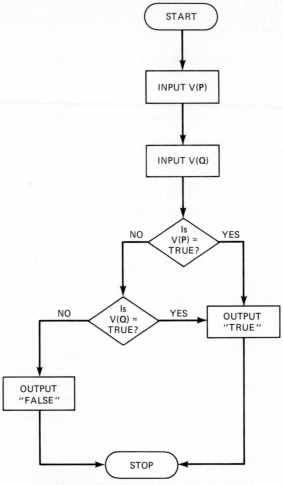

Figure 3-4 Flowchart for computing FDSJ.

In our program design language, an algorithm is:

1. INPUT V(**P**).
2. INPUT V(**Q**).
3. IF V(**P**) = TRUE
    THEN (a) OUTPUT "TRUE."
            (b) STOP.
4. IF V(**Q**) = TRUE
    THEN (a) OUTPUT "TRUE."
            (b) STOP.
5. OUTPUT "FALSE."
6. STOP.

Returning to the arithmetical associations, we see that the truth table for FDSJ would be:

V(P)	V(Q)	FDSJ(V(P), V(Q))
0	0	0
0	1	1
1	0	1
1	1	1

There are several arithmetical functions that would take these inputs and generate the same outputs as shown in this truth table. We are going to give an algorithm for computing FDSJ that uses an arithmetical function, the "maximum" function. The *maximum* function selects the *larger* of the values it operates on. That is,

MAX(2, 5) = 5
MAX(5, 2) = 5
MAX(5, 5) = 5

Thus the algorithm is:

1. INPUT V(P).
2. INPUT V(Q).
3. OUTPUT MAX (V(P), V(Q)).
4. STOP.

Applied to our truth values 0 and 1, this algorithm does exactly what FDSJ does.

Inclusive and Exclusive Disjunction

Frequently, disjunctions in English have to be rewritten so that their status as disjunctions of two sentences is revealed. Consider:

Helen or Mary is the winner.

This must be rewritten as

Helen is the winner or Mary is the winner.

so that we can see that it is a disjunction of two sentences.

A sentence such as the one above is frequently, however, understood in the *exclusive* sense, namely, as asserting that either Mary or Helen is the winner *but not both*. Our discussion of disjunctions in this section has addressed only the *inclusive* sense, because it *includes* the possibility of both disjuncts being TRUE. For instance, our use

CHAPTER 3

of disjunction in the sentence above allows for the possibility that both Helen and Mary have won. In the next chapter, we shall consider a special connective for the exclusive sense of disjunction.

Sentences with Several Connectives

Now is the time to work a few examples to make sure that we understand how to deal with sentences that are mixtures of negation, conjunction, and disjunction. Before we do some examples, though, we need to add another rule to our rules for determining which strings are sentences:

4. If strings **P** and **Q** are sentences,
   then their disjunction, **(P v Q)**, is a sentence.

According to this new rule (and also rules 2 and 1 from page 52)

$(\sim A \lor B)$

is a sentence, because:

'A' and 'B' are both sentences (by rule 1).
So, '$\sim$A' is a sentence (by rule 2).
Therefore, '$(\sim A \lor B)$' is a sentence (by rule 4).

Its truth value can be calculated by this expression:

FDSJ(FNEG(V(A)), V(B))

We have obtained this by reasoning as follows: For every sentence connective, there is a truth function uniquely associated with it. For $\sim$ it is FNEG, for & it is FCNJ, and for v it is FDSJ. Working from the "inside" of the original sentence "out," we first find the truth value of '$\sim$A':

$V(\sim A) = FNEG(V(A))$

Next, we see that

$V(\sim A \lor B) = FDSJ(V(\sim A), V(B))$

Substituting our previous result, we get

$V(\sim A \lor B) = FDSJ(FNEG(V(A)), V(B))$

Consider this sentence: $((A \lor B) \& \sim C)$. (You should verify that this is indeed a sentence according to rules 1 to 4.) A step-by-step analysis of this sentence leads to the expression:

V((A v B) & ~C) = FCNJ(FDSJ(V(A), V(B)), FNEG(V(C)))

We arrived at this formula by reasoning as we did in the previous example, associating the appropriate truth functions with every sentence connective. You should evaluate this expression for various truth values of A, B, and C.

For instance, when V(A) = TRUE, V(B) = FALSE, and V(C) = TRUE, the value is FALSE. We arrived at this answer in the following way. When V(A) = TRUE and V(B) = FALSE, the output of the function FDSJ(V(A), V(B)) is TRUE. So, replacing 'FDSJ(V(A), V(B))' with 'TRUE', we would have

FCNJ(TRUE, FNEG(V(C)))

When V(C) = TRUE, then FNEG(V(C)) is FALSE. So, replacing 'FNEG(V(C))' with 'FALSE', we have:

FCNJ(TRUE, FALSE)

With these inputs (TRUE and FALSE), the output of the FCNJ function is FALSE. But when V(A) = TRUE, V(B) = FALSE, and V(C) = FALSE, the truth value of the sentence is TRUE.

Another example is:

(A & ~(B v C))

The truth value of (B v C) is FDSJ(V(B), V(C)). And the truth value of ~(B v C) is:

FNEG(FDSJ(V(B), V(C)))

Thus the whole sentence has the truth value

FCNJ(V(A), FNEG(FDSJ(V(B), V(C))))

Other Connectives

The three connectives we have examined are not the only possible ones. There are many other ways to form new sentences from old ones. Some of these ways use truth-functional connectives, but others don't. An example of a connective that is *not* truth-functional is the one-place connective 'My friend believes that. . .'. This may seem like a strange connective, but it behaves very much like the truth-functional, one-place connective 'It is not the case that'. To see why 'My friend believes that' is not truth-functional, consider the sentence A = 'My friend believes that our team will win the game'. Its truth value is not a function of the truth value of B = 'Our team will win the game', because V(A) might be TRUE whether V(B) = TRUE or V(B) = FALSE. That is, the truth value of A does not depend solely on the truth value of B. More precisely, there is no algorithm that outputs V(A) when only V(B) is input.

CHAPTER 3

However, there are many connectives besides those discussed in this chapter that *can* be associated with a truth function. Most important among these new connectives are 'if . . . then . . .' and, especially for computer science, 'NAND' and 'NOR'. Just as with 'not', 'and', and 'or', each of these connectives can be expressed in English by many different words. We have not sought to make the translation from English into symbolic notation, or from our symbolic notation back into English, a "mechanical" matter. Perhaps it would not be possible. Here is one province that seems, for now, best reserved for nonmechanical processes. (But for an attempt to make it mechanical, see Otto, 1978; and for a discussion of related research in "computational linguistics"—a branch of computer science dealing with natural-language understanding—see Winograd, 1983.)

There is a sense, however, in which our discussion of the three connectives introduced in this chapter is complete. Namely, it can be shown that any proposition that one might wish to express can be expressed by a sentence that uses only negation, conjunction, and disjunction. In fact, only negation and *one* of the other two connectives are sufficient. Further discussion of this fact must await a later chapter, however.

Summary

In this chapter, we began our study of *sentential logic*. We viewed a sentence as a string of symbols that expresses a proposition, and we saw how to construct complex *molecular* sentences from simpler molecular ones or from *atomic* sentences by using three connectives: *negation, conjunction,* and *disjunction.*

While there are many ways to negate English sentences, a standard way is by prefixing the phrase 'It is not the case that' to a sentence. If **P** is a sentence in our symbolic notation, then ~**P** is its negation. The truth value of a negation is TRUE (or FALSE) if the truth value of the nonnegated sentence is FALSE (or TRUE).

A *function* associates a single output with given inputs. Negation is a *truth-functional* connective, and FNEG is the function that outputs TRUE (FALSE) when its input is FALSE (TRUE). Functions can be characterized *extensionally* by listing all possible inputs and corresponding outputs. In the case of a *truth function* such as FNEG, the inputs and outputs can be displayed in a *truth table.* Functions can also be characterized *intensionally* by giving an algorithm for computing the output that corresponds to each set of inputs. In the case of FNEG, we looked at algorithms that use the arithmetical operation of subtracting the input (0 for FALSE, 1 for TRUE) from 1.

Our standard way of forming a conjunction in English is to connect two sentences with the word 'and': symbolically, if **P** and **Q** are sentences, then (**P** & **Q**) is a sentence. The truth value of a conjunction of two sentences is TRUE if the truth values of both *conjuncts* are TRUE, and it is FALSE otherwise. FCNJ is the truth function that outputs TRUE when both of its inputs are TRUE and outputs FALSE otherwise. We looked at algorithms for FCNJ that use the arithmetical function MIN.

If **P** and **Q** are sentences, then their disjunction is the sentence (**P** v **Q**)—in English, we would use the word 'or'. The truth value of a disjunction of two sentences is TRUE if at least one of the two *disjuncts* has the truth value TRUE, and it is FALSE otherwise. This is the *inclusive* sense of disjunction, since it allows for the possibility that both disjuncts are TRUE. The truth function FDSJ outputs FALSE when both of its inputs are

FALSE and outputs TRUE otherwise. Our algorithms for characterizing FDSJ inten-sionally used the arithmetical function MAX.

Finally, we presented four rules to help us in determining whether a string is a sentence, and we discussed how to find the truth values of molecular sentences con-taining more than one connective.

Exercises

A. Using the following abbreviations, think of an English sentence that as clearly as possible says what each formula expresses.

A = 'It is raining.'
B = 'The sky is clear.'
C = 'It is snowing.'
D = 'It is cold.'

Example: ~(A & B)

Answer: It is not the case both that it is raining and that the sky is clear.

1. ~C
2. ~~D
3. (A & C)
4. (B v D)
5. (~B & D)
6. (B & ~D)
7. ~(A v C)
8. ~(B & C)
9. (A & (B v C))
10. (~B v (C & D))
11. (C & (~D v A))
12. ((A v B) & (C v D))
13. ~(B v D)
14. (~B & ~D)

B. For each of the formulas 1 to 14 above, state whether the sentence is TRUE or FALSE, assuming:

V('It is raining.')   = V(A) = TRUE
V('The sky is clear.') = V(B) = FALSE
V('It is snowing.')   = V(C) = TRUE
V('It is cold.')   = V(D) = FALSE

Example: ~(A & B)

Answer: TRUE   [The truth value of (A & B) is FALSE because B is FALSE. So the truth value of ~(A & B) is the opposite value, which is to say, TRUE.]

C. Symbolize the sentences below using the following abbreviations:

A = 'Computers think.'
B = 'Computers feel.'

C = 'Animals think.'
D = 'Animals feel.'

Example: Computers do not think.
Answer: ~A

1. Computers both think and feel.
2. Animals feel but computers don't.
3. Either computers think or animals do.
4. It is not the case that animals don't feel.
5. Either computers both feel and think or animals do.
6. Either animals think, or computers don't think but do feel.
7. Neither animals nor computers think.
8. Either animals feel or computers don't.
9. Computers and animals both think and feel.
10. Either computers think, animals do, or computers feel, or animals do.
11. Neither animals nor computers think or feel.
12. Neither animals nor computers both think and feel.

D. Determine the truth value of each of the above sentences, assuming:

V('Computers think.') = TRUE
V('Computers feel.')   = FALSE
V('Animals think.')   = FALSE
V('Animals feel.')   = TRUE

Example: Computers do not think.

~A

Answer: FALSE, since the truth value of ~A is the opposite of the truth value of A.

E. Sometimes we do not know in advance the truth values of the atomic sentences in a molecular sentence. We can nevertheless give an algorithm for determining the truth value of a molecular sentence from inputs consisting of the truth values of the atomic sentences.

Example: ~(A & B)

Answer: Using a flowchart and arithmetical functions, see Figure 3-5.

Using our program design language, but without using arithmetical functions:

1. INPUT V(A).
2. IF V(A) = FALSE
   THEN (a) OUTPUT "TRUE."
        (b) STOP.
3. INPUT V(B).
4. IF V(B) = FALSE
   THEN (a) OUTPUT "TRUE."
        (b) STOP.
5. OUTPUT "FALSE."
6. STOP.

Construct an algorithm for each of the following formulas. (Your instructor will tell you whether to use flowchart language or program design language.)

'NOT', 'AND', 'OR'

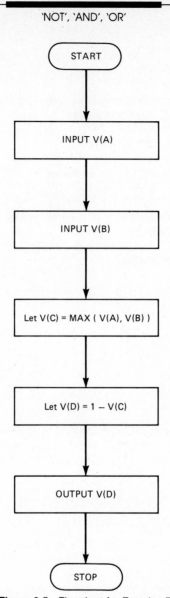

Figure 3-5 Flowchart for Exercise E.

1. ~~A
2. (A & ~B)
3. (~A v B)
4. ((A & B) v C)
5. (~A & (B v C))
6. ((A & ~B) v (~C v D))

    7. ~(A v B)
    8. (~A v A)
    9. (B & ~B)

F. Given the molecular sentences below, determine the truth functions that would allow one to calculate their truth values.

Example: (A v ~B)

Answer: FDSJ(V(A), FNEG(V(B)))

Explanation: Work from the "inside" out; that is, begin with the innermost subformula. In this case, the innermost sentence is '~B'. The truth value of '~B' is given by:

    FNEG(V(B))

But '~B' is part of a disjunction, whose truth value is calculated by:

    FDSJ(V(A), V(~B))

Since V(~B) = FNEG(V(B)), we have by substitution:

    FDSJ(V(A), FNEG(V(B)))

    1. ~(A v B)
    2. ~(~A v B)
    3. (A & B)
    4. (~A & B)
    5. ~(A & B)
    6. ~(~A & ~B)
    7. (A & (B v C))
    8. (~B v (C & ~D))
    9. (~B & (~C & ~D))
  10. ~(A & (~B v C))

G. Given the following truth-value assignments:

    V(A) = 1
    V(B) = 0
    V(C) = 0
    V(D) = 1

calculate the output of each of the functions listed below.

Example: MAX(V(A), 1 − (1 − V(B)))

Answer: 1 (that is, TRUE)

Explanation: The value of A is 1. So if we substitute 1 for V(A), the expression becomes:

    MAX(1, 1 − (1 − V(B)))

But since we are looking for the maximum value of this expression, it must be 1—we don't really have to go any further. If we did go further, we would substitute 0 for V(B), and the result would be:

    MAX(1, 1 − (1 − 0))

This is:

    MAX(1, 1 − 1)

which is nothing but

    MAX(1, 0)

and the maximum of 1 and 0 is

    1

just as we had earlier concluded.

'NOT', 'AND', 'OR'

1. $1 - (1 - V(B))$
2. $1 - MAX(V(A), V(B))$
3. $FCNJ(V(A), V(B))$
4. $MIN(1 - V(A), V(B))$
5. $FCNJ(1 - V(B), 1 - V(C))$
6. $MAX(V(B), 1 - V(D))$
7. $FCNJ(V(A), FDSJ(V(B), V(C)))$
8. $MAX(V(B), MAX(V(C), V(D)))$
9. $FCNJ(1 - FDSJ(V(A), V(B)), V(A))$
10. $MIN(1 - MAX(V(B), V(C)), MIN(V(A), 1 - (V(D)))$
11. $1 - FDSJ(1 - V(B), FCNJ(FDSJ(V(B), V(C)), 1 - V(D)))$
12. $1 - (1 - (1 - (FCNJ(V(A), V(B)))))$

H. For each of the expressions in the above problem, determine the sentence that corresponds to it.

Example: $1 - MIN(V(A), V(B))$

Answer: ~(A & B)

Explanation: Work from the outside in. A formula beginning with '1 −' is certain to be a negation, so we can write a negation sign:

~

The next function we encounter is

$MIN(V(A), V(B))$

The sentence that corresponds to this is

(A & B)

So we can add this to our lonely negation sign, obtaining

~(A & B)

I. Negation.
Write an algorithm for computing the truth value of a negation, using a different arithmetical function from the one given in the text [that is, a function other than $1 - V(P)$].

J. Conjunction.
1. Write two algorithms for computing the truth value of a conjunction, using arithmetical functions other than the one given in the text.
2. Rewrite either of the algorithms for FCNJ given on pages 49–50, with the first test being $V(\mathbf{P}) = FALSE$.

K. Disjunction.
1. Write an algorithm for computing the truth value of a disjunction, using an arithmetical function other than the one given in the text.
2. Rewrite the algorithm for FDSJ given on page 54, with the first test being $V(\mathbf{P}) = FALSE$.

L. We have defined the notions of conjunction and disjunction for only two sentences. Similarly, we have spoken of 'and' and 'or' as connecting just two English sentences. But we might sometimes wish to speak of a more general truth function or connective that can take as input two or more truth values or connect two or more sentences. Consider this sentence:

Thomas Jefferson was an American, a Virginian, and a slaveholder.

When is it TRUE? What arithmetical function (other than the one given in the text) would be suitable for use in an algorithm for computing the truth value of such a sentence with more than two conjuncts?

M. 1. Construct a sentence using just conjunction and negation that is FALSE in the single case where A, B, and C are all TRUE.

2. Construct a sentence using only negation and conjunction that is TRUE whenever just one of A and B is TRUE and that otherwise is FALSE.

3. Construct a sentence using only negation and conjunction that is FALSE whenever A and B are either both TRUE or both FALSE.

4. Construct a sentence using just conjunction and negation that is TRUE whenever exactly two of A, B, and C are FALSE and that is otherwise FALSE.

Suggestions for Computer Implementation

Although the creation of algorithms for computing FNEG, FCNJ, and FDSJ is neither especially complicated nor, at this point, especially useful, these algorithms will later be of great importance. Without them, we would not be able to determine the truth value of an arbitrary molecular sentence.

Depending on the computer and programming language available, there are several ways to design a program to compute these truth functions. For instance, in Pascal and in dialects of BASIC in which definitions of functions are permitted to be spread over several lines (so-called "multistatement function definitions"), matters are at their simplest: FNEG, FCNJ, and FDSJ can be defined almost exactly as indicated by our program design language algorithms in the text.

If multistatement function definitions are not permitted, then more careful planning must be employed. Perhaps the simplest way would then be to resort to the arithmetical association of 1 with TRUE and 0 with FALSE. This convention will usually allow the definition of a truth function to be placed on a single line.

Sometimes, the Boolean operations, NOT, AND, and OR can be used directly. Otherwise, one can resort to the arithmetical functions we mentioned in the text. Let p and q be the arithmetic truth values of **P** and **Q**, respectively. Then:

Let FNEG(p) be $1 - p$.
Let FCNJ(p, q) be MIN(p, q).
Let FDSJ (p, q) be MAX(p, q).

The MIN and MAX functions might in turn have to be defined, or we could use other arithmetical functions that behave in the appropriate manner for FCNJ and FDSJ. For example, two functions are:

Let FCNJ(p, q) be ($p * q$).
Let FDSJ (p, q) be ($p + q$) $-$ ($p * q$).

(As is usual in computer science, $*$ is the multiplication operator.) This identification of a conjunction function with multiplication and of a disjunction function with a special kind of addition was discovered by George Boole in the 1830s and 1840s and is the heart of an area of mathematics known as Boolean algebra.

Instead of a definition of functions, some sort of explicit subroutine can be used—such as GOSUB in BASIC or procedures in Pascal. Whenever we would want to apply a truth function, we would instead switch control to some other point in the program, which would then perform the necessary operations and return control to the original place in the program. For example, in a limited microcomputer BASIC, to calculate the truth value of a conjunction, (A$ & B$)—where A$ and B$ are the conjuncts and A and B are their respective truth values—we might have:

```
100 INPUT A
200 INPUT B           [Inputting and storing truth values of A$ and B$ in variables
                       A and B]
300 LET P = A
400 LET Q = B         ["Passing off" the truth values of A and B to variables P
                       and Q used in the subroutine]
500 GOSUB 1000        [Switching control to line 1000 if we encounter a conjunc-
                       tion]
  .
  .
  .
1000 IF P = 0 THEN GOTO 1400
1100 IF Q = 0 THEN GOTO 1400
1200 LET R = 1        [Value of entire conjunction is TRUE, i.e., 1]
1300 RETURN
1400 LET R = 0        [Value of entire conjunction is FALSE, i.e., 0]
1500 RETURN
```

The value of the conjunction when the subroutine returns control is stored in the variable called R. Line 500 would actually be more involved in a real program, because we would want to know that we had encountered a conjunction, and only then would we apply the subroutine beginning at 1000. The variables P and Q are necessary if we wish to apply the subroutine to any two conjuncts—A$ and B$, C$ and D$, and so on—anywhere in the program. So the information about the truth values of the two conjuncts—whatever they were originally called—is temporarily stored in P and Q.

SENTENTIAL LOGIC: The Connective 'If . . . Then . . .' and Additional Connectives

In the previous chapter, we looked at the one-place connective 'not' ($\sim$) and the two-place connectives 'and' (&) and 'or' (v). We now turn to an examination of several other two-place connectives: 'if . . . then . . .' ($\rightarrow$), 'if and only if' ($\leftrightarrow$), exclusive disjunction (XOR), 'neither . . . nor . . .' (NOR), and 'not both . . . and . . .' (NAND). Finally, we shall present a complete listing of all possible two-place connectives.

These additional connectives are not strictly speaking required. The two connectives $\sim$ and & are sufficient to express any sentence in sentential logic. Yet these additional connectives we are about to discuss correspond to phrases commonly used in English, and so the addition of special symbols for these connectives allows us to translate English sentences very smoothly into symbolized ones. We are, however, faced with a trade-off when we decide whether to introduce such additional connectives. When the number of connectives we are using is very small, the resulting account of logic is compact, elegant, and easy for a computer to "understand"—but it is not always convenient for us human users, accustomed as we are to thinking in a natural language like English. On the other hand, when we introduce a full range of special symbols that correspond to commonly used English connectives, the resulting account makes us humans feels very "at home"—but the account is then repetitive, certain truth-functionally synonymous expressions are not easy to identify, and the amount of work that is required to program a computer to understand our notation will have multiplied. We shall in later chapters see similar decisions that will have to be made and that also involve trade-offs between human and computer convenience, and even between algorithmic convenience of one sort and algorithmic convenience of another.

The Conditional

In ordinary conversation, we sometimes wish to qualify our statements by using an "if" clause. Such qualified statements are called *conditionals*. Rather than promise you outright a bag of peanuts, I might say:

If you go to the hockey game with me, then I'll give you a bag of peanuts.

What is important about this example is that the *only* circumstance under which I have broken my promise is when you do go to the hockey game with me, but I do not give you a bag of peanuts. Suppose, on the other hand, that you do *not* go to the hockey game with me. In that case, I will *not* have broken my promise—whether or not I give you a bag of peanuts anyway—because my promise was a conditional one. Since the condition (your going to the hockey game with me) was not met, there is no way for me to break my promise.

Sentences about future events are typically phrased in conditional form:

If the Red Sox win the pennant, then the first play-off game is in Boston.

When would this sentence be FALSE? Clearly, it would be FALSE when the Red Sox do win the pennant, but (it turns out) the first play-off game is not in Boston. What if the Red Sox do not win the pennant? Is the conditional TRUE, or is it FALSE, or have we found a kind of sentence that is neither TRUE nor FALSE?

If the Red Sox do not win the pennant, there are several reasons for taking the whole conditional sentence to be TRUE. One reason involves making this conditional analogous to a conditional promise—which, as we have seen, is considered broken only when the "if" clause is TRUE (and the promised action is not done).

Keeping things tidy, and insisting that all our sentences be TRUE or FALSE depending only on the truth or falsity of their components, we shall stipulate that all sentences of the form

If **P,** then **Q.**

will be FALSE whenever both **P** is TRUE and **Q** is FALSE. In any other case, the conditional will be TRUE. A conditional that obeys this stipulation is called a *material conditional.* A conditional sentence has two parts that are themselves sentences (just like conjunctions and disjunctions, but unlike negations, which have only one component sentence). The sentence setting the condition, which usually follows immediately after the word 'if', is called the *antecedent* of the conditional. The second part of a conditional, often following the word 'then', is called the *consequent* of the conditional.

ADDITIONAL CONNECTIVES

In logic, we are primarily concerned with those conditionals whose consequents are declarative sentences, rather than those whose consequents are promised actions, threats, or commands. In computer science, on the other hand, the most frequently encountered conditional is one whose consequent is an instruction: If <something is TRUE>, then do <some action>.

We have already seen a conditional whose consequent is a promise. Other variations include conditionals with threats or commands as consequents:

If you take my book, I will report you.
If you cannot keep from laughing, leave the room.

So there are at least three other kinds of conditionals besides material conditionals (which, remember, are composed entirely of declarative sentences): conditional promises, conditional threats, and conditional commands. An examination of them can help us see more clearly when material conditional sentences are TRUE or FALSE. Consider the following claims about promises, threats, and commands:

A conditional promise is broken exactly in those cases when the antecedent is TRUE, but the action described in the consequent is *not* done; otherwise, the promise is not broken.

A conditional threat is not carried out exactly in those cases when the antecedent is TRUE, but the action described in the consequent is *not* performed; otherwise, the threat is still in force.

A conditional command is disobeyed exactly in those cases when the antecedent is TRUE, but the action described in the consequent is *not* performed; otherwise, the command is not disobeyed.

The truth conditions for a material conditional sentence follow this pattern exactly:

A material conditional sentence is FALSE exactly when the antecedent is TRUE, but the consequent is FALSE; otherwise, the material conditional is not FALSE.

Sentences, however, are either TRUE or FALSE. So, if a material conditional sentence is not FALSE, then it is TRUE.

Besides the material conditional, there are several other types of conditional sentences in English. Conditional sentences can be used to express causal connections between two events, as in 'If the temperature of water reaches 100°C, then the water will boil.' They can also be used to express counterfactual situations: 'If the match had not been wet, then it would have lit when you struck it.' And they sometimes are used to express temporal connections: 'If it was 3 P.M. five minutes ago, then it is now 3:05 P.M.' In material conditionals, there is not considered to be any such "connection" between the antecedent and the consequent. A good example of a "pure" material conditional might be 'If our team wins, then I'm a monkey's uncle'. From now on, the only conditional sentences we shall study will be material ones—even if they look like one of the other kinds.

Perhaps the most important thing to keep in mind when evaluating a conditional is that one must differentiate between the truth value of the antecedent and the truth value of the whole conditional. In other words, one must distinguish between sentences such as

Horses have wings.

and

If horses have wings, then they fly.

The first, atomic, sentence is FALSE: horses do not have wings. This is not to say, however, that the conditional ('If horses have wings, then they fly') is FALSE. The conditional is TRUE precisely because its antecedent is FALSE. The truth value of a material conditional depends not on any causal, counterfactual, or temporal "connection" between its antecedent and its consequent but only on their truth values. Whenever its antecedent is FALSE, a material conditional is TRUE.

Conditional sentences can be expressed in English in a number of ways. We have already seen these patterns:

If **P, Q.**
If **P,** then **Q.**

A few other forms for conditionals are:

Q, if **P.**
Q, provided that **P.**
When **P, Q.**

The special symbol we shall use for symbolizing conditional sentences is →. Thus, if we wanted to symbolize a sentence such as 'If the sunset tonight is especially pretty, then the weather will be bad tomorrow', where

A = 'The sunset tonight is especially pretty.'
B = 'The weather will be bad tomorrow.'

we would write:

$(A \rightarrow B)$

In general, for any sentences **P** and **Q,**

$(P \rightarrow Q)$

is a conditional sentence. (Of course, '$(Q \rightarrow P)$' is also a conditional sentence, but a different one.)

The Truth Function FCND

Corresponding to the sentence connective → is a truth function we shall call FCND. This function describes the way that the truth value of a conditional depends on the truth values of its antecedent and consequent. Its extensional characterization is as follows:

FCND(FALSE, FALSE) = TRUE
FCND(FALSE, TRUE) = TRUE
FCND(TRUE, FALSE) = FALSE
FCND(TRUE, TRUE)   = TRUE

The first of the pair of truth values that FCND is applied to is the truth value of the antecedent, and the second member of the pair is the truth value of the consequent. Looking at this characterization of FCND, we notice that its output is TRUE if the truth value of the antecedent is FALSE or if the truth value of the consequent is TRUE (or both). Put another way, the output of FCND is FALSE if (and only if) the truth value of the antecedent is TRUE and the truth value of the consequent is FALSE.

As we have done for the other sentence connectives, we present the truth conditions for a conditional in tabular form:

V (P)	V (Q)	V (P → Q)
FALSE	FALSE	TRUE
FALSE	TRUE	TRUE
TRUE	FALSE	FALSE
TRUE	TRUE	TRUE

With this information about the behavior of the FCND function, we can construct algorithms to compute it. A flowchart for computing FCND is:

Figure 4-1 Flowchart for computing FCND.

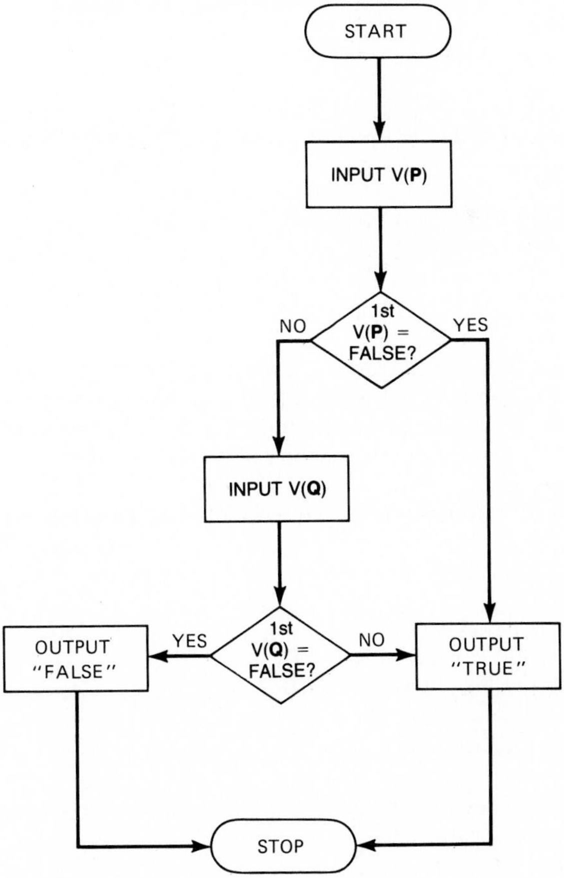

An algorithm in our program design language is:

```
1. INPUT V(P).
2. INPUT V(Q).
3. IF V(P) = FALSE
      THEN (a)  OUTPUT "TRUE."
           (b)  STOP.
4. IF V(Q) = TRUE
      THEN (a)  OUTPUT "TRUE."
           (b)  STOP.
5. OUTPUT "FALSE."
6. STOP.
```

Using our arithmetical associations, we find that one arithmetical expression for computing FCND is:

MAX(1 − V(**P**), V(**Q**))

At this point, you should take the four possible pairs of truth values for **P** and **Q** and compute MAX(1 − V(**P**), V(**Q**)) to verify that this expression can indeed be used for computing FCND(V(**P**), V(**Q**)) as the truth table shows.

Symbolizing Conditionals

Working with conditionals requires a little more care than working with conjunctions or disjunctions. The examples of conditionals that we have examined so far have all had atomic antecedents and atomic consequents. But this is not always the case. The antecedent or the consequent can itself be a molecular sentence. For example, consider:

If yesterday was Tuesday or tomorrow is Thanksgiving, then today is Wednesday.

Here, the antecedent of the conditional is itself a disjunction:

Yesterday was Tuesday or tomorrow is Thanksgiving.

If we had to call attention to this fact in print, we could write something like this:

If (yesterday was Tuesday or tomorrow is Thanksgiving), then today is Wednesday.

We shall similarly clarify this sentence in our notation by using parentheses. If we use the abbreviations

ADDITIONAL CONNECTIVES

A = 'Yesterday was Tuesday.'
B = 'Tomorrow is Thanksgiving.'
C = 'Today is Wednesday.'

then to express the above conditional, we write:

$$((A \vee B) \rightarrow C)$$

The parentheses are absolutely necessary where they are, as the following remarks show. If we had written

$$(A \vee (B \rightarrow C))$$

we would be symbolizing a quite different sentence, namely:

Either yesterday was Tuesday or (if tomorrow is Thanksgiving, then today is Wednesday).

You should evaluate the truth values of

$$((A \vee B) \rightarrow C)$$

and

$$(A \vee (B \rightarrow C))$$

for various truth values of A, B, and C to see that these different sentences sometimes have different truth values. You may use any method of evaluation you wish: truth tables with TRUE and FALSE, truth tables with 0 and 1, or any of the algorithms.

Deciding where the parentheses are to be placed in a symbolization of an English sentence containing 'if . . . then . . .' is a delicate and sometimes difficult matter. We can give only some general hints here. If the sentence begins with 'If' and what follows a 'then' (or a comma) is said naturally in one breath, then—assuming that our sentence has the pattern

If **P**, then **Q**.

—its correct symbolization is probably

$$(\mathbf{P} \rightarrow \mathbf{Q})$$

Here are some examples:

Sentence:
If gold is valuable and portable, then it should be hidden or securely stored.
Symbolization:
$$((A \& B) \rightarrow (C \vee D))$$

Sentence:
> If a nation's enemies have the means, then if they have the will to use those means, they may disrupt the balance of power.

Symbolization:
> $(E \rightarrow (F \rightarrow G))$

However, when the sentence does not begin with 'If' or when the consequent—what follows the 'then'—is broken by a comma, or a natural pause, the conditional might actually be buried within another sentence. Here are some examples:

Sentence:
> It's just not true that if I take a shortcut by walking through the grass, then everyone will do so.

Symbolization:
> $\sim(H \rightarrow J)$

Sentence:
> If we pay our taxes, then we shall have less to spend, but if we don't pay our taxes, then we shall live in fear.

Symbolization:
> $((A \rightarrow B) \ \& \ (\sim A \rightarrow C))$

Only if

Another way to express a conditional uses the phrase 'only if'. The sentence

1. Combustion occurs only if oxygen is present.

is also a conditional sentence. But what is the antecedent? And what is the consequent? There are two possible candidates for this conditional sentence:

2. Combustion occurs $\rightarrow$ oxygen is present.
3. Oxygen is present $\rightarrow$ combustion occurs.

With some thought, you should realize that the first representation is correct. So, the sentence following 'only if' is the *consequent* of (1). As a general rule, one should directly replace 'only if' with $\rightarrow$ in symbolizing English sentences.

Another example is:

I'll take the test only if my brother feels better.

When someone who has said this comes for the test, I know that her brother feels better, because if her brother had *not* felt better, then she would *not* have taken the test.

Necessary and Sufficient Conditions

Another way to say that combustion occurs only if oxygen is present is to say:

The presence of oxygen is a necessary condition for combustion to occur.

That is, *if* combustion occurs, *then* oxygen is present, for if oxygen is *not* present, then combustion does *not* occur. Thus **P** is a *necessary condition* for **Q** when the absence of **P** guarantees the absence of **Q**. (Notice that 'the presence of oxygen' is not a sentence. However, such phrases can easily be converted into sentences, and vice versa. So, for convenience, we shall use the same notation for both.)

A correlative notion is that of a "sufficient condition": **P** is a *sufficient condition* for **Q** when the presence of **P** guarantees the presence of **Q**. When **P** is a sufficient condition for **Q,** we write 'If **P,** then **Q**'. For example,

Cessation of blood flow for an hour is a sufficient condition for death in a human being.

can be translated into:

If a person's blood ceases to flow for an hour, then he or she will die.

When **P** is a necessary condition for **Q,** we write 'If **Q,** then **P**'. For example,

Breathing is a necessary condition for being alive.

can be translated into:

If something is alive, then it is breathing.

Notice that

P is a sufficient condition for **Q.**

means the same as

Q is a necessary condition for **P.**

and that both of these are written in the form

If **P,** then **Q.**

CHAPTER 4

The Biconditional

It sometimes happens that **P** is both a necessary and sufficient condition for **Q**. In this case, we would say:

If **Q** then **P,** and if **P** then **Q.**

This is the same as:

If **P** then **Q,** and if **Q** then **P.**

This expression could be symbolized as:

$$((P \rightarrow Q) \ \& \ (Q \rightarrow P))$$

and is frequently read as:

P if and only if **Q**

Now, in principle, we have nothing new here. We can symbolize the "if and only if" sentence as we did here, using & and →, and by careful use of FCND and FCNJ, we can evaluate the truth value of any such sentence. But because the expression 'if and only if' occurs so often in logical studies, we shall call it the *biconditional* connective and use a special symbol for it, namely, the double-headed arrow: ↔. So, '**P** if and only if **Q**' will be written like this:

$$(P \leftrightarrow Q)$$

There are other ways to express the biconditional in English. One common way that often appears in logical and mathematical writings is to abbreviate 'if and only if' with 'iff'. Other phrases that are sometimes used are 'just when', 'just in the case that', and 'exactly when'. You should also pay special attention when you read a sentence of the form '**P,** if **Q**' or '**P** only if **Q**', because the author often *means* '**P** if and only if **Q**', even though that is not what he or she wrote. (And when an author does write a sentence of the form '**P** if and only if **Q**', make sure that *both* 'If **P**, then **Q**' *and* 'If **Q**, then **P**' are meant!)

When '$(P \leftrightarrow Q)$' is understood as '$((P \rightarrow Q) \ \& \ (Q \rightarrow P))$', one algorithm for computing its truth value might be:

1. INPUT V(**P**).
2. INPUT V(**Q**).
3. Let V1 = FCND (V(**P**), V(**Q**)).
   (That is, V1 = V(**P** → **Q**).)
4. Let V2 = FCND(V(**Q**), V(**P**)).
   (That is, V2 = V(**Q** → **P**).)
5. OUTPUT FCNJ(V1, V2).
6. STOP.

If we follow this algorithm, we can produce the following extensional characterization of the truth function, which we shall call FBIC:

FBIC(FALSE, FALSE) = TRUE
FBIC(FALSE, TRUE) = FALSE
FBIC(TRUE, FALSE) = FALSE
FBIC(TRUE, TRUE)   = TRUE

If we now examine just how the truth value of '$(P \leftrightarrow Q)$' is determined by the truth values of **P** and of **Q,** we see that $V(P \leftrightarrow Q)$ = TRUE if and only if $V(P) = V(Q)$. That is, if $V(P) = V(Q)$, then $V(P \leftrightarrow Q)$ = TRUE, and if $V(P) \neq V(Q)$, then $V(P \leftrightarrow Q)$ = FALSE. We can use this fact, and the trivial arithmetical observation that subtracting a number from itself leaves a remainder of zero, to construct an arithmetical algorithm for computing FBIC.

To do this, we shall use the *absolute-value* function, ABS, which can be defined as follows:

$ABS(n) = n$, if $n \geqslant 0$
$ABS(n) = -n$, if $n < 0$

For example, $ABS(5) = 5$, $ABS(0) = 0$, and $ABS(-5) = 5$. ABS will provide the information we need about whether $V(P) = V(Q)$, since—using 1 for TRUE and 0 for FALSE—$V(P) \neq V(Q)$ iff $ABS(V(P) - V(Q)) = 1$ and $V(P) = (VQ)$ iff $ABS(V(P) - V(Q)) = 0$. But since $V(P \leftrightarrow Q) = 1$ iff $V(P) = V(Q)$ and $V(P \leftrightarrow Q) = 0$ iff $V(P) \neq V(Q)$, we need to "reverse" the output of ABS. Here, then, is the algorithm for computing FBIC:

1. INPUT V(**P**).
2. INPUT V(**Q**).
3. OUTPUT 1 − ABS (V(**P**) − V(**Q**)).
4. STOP.

Exclusive Disjunction

In Chapter 3, we said that disjunction could be understood in two senses: an *inclusive* sense and an *exclusive* sense. You should recall that the truth value of a sentence that is an inclusive disjunction can be calculated by means of the truth function FDSJ. In truth-table form, this was:

V (**P**)	V (**Q**)	V (**P** v **Q**)
FALSE	FALSE	FALSE
FALSE	TRUE	TRUE
TRUE	FALSE	TRUE
TRUE	TRUE	TRUE

This sense of disjunction is said to be "inclusive" because it includes the possibility that both disjuncts are TRUE. For instance, suppose you are asked how you are doing in school and you reply by saying "I'll pass French or math." No one would accuse you of being incorrect if in fact you passed both French and math. It's certainly possible to pass both courses, and if you think you'll pass at least one of them, then your use of the word 'or' in 'I'll pass French or math' is in the inclusive sense.

Often, however, we want to exclude the possibility of both disjuncts being TRUE. Sometimes this possibility is excluded automatically: if you ask someone what today's date is and the reply is "It's either the 21st or the 22d," you know it can't be both. This is an example of an *exclusive* disjunction.

At other times, however, it's not clear whether an English disjunction is exclusive or inclusive. For instance, if a college adviser says that you can major in the sciences or the humanities, this might mean that you must choose which one area to major in. But it might mean that you can have a double major. In the first case, the adviser's offer was an exclusive disjunction; in the second case, the offer was an inclusive disjunction. Given only the information in this example, there is no way to know which kind of disjunction is involved. In a real situation, if it is not immediately obvious which is meant, you will need more information to decide. Sometimes the phrase 'and/or' is used as the connective in English to specify the inclusive sense. Similarly, the phrase 'but not both' is often added to specify the exclusive sense. In other cases, the best strategy is to assume that the inclusive sense is intended, unless you have evidence to the contrary.

There are several symbols that can be used to represent exclusive disjunction; we shall simply use the three-letter abbreviation xor. Thus

    (P xor **Q)**

will be our way of symbolizing a sentence of the form

    P or **Q,** but not both.

When we connect two sentences by an exclusive disjunction, we mean that at least one of them is TRUE and at most one of them is TRUE. We shall use the truth function FXOR for exclusive disjunction:

    $V(\textbf{P} \text{ xor } \textbf{Q}) = \text{FXOR }(V(\textbf{P}), V(\textbf{Q}))$

This function can be extensionally characterized as follows:

    FXOR(FALSE, FALSE) = FALSE
    FXOR(FALSE, TRUE) = TRUE
    FXOR(TRUE, FALSE) = TRUE
    FXOR(TRUE, TRUE)   = FALSE

To make sure you understand this, consider the sentence

    Today is the 22d or the 23d.

If we let

A = 'Today is the 22d.'   B = 'Today is the 23d.'

then our sentence can be symbolized as

(A xor B)

Suppose both A and B are FALSE. Then surely '(A xor B)' must be FALSE. But if A is TRUE, then B can't be TRUE, so '(A xor B)' is TRUE. Similarly, when B is TRUE and A isn't, then '(A xor B)' is TRUE. In the case of this sentence, it really doesn't make much sense to suppose that both A and B are TRUE, but you should note that if they were, somehow, both TRUE, then '(A xor B)' would indeed be FALSE! A more plausible example to illustrate the fourth possibility is this: Suppose your logic professor says at the beginning of the semester that you will have a final exam or a midterm, but not both. If you are then given both tests, your professor was not truthful.

An algorithm for computing FXOR can be written using the arithmetical function ABS, which we also used in the algorithm for FBIC. Once again, we can use the fact that V(P) = V(Q) if ABS(V(P) − V(Q)) = 0:

1. INPUT V(P).
2. INPUT V(Q).
3. OUTPUT ABS (V(P) − V(Q)).
4. STOP.

xor can be expressed in terms of conjunction and inclusive disjunction, as follows:

(P xor Q)

just means:

1. P or Q but not both.

Remembering that 'but' is represented logically as conjunction, and noting that 'both' is short for 'both P and Q', we can symbolize (1) as

((P v Q) & (P & Q))

Unless

In ordinary English, we often express propositions with sentences containing the connective 'unless'. As we shall see in this section, 'unless' is not really a "new" connective, since it can be expressed in terms of the connectives that we are already familiar with.

Consider the sentence

> 1. I'll take the test, unless my sister is sick.

Sentence (1) means that if my sister is *not* sick, then I *will* take the test. Letting

> A = 'I'll take the test.'
> B = 'My sister is sick.'

we can symbolize (1) as

> 2. ($\sim$B $\rightarrow$ A)

You should also notice that we could have paraphrased (1) as meaning that if I do *not* take the test, then my sister *is* sick, which would be symbolized as

> 3. ($\sim$A $\rightarrow$ B)

Fortunately, these two symbolizations can be shown to be TRUE in exactly the same situations and FALSE in exactly the same situations; so, both (2) and (3) are proper ways to symbolize (1).

You may be wondering why we didn't symbolize (1) as

> 4. (B $\rightarrow$ $\sim$A)

that is, if my sister is sick, then I will not take the test. But very often a person who uses a sentence such as (1) is simply expressing what he or she will do if the sister is *not* sick, leaving open the options of what to do if the sister *is* sick. After all, one might take the test anyway.

Let us call the interpretation of (1) in which we symbolize it as (2) the "weak" interpretation. An "unless" sentence always means at least the weak interpretation. In some contexts, it also means (4). We call the interpretation in which (1) means both (2) and (4) the "strong" interpretation. Deciding which interpretation is meant is a matter of context, just as with deciding whether the English word 'or' should be symbolized by v or by xor. In fact, the parallel is exact, as we'll shortly see.

For another example, consider

> 5. We'll eat dinner at 8, unless we go to a movie.

Letting

> E = 'We'll eat dinner at 8.'
> F = 'We'll go to a movie.'

the weak interpretation of (5) is

> 6. ($\sim$F $\rightarrow$ E)

But suppose the context in which (5) was used made it clear that what was meant was:

    7. We'll eat dinner at 8, unless we go to a movie, in which case, we'll eat dinner at 6.

The reasonable assumption is that if we eat dinner at 6, then we do not eat dinner at 8. Thus (5) in this context is to be understood as meaning that if we don't go to a movie, then we'll eat dinner at 8, but if we do go to a movie, then we won't eat dinner at 8. In other words, we'll eat dinner at 8 iff we don't go to a movie—which is the strong interpretation:

    8. $(E \leftrightarrow \sim F)$

Simple calculations with truth tables reveal that on the weak interpretation, (5) could also be expressed by the inclusive disjunction

    9. $(E \vee F)$

and on the strong interpretation, it could be expressed by the exclusive disjunction

    10. $(E \text{ XOR } F)$

NOR

Yet another common connective in English is expressed by the word 'nor', as in the sentence

    1. Neither Ann nor Bob was at the party.

This simply means that Ann was not at the party and Bob was not at the party. Suppose that someone asks whether Ann *or* Bob was at the party. If (1) is true, then the answer is no: in other words, (1) is the negation of

    Ann or Bob was at the party.

Thus a "neither . . . nor . . ." sentence is the negation of a disjunctive sentence. For this reason, one common symbol for 'nor' is the disjunction sign with a bar through it, often called a "dagger": $\downarrow$. But for convenience we shall just use the three-letter symbol NOR. Using obvious abbreviations, we can symbolize (1) as follows:

    $(A \text{ NOR } B)$

We can easily see that the truth value of a NOR sentence is calculated by the function FNOR, extensionally characterized as follows:

FNOR(FALSE, FALSE) = TRUE
FNOR(FALSE, TRUE) = FALSE
FNOR(TRUE, FALSE) = FALSE
FNOR(TRUE, TRUE) = FALSE

You should notice that V(**P** NOR **Q**) = V($\sim$(**P** v **Q**)).

NAND

If NOR is the negation of an (inclusive) disjunction, then it seems reasonable to consider what the negation of a conjunction is. Unfortunately, there is no ordinary English word for this, but computer scientists have coined the word 'nand'. Thus

(**P** NAND **Q**)

means:

$\sim$(**P** & **Q**)

There is also a common logical symbol for this, the stroke: |. But we shall use the four-letter symbol NAND both because it is more common in computer use and because the stroke has another meaning in some programming-language contexts—confusingly, it stands for disjunction! Because of the possibility of expressing NAND in terms of $\sim$ and &, we shall leave the development of the truth function FNAND, together with its extensional characterization and appropriate algorithms, to the exercises (specifically, Exercise F on page 86).

The Two-Place Truth-Functional Connectives

We should now add the following to our rules for sentences:

5. If strings **P** and **Q** are sentences,
   then the conditional, (**P** $\rightarrow$ **Q**), is a sentence.
6. If strings **P** and **Q** are sentences,
   then the biconditional, (**P** $\leftrightarrow$ **Q**), is a sentence.
7. If strings **P** and **Q** are sentences,
   then their exclusive disjunction, (**P** XOR **Q**), is a sentence.
8. If strings **P** and **Q** are sentences,
   then (**P** NOR **Q**) is a sentence.
9. If strings **P** and **Q** are sentences,
   then (**P** NAND **Q**) is a sentence.

We have looked at seven two-place truth-functional connectives so far (not including 'unless'): &, v, →, ↔, XOR, NOR, and NAND. Two reasonable questions to ask at this stage are: How many such connectives are there? Are they related to each other in any interesting ways?

The best way to answer these questions is by finding a systematic way of listing all the connectives. To see how to do this, consider what any two-place truth function must be like: It must have as an output either 0 or 1 (that is, FALSE or TRUE) for all possible pairs of truth values as inputs. Since there are only four such pairs (namely 00, 01, 10, 11), we can list all possible outputs as shown in Table 4-1.

We have only discussed the seven functions to which we gave names beginning with 'F', but each of the sixteen functions whose extensional characterizations are given in the table can be dealt with in a similar fashion. That is, there are algorithms for computing them, arithmetical functions that can be used in such algorithms, and ways of expressing them in English (although some ingenuity may be needed to do this!).

Summary

In this chapter, we finished our introduction to the two-place truth-functional connectives. We looked at extensional characterizations of the corresponding truth functions, and we presented algorithms for computing each of them.

We discussed *conditionals,* paying special attention to *material conditional sentences*—'If **P,** then **Q**'—and the different ways they can be expressed in English, including the language of *necessary and sufficient conditions.* We then turned to the *biconditional* ('**P** if and only if **Q**'), *exclusive disjunction,* XOR ('**P** or **Q,** but not both'), and the two connectives NOR and NAND. We also looked at the connective 'unless'. Finally, we gave a complete list of all sixteen two-place truth functions.

Exercises

A. Symbolize the following sentences using the indicated symbolic abbreviations:

A = 'Arthur is innocent.'   B = 'Barbara is innocent.'
C = 'Charles is innocent.'   D = 'Charles tells the truth.'

1. If Arthur is innocent, then so is Barbara.
2. Charles is innocent only if Arthur is too.
3. If neither Arthur nor Barbara is innocent, then Charles is innocent.
4. Only if Charles tells the truth is Arthur innocent.
5. Unless Charles tells the truth, Barbara is not innocent.
6. Arthur is innocent, unless Charles does not tell the truth.
7. Barbara is innocent in case Charles tells the truth.
8. If Barbara and Charles are innocent, then Arthur isn't.
9. If, but only if, Charles tells the truth, then Arthur is innocent.

TABLE 4-1. The Two-Place Truth Functions

No.	INPUTS				Name	Function	Symbol	English expression
	V(P) 0 V(Q) 0	V(P) 0 V(Q) 1	V(P) 1 V(Q) 0	V(P) 1 V(Q) 1				
	OUTPUTS							
0	0	0	0	0	(none)	(none)	(none)	(none)
1	0	0	0	1	Conjunction	FCNJ	&	P and Q
2	0	0	1	0	Material Non-Conditional*	(none)	↛	P but not Q
3	0	0	1	1	(none)	(none)	(none)	(none)
4	0	1	0	0	Converse Non-Conditional*	(none)	↚	Q but not P
5	0	1	0	1	(none)	(none)	(none)	(none)
6	0	1	1	0	Exclusive Disjunction	FXOR	XOR	P or Q, but not both
7	0	1	1	1	(Inclusive) Disjunction	FDSJ	v	P or Q
8	1	0	0	0	Nor	FNOR	NOR	Neither P nor Q
9	1	0	0	1	Biconditional	FBIC	↔	P if and only if Q
10	1	0	1	0	(none)	(none)	(none)	(none)
11	1	0	1	1	Converse Conditional*	(none)	↓	P if Q
12	1	1	0	0	(none)	(none)	(none)	(none)
13	1	1	0	1	Material Conditional	FCND	↑	If P, then Q
14	1	1	1	0	Nand	FNAND	NAND	Not both P and Q
15	1	1	1	1	(none)	(none)	(none)	(none)

*Names suggested in Church (1956)

84

ADDITIONAL CONNECTIVES

10. Barbara is innocent if and only if Arthur is innocent and Charles tells the truth.
11. Charles is innocent if either Barbara or Arthur is.
12. Charles tells the truth when, and only when, he is innocent.
13. Charles tells the truth and is innocent if and only if Arthur is not innocent.
14. Whenever Charles tells the truth, he is innocent.
15. If Charles tells the truth, then Arthur and Barbara are innocent.
16. Arthur is innocent if and only if it is not the case that both Barbara and Charles are innocent.

B. Symbolize the following sentences, using your own abbreviations for the atomic sentences.
   1. If you want to get a good grade, you will be successful if you study hard.
   2. If you want to get a good grade, and if you study hard, you will be successful.
   3. If you want to get a good grade, you will be successful only if you study hard.
   4. Unless you have a credit card, you can rent the car if and only if you leave a deposit of $100.
   5. You are not responsible for damages unless, of course, the accident is your fault, in which case, the company will pay if and only if you pay the first $100.
   6. You cannot beat the stock market if you are not lucky, unless you have inside information.

C. Calculate the truth value of each of the following sentences, using the given truth values of the atomic sentences:

   $V(A) = TRUE$
   $V(B) = TRUE$
   $V(C) = FALSE$
   $V(D) = FALSE$

   1. $(A \rightarrow (B \lor C))$
   2. $(B \rightarrow (A \& D))$
   3. $((A \lor C) \rightarrow D)$
   4. $((C \lor D) \rightarrow (A \lor C))$
   5. $(A \rightarrow (B \rightarrow \sim C))$
   6. $((C \& D) \rightarrow \sim A)$
   7. $(B \rightarrow \sim (A \lor C))$
   8. $(A \rightarrow (D \rightarrow \sim (B \& C)))$
   9. $((B \rightarrow (A \lor C)) \rightarrow (D \& B))$
   10. $((B \& D) \rightarrow (C \lor (A \& B)))$
   11. $(A \leftrightarrow (B \lor C))$
   12. $(C \leftrightarrow (A \leftrightarrow D))$
   13. $(B \leftrightarrow (C \text{ NOR } D))$
   14. $(C \leftrightarrow \sim (A \text{ NAND } D))$
   15. $(\sim (A \& C) \leftrightarrow (A \text{ NAND } C))$
   16. $((C \lor (A \leftrightarrow D)) \rightarrow (A \rightarrow C))$

17. (~A ↔ (A NOR A))
18. ((B NAND B) ↔ (B NOR B))
19. ((C NOR C) ↔ (C NAND C))
20. ((A NAND A) ↔ (~A ∨ C))
21. ((A XOR B) XOR C)
22. ((A XOR C) XOR D)
23. ((D XOR A) NAND C)
24. (C NOR (A XOR B))
25. ~(A XOR B)
26. (~A XOR ~B)
27. (~A XOR B)
28. (A XOR ~B)
29. ((A XOR B) & C)
30. (A XOR (B & C))
31. ((A XOR B) & ~(A XOR B))
32. ((~A XOR B) & (~B XOR A))

D. Exclusive Disjunction
   1. Consider the following sentence:
      "If a college adviser says that you can major in the sciences or the human-
      ities, this might mean that you must choose which one area to major in, *or*
      it might mean that you can have a double major."
      Is the italicized occurrence of the word 'or' in this sentence inclusive or
      exclusive? Why?
   2. Write an algorithm for computing FXOR in terms of MAX and MIN.
   3. Write an algorithm for computing FXOR using FBIC.
   4. Write an algorithm for computing FBIC using FXOR.
   5. Use the fact that '(**P** XOR **Q**)' can be expressed as '((**P** ∨ **Q**) & ~(**P** & **Q**))' to
      write an algorithm for computing FXOR.

E. NOR
   1. Write an algorithm for computing FNOR in terms of FDSJ.
   2. Write algorithms to evaluate (**P** NOR **Q**) and ~(**P** ∨ **Q**) showing that the out-
      puts are identical for given inputs.

F. NAND
   1. Give an extensional characterization of a truth function FNAND for the
      connective NAND.
   2. Write an algorithm for FNAND using an appropriate arithmetical function.
   3. Show how XOR can be expressed in terms of ~, &, and NAND.
      [*Hint:* '(**P** NAND **Q**)' is TRUE if at most one of **P**, **Q** is TRUE.]
   4. Write an algorithm for computing FXOR in terms of the arithmetical functions
      for ~, &, and NAND.

G. Find appropriate English sample sentences using connectives 0, 3, 5, 10, 12,
   and 15 in Table 4-1.

CHAPTER 5

SENTENTIAL LOGIC: Algorithms for Calculating Truth Values and Determining Well-Formedness

Up to this point, we have not extensively considered how to calculate the truth values of relatively complex molecular sentences from the truth values of the atomic sentences that compose them. Instead, we have concentrated on rather simple molecular sentences, which demonstrated the behavior of our main sentence connectives: ~, &, v, and →.

There are, however, more complicated examples than these, and we must find an *algorithm* for calculating their truth values. Having such a procedure, as we shall see later, will prove to be extremely useful in determining whether an argument in sentential logic is valid or invalid.

Our method for discovering an algorithm for calculating the truth value of a molecular sentence will follow a familiar pattern. We shall first examine how *we* would do it (just as we first considered how *we* add in order to discover an algorithm for addition). Then we shall refine the procedure so that *anyone*—even a computer—could follow it, knowing nothing about logic or truth values.

CHAPTER 5

An Informal Method for Calculating Truth Values

Consider these assignments of truth values to atomic sentences:

$V(A) = 1$
$V(B) = 0$
$V(C) = 1$
$V(D) = 0$

Note that we shall assume for convenience in this and the next chapter that TRUE and FALSE are represented by the numbers 1 and 0. Next, consider a molecular sentence composed of these atomic sentences, say:

$(A \rightarrow (\sim B \& (C \lor D)))$

What is the truth value of this molecular sentence, given the assignment of truth values to the atomic sentences?

To calculate this truth value, we can begin by replacing the atomic-sentence letters ('A', 'B', 'C', and 'D') with their truth values. Making these substitutions, we would have:

$(1 \rightarrow (\sim 0 \& (1 \lor 0)))$

It is important to note that this is *not* itself a sentence according to our rules. It is a hybrid creation, which we shall call a "hybrid formula," formed by mixing truth values (1, 0) and sentence connectives. To say "If TRUE, then both not FALSE and either TRUE or FALSE" does not make any sense in English—but it *is* a useful creation, as we shall see.

But now what do we do? We should look for something in this formula that we do know something about from our reading in the previous chapters, namely, simple combinations of truth values and sentence connectives. Our eye should spot two such combinations in the above formula. They are:

~ 0

and

$(1 \lor 0)$

We shall call these *subformulas* of the formula that we are considering, because they are *parts* of the whole formula and because they have the patterns of the simple molecular sentences that we saw in the last two chapters.

The first subformula, '~ 0', can be replaced by the truth value 1, since the logical function (FNEG) associated with negation "reverses" the truth value of the sentence following it. That is, we can replace '~ 0' in the formula with the output of FNEG(0), namely, 1. Similarly, '$(0 \lor 1)$', we should know, can be replaced by the truth value 1. To see this, we need only consult the truth table for v or apply FDSJ to the truth values 0 and 1. Informally, we may recall, a disjunction is TRUE if even one of its disjuncts is TRUE. So we can replace '$(1 \lor 0)$' with the truth value 1.

If we had been writing down these reflections, we would now have:

$(A \rightarrow (\sim B \& (C \lor D)))$
$(1 \rightarrow (\sim 0 \& (1 \lor 0)))$
$(1 \rightarrow (1 \quad \& (1 \lor 0)))$ [Replacing '~ 0' with '1']
$(1 \rightarrow (1 \quad \& \quad 1 \quad))$ [Replacing '$(1 \lor 0)$' with '1']

Our next step is again to apply what we know about truth values and sentence connectives to the simplest parts of this last formula. We see that '$(1 \& 1)$' is a subformula of it, and we should recognize from our study of conjunction that this can be replaced by the truth value 1. (We could determine this by examining the truth table for & or by applying the FCNJ function.) So our next steps would be:

$(1 \rightarrow (1 \& 1))$
$(1 \rightarrow \quad 1 \quad)$
    1

The last line, a single truth value, was arrived at by reasoning that the hybrid formula '$(1 \rightarrow 1)$' can be replaced by the truth value 1. (Again, we could consult our truth tables or apply FCND to determine this.) The last line tells us that the truth value of our original molecular sentence is 1 (that is, TRUE) *given* our original assignment of truth values to the atomic sentences.

Observations about the Informal Method

Several observations on what we just did are in order. Notice, first, that in order to determine the truth value of a molecular sentence, we need only look at the *last line.* That is, we don't need to look at the calculations that led up to it, unless we are checking the whole calculation for errors after we are done. Second, at each step after the replacement of atomic sentences by truth values, our eye looks for those parts of the formula to which we can directly apply the truth functions for $\sim$, &, $\lor$, and $\rightarrow$, such as '~ 1', '$(0 \& 0)$', '$(1 \lor 0)$', or '$(1 \rightarrow 1)$'. Once we find such subformulas, we replace each one and its immediately surrounding parentheses (if any) with the single truth value as given by the appropriate truth function. Finally, we stop this process when we are left with only a single truth value.

Let's look at another example. Consider the molecular sentence

$(\sim A \& (A \rightarrow ((C \lor D) \rightarrow D)))$

and the atomic truth-value assignments:

$V(A) = 0 \qquad V(C) = 1$
$V(B) = 1 \qquad V(D) = 0$

To find the truth value of the molecular sentence, we would proceed as follows (omitting explanations):

```
(~A & (A → ((C v D) → D)))
(~0 & (0 → ((1 v 0) → 0)))
(1  & (0 → ((1 v 0) → 0)))
(1  & (0 → (  1    → 0)))
(1  & (0 →         0  ))
(1  &   1              )
   1
```

Let us look at one last example, carefully keeping the replacing truth value directly under the sentence connective of the replaced subformula. Consider:

(B v (C → ((D & ~D) → A)))

with the truth values

V(A) = 1   V(C) = 1
V(B) = 0   V(D) = 0

Our calculation would proceed as follows:

```
(B v (C → ((D & ~D) → A)))
(0 v (1 → ((0 & ~0) → 1)))
(0 v (1 → ((0 & 1 ) → 1)))
(0 v (1 → (  0      → 1)))
(0 v (1 →           1  ))
(0 v   1               )
   1
```

Innermost Subformulas

We are now almost in a position to give an algorithm for what we have just done. One important concept is necessary, namely, that of an "innermost subformula." This concept, when made precise, will allow us to state explicitly the procedure that we earlier described as looking for the subformula to which we could straightforwardly apply what we know about the simple truth functions.

After replacing atomic-sentence letters with truth values, and after replacing '~0' with '1' and '~1' with '0', we obtain a formula having no negation signs in front of atomic parts. Suppose that we have such a formula that has no negated atomic parts. Then the *innermost subformulas* (there may be more than one) of this formula can be identified as those subformulas of the given formula that are surrounded by the most parentheses. For example, in

(1 → ((0 & (1 v 0)) & 1))

the innermost subformula—here, there is only one—is '(1 v 0)'. It is the part of the formula most deeply "buried" in parentheses. Four sets of parentheses surround it, including the set that is part of the subformula itself. In the formula

$$((0 \rightarrow 1) \text{ v } (1 \rightarrow 0))$$

the innermost subformulas are '(0 → 1)' and '(1 → 0)', which are each enclosed by just two sets of parentheses. Note that the innermost subformula of '(1 v 0)' is '(1 v 0)' itself.

The Algorithm: TRUTH-VALUE CALCULATOR

Using this notion of the innermost subformula, we can give the full algorithm for calculating the truth value of a complex molecular sentence:

ALGORITHM TRUTH-VALUE CALCULATOR

1. INPUT a sentence **P**.
2. INPUT the truth values of **P**'s atomic sentences.
3. Replace each atomic sentence in **P** with its assigned truth value to produce a hybrid formula.
4. Reading the hybrid formula from left to right, delete all occurrences of ~~ (that is, delete all double negation signs).
5. WHILE the formula has more than 1 character,

   (a) Reading the formula from left to right, replace all occurrences of '~1' with '0'.
   (b) Reading the formula from left to right, replace all occurrences of '~0' with '1'.
   (c) IF a single truth value remains,
       THEN

       (i) OUTPUT it.
       (ii) STOP.

   (d) Find the innermost subformulas.
   (e) FOR each innermost subformula:

       (i) IF the middle symbol in the subformula is &,
           THEN

           (1) Apply FCNJ to the two truth values in the subformula.
           (2) Replace the subformula with the output.

       (ii)–(iv) Do similarly for v, →, and ↔.

6. OUTPUT the single truth value.
7. STOP.

This algorithm has a "loop" in step 5 that allows us to whittle down our formula until only a single truth value remains. The algorithm describes in most respects what we were doing in our previous, informal evaluations of the truth value of a molecular sentence. Note the difficulties created by negation in TRUTH-VALUE CALCULATOR, since it is a one-place connective; it requires its own steps: 4, 5(a), and 5(b).

Steps 5(d) and 5(e) remain at a somewhat abstract level, so let us refine them.

Refining Step 5(d): Finding the Innermost Subformulas

The essential idea, as we have already observed, is simply to determine which parts of the formula are most deeply buried in parentheses. But how do we *mechanically* determine this?

Suppose that we number the characters in our string (other than blanks). For example, numbering the (nonblank) characters in a sample formula, we would have:

$$((1 \rightarrow 0) \rightarrow 0)$$
123 4 567 89

Now imagine a "counter" passing from left to right over the numbered characters in the string. The counter starts with a value of 0. When it encounters a *left* parenthesis, it *adds* 1 to its value. When it encounters a *right* parenthesis, it *subtracts* 1 from its value. Otherwise, it does not change its value. The counter has a value of 0 before it begins, and it *should* have a value of 0 after it ends. (If it does not, there are an unequal number of right and left parentheses. This indicates that the original string was not a sentence according to our rules.)

Let us record the *highest* value that this counter achieves when passing from left to right. After the highest value of this counter has been recorded, let us start with a second counter, also set initially to 0 and passing from left to right with the same rules: '(' adds 1, ')' subtracts 1.

1. The first innermost subformula *begins* at the position where the second counter first equals the highest value of the first counter.
2. This innermost subformula *ends* at the first position where the second counter becomes less than this value.

Because there may be more than one such innermost subformula, the second counter should continue sweeping right through the string, recording the positions that mark the beginnings and endings of innermost subformulas. These recorded positions can then be used to "extract" the subformulas for the analysis and evaluation that the next step, step 5(e), requires.

One example should suffice to demonstrate the workings of these two counters.

Formula:	(	1	→	(	0	&	(	0	v	1	)	)	)
Position:	1	2	3	4	5	6	7	8	9	10	11	12	13
First Counter: 0	1	1	1	2	2	2	3	3	3	3	2	1	0

The highest value of the first counter is 3. So the second counter will record that the innermost subformula begins at position 7 and ends at position 11. (You should be aware that some of the extraordinary lengths that we had to go to with regard to parentheses can be avoided by adopting a notational system without parentheses. We shall look at one such system, *Polish notation,* in Chapter 7.)

Refining Step 5(e): Replacing Innermost Subformulas with Truth Values

Every innermost subformula should have the form

(<truth value 1> ☆ <truth value 2>)

where <truth value 1> and <truth value 2> are either 0 or 1, and where ☆ is the symbol for a two-place sentence connective (such as &, v, or →). Step 5(e) will tell us what truth value to replace the entire subformula with, including its parentheses. A flowchart for the procedure of step 5(e) is given in Figure 5-1. In other words, every innermost subformula is replaced by a truth value, according to the truth functions studied in the previous chapters.

For example:

(1 & 1)

is replaced by the output of

FCNJ(1, 1)

which is just

1

Similarly:

(1 → 0)

is replaced by the output of

FCND(1, 0)

which is just

0

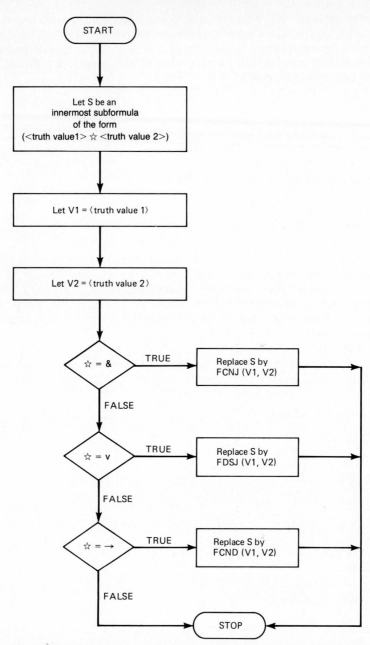

Figure 5-1 Flowchart for replacing innermost subformulas with truth values.

Formulas and Sentences

There is a topic that we have not yet dealt with in detail: the relationship between sentences and our hybrid formulas. A string, you should recall, is any sequence of characters. We have defined a sentence as any string satisfying our rules 1 to 9 from Chapters 3 and 4:

1. A string consisting of one of the single letters
   'A', 'B', . . .,'O' (possibly with numerals) is a sentence.
2. If **P** is a sentence,
   then ~**P** is a sentence.
3. If **P** and **Q** are sentences,
   then (**P** & **Q**) is a sentence.
4. If **P** and **Q** are sentences,
   then (**P** v **Q**) is a sentence.
5. If **P** and **Q** are sentences,
   then (**P** → **Q**) is a sentence.
6. If **P** and **Q** are sentences,
   then (**P** ↔ **Q**) is a sentence.
7. If **P** and **Q** are sentences,
   then (**P** xor **Q**) is a sentence.
8. If **P** and **Q** are sentences,
   then (**P** nor **Q**) is a sentence.
9. If **P** and **Q** are sentences,
   then (**P** nand **Q**) is a sentence.
10. Only strings constructed from rules 1 to 9 are sentences.

Rule 10 is called a "closure" clause. In the future, for convenience, we shall usually omit the last few connectives, and we shall usually not explicitly state the closure clause.

We can then define a *hybrid formula* as a string obtained from a sentence by replacing all sentence letters with truth values.

But how do we determine when a formula *could not* have arisen in this way, and hence was not originally a sentence? A string that is a sentence will be called "well-formed."

One answer conveniently lies in what we have just been considering, namely, the algorithm for calculating the truth values of molecular sentences. Before we examine this, however, we should perhaps look at some of the ways strings can "go wrong" and fail to be sentences. Here are some examples of strings that are *not* sentences, along with their diagnoses:

(((A & B) v C)	Too many left parentheses.
((A → B)) & C)	Too many right parentheses.
((AB) & C)	Run-on: needs a connective between 'A' and 'B'.
)A & B(	Left and right parentheses in wrong order.
(A → → B)	Two connectives together.
(A ~ v B)	Two connectives together.
A &	The & requires two sentences.

CHAPTER 5

An Algorithm for Determining Well-Formedness

With a little practice, it becomes possible to detect non-well-formed strings just by looking at them. But how can we be *sure* that a string we are looking at is well-formed? This question requires us to construct an algorithm that, when we apply it to a suspect string, correctly outputs—after a finite time—a message such as either "No, not well-formed" or "Yes, well-formed." Fortunately, we have already done most of the work and need only to insert some steps in our algorithm TRUTH-VALUE CALCULATOR.

Problems with parentheses are easiest to detect. Recalling the first counter from our procedure for finding innermost subformulas [step 5(d)], we can observe:

> If the count after the final character is greater than 0, then there are too many left parentheses.
> If the count after the final character is less than 0, then there are too many right parentheses.
> If the count is ever negative in the process of sweeping from left to right, then the parentheses are incorrectly matched.

If any one of these conditions arose, then we could add a step in the original procedure that would output "Not well-formed" and bring the procedure to a halt immediately.

But what about the many things that could go wrong in a string but that do not involve mistakes with parentheses? To answer this question, we must examine in still more detail what we said about step 5(e). When we were examining innermost subformulas in a gradually dwindling formula, we mentioned that every innermost subformula *should* have the form

(<truth value 1> ☆ <truth value 2>)

where <truth value 1> is 0 or 1, <truth value 2> is 0 or 1, and ☆ is &, v, ↔, or →. Examples are '(1 & 0)' and '(0 → 1)'. If an innermost subformula ever does *not* have this form, then the original string was not well-formed. Furthermore, if the innermost subformulas always have this form down to the last, single truth value, then the original string *was* well-formed.

In other words, at each stage in our analysis of the innermost subformula, the subformula under consideration must be such that:

1. It has precisely five symbols.
2. The first symbol is '(',
   the second symbol is a truth value ('0' or '1'),
   the third symbol is a two-place connective (&, v, →, or ↔),
   the fourth symbol is a truth value ('0' or '1'), and
   the fifth symbol is ')'.

A procedure in our program design language for determining whether an innermost subformula satisfies these two criteria is as follows:

PROCEDURE CHECK-SUBFORMULA

FOR each innermost subformula (from step 5(d),

    (a) IF the subformula does not contain exactly five symbols,
        THEN OUTPUT "Not well-formed" and STOP.
    (b) IF the first symbol is not '(',
        THEN OUTPUT "Not well-formed" and STOP.
    (c) IF the second symbol is not '0' or '1',
        THEN OUTPUT "Not well-formed" and STOP.
    (d) IF the third symbol is not a two-place connective (such as &, v, →, ↔),
        THEN OUTPUT "Not well-formed" and STOP.
    (e) IF the fourth symbol is not '0' or '1',
        THEN OUTPUT "Not well-formed" and STOP.
    (f) If the fifth symbol is not ')',
        THEN OUTPUT "Not well-formed" and STOP.

This procedure should be inserted between steps 5(d) and 5(e) of TRUTH-VALUE CALCULATOR.

The idea behind the insertion of this procedure is actually quite simple. It will test each subformula, as identified by step 5(d), to see if it is of the proper form, and it will repeat this test as the formula is whittled down by the replacement and loop process. But the insertion of this procedure will detect only some features of a string that disqualify it from being well-formed. To modify TRUTH-VALUE CALCULATOR so that it can find all errors, we must modify TRUTH-VALUE CALCULATOR more drastically. We will call the resulting algorithm "SENTENCE-CHECKER."

ALGORITHM SENTENCE-CHECKER

1. INPUT a string, **S.**
2. IF **S** contains other than sentence letters or connectives
    THEN OUTPUT "Not well-formed" and STOP.
3. Replace all atomic sentence letters in the string with arbitrary truth values (all 0's and 1's, for example).
4. Reading the string from left to right, delete all occurrences of ~~ (that is, delete all double negation signs).
5. WHILE the string has more than one character,

    (a) Reading the string from left to right, replace all occurrences of '−1' with '0'.
    (b) Reading the string from left to right, replace all occurrences of '−0' with '1'.
    (c) IF a single truth value remains
        THEN OUTPUT "Well-formed" and STOP.

> (d) IF there are no innermost subformulas
>   THEN OUTPUT "Not well-formed" and STOP.
> (e) FOR each innermost subformula:
>   (i) CHECK-SUBFORMULA.
>   (ii) Replace the subformula with '0'.
> 6. OUTPUT "Well-formed".
> 7. STOP.

Observe that to apply SENTENCE-CHECKER we do not need to input an assignment of truth values for atomic sentences. At step 3, absolutely any arbitrary assignment—such as 0 to each atomic sentence—would suffice for our purposes in SENTENCE-CHECKER. This is the case because in SENTENCE-CHECKER we are concerned only with whether the input string is well-formed and not with its truth value (if it is a sentence at all).

Summary

In this chapter, we presented algorithms for calculating the truth value of a molecular sentence, given truth values for its atomic parts. Informally, the method consists of replacing the sentence with a formula having truth values in place of atomic sentences and then applying our truth functions to the *subformulas* in order to reduce each of them to a single truth value. Repeating this until there are no subformulas left, we finally arrive at the truth value of the original sentence. The crucial notion needed to make this procedure precise is that of *innermost subformulas*—the subformulas surrounded by the most parentheses.

The main algorithm is TRUTH-VALUE CALCULATOR. Two important procedures, for which we gave refinements, are a procedure for finding the innermost subformula of a string by counting parentheses and a procedure for replacing an innermost subformula with a truth value by using the truth functions from Chapters 2 and 3.

We gave rules that characterize a sentence as a well-formed string: it must either be a single letter ('A', . . .,'O') or have the form ~**P** or the form (**P** ☆ **Q**), where **P** and **Q** are themselves sentences and ☆ is any two-place connective. We also gave algorithms for testing these criteria.

Exercises

A. Consider the following task (which is a "miniature" version of the project in this chapter).

   A formula is given to you. It comes from either a conjunction or a disjunction, and each of its conjuncts (or disjuncts) has the truth value 0 or 1. Examples of such a formula are:

TRUTH VALUES AND WELL-FORMEDNESS

    (1 & 0)
    (0 v 1)
    (0 & 1)

In other words, you know beforehand that the given string is five symbols long, that the first symbol is '(', that the second is a truth value (0 or 1), that the third is a connective (& or v), that the fourth is a truth value (0 or 1), and that the fifth is ')'. Write an algorithm to determine the truth value of the entire expression.

    For example, if the input is

    (1 & 0)

then the output should be

    0

Hint: One of your first instructions should be to INPUT the formula. Your algorithm should then promptly decide whether the input formula comes from a conjunction or a disjunction (that is, whether the middle symbol is & or v) and branch accordingly.

    Do *not* use the FCNJ and FDIS functions, but instead write a section of the algorithm to do what they would do.

B. Consider the "first counter" described in the refinement of step 5(d) of TRUTH-VALUE CALCULATOR.
  1. With the string
     (A → (B v (~C & D)))
    what is the value of the first counter at the following positions?
    (a) 2
    (b) 4
    (c) 5
    (d) 7
    (e) 10
    (f) 11
    (g) 12
  2. With the string
     (((A & ~B) → ~C) v (C & (D & ~E)))
    what is the value of the first counter at the following positions?
    (a) 3
    (b) 5
    (c) 7
    (d) 9
    (e) 12
    (f) 15
    (g) 23
    (h) 24

C. Apply the "second counter" described in the refinement of step 5(d) to the following strings.
Example: (A & (B & C))
Answer: 4, 8
since the innermost subformula begins at position 4 and ends at position 8.

1. $(((A \rightarrow B) \& C) v \sim D)$
2. $((A \& B) \& C)$
3. $((A \& B) \& (C \& D))$
4. $((A \& (B v \sim C)) \rightarrow (C \& (D v E)))$
5. $(\sim(A v \sim C) \rightarrow (F \rightarrow (F \& F)))$
6. $((A \rightarrow \sim(B \& C)) \rightarrow D)$

D. Step 3 of TRUTH-VALUE CALCULATOR ("Replace each atomic sentence with its assigned truth value") was left at an intuitive level. Let us, however, consider the limited case of strings with only two distinct atomic-sentence letters, 'A' and 'B'.

   Write an algorithm for inputting a string and replacing each of the two sentence letters with its associated truth value, $V(A)$ or $V(B)$.

E. Some of the following formulas do not come from well-formed strings. Apply SENTENCE-CHECKER, stopping when an error has been discovered. Explain what is wrong with the formula.

1. $(1 \sim 0)$
2. $(1 \& (0 v \& 1))$
3. $((0 \& 1)(1 \rightarrow 1))$
4. $\sim(\sim 0 \& 1)$
5. $((0 \rightarrow 1) v (0(0 \& 1)))$
6. $(((0 v 1) \& 1)$
7. $v (0)$
8. $(\& (1 v 0))$
9. $(1 \rightarrow (0 v (1 \& 1)))$
10. $(((1 \& \sim 0) v \sim (0 \& 0) \rightarrow 1)$

F. Using TRUTH-VALUE CALCULATOR and the indicated truth values below, determine the truth value of each of the following sentences. Display the resulting truth value, and the calculation leading up to it, as on pages 89 and 90.

1. Using the truth values
   $V(A) = 0 \quad V(C) = 1$
   $V(B) = 1 \quad V(D) = 1$
   determine the truth values of (a) to (r) below.

2. Using the truth values
   $V(A) = 1 \quad V(C) = 0$
   $V(B) = 0 \quad V(D) = 1$
   determine the truth values of (a) to (r) below.
   a. $\sim(A \rightarrow (B \& (C v D)))$
   b. $(C \& \sim(B \& D))$
   c. $(\sim\sim D \& (A \rightarrow (B v C)))$
   d. $(B v (C v \sim D))$
   e. $(A \& (B \& C))$
   f. $((A \& B) \& C)$
   g. $(A \& (B v C))$
   h. $((A \& B) v C)$
   i. $((A \& (B \rightarrow A)) \rightarrow B)$

j. ((A & (A → B)) → B)
k. (B → A)
l. (~B → ~A)
m. (A → B)
n. (~A v B)
o. (A & ~B)
p. ~(A & B)
q. (~A v ~B)
r. (~A & ~B)

Suggestions for Computer Implementation

The initial steps of any computer program implementing TRUTH-VALUE CALCULATOR would begin by inputting a string: the sentence to be tested. The program should then input for every distinct sentence letter contained in the initial input string, the truth values (either as TRUE and FALSE or as 1 and 0). Because of the later importance of having every significant symbol occupy just one position, and because of the necessity of using symbols on a standard keyboard, the conditional should be represented by a single symbol, such as >. That is, let → be >. Where there is a choice, it will often prove useful to use only capital letters for atomic sentences.

The conversion of the algorithm described in this chapter into a computer program might require the extensive use of "string manipulation" functions. The available such functions vary widely from computer language to computer language. Consequently, very little of a specific nature can be said about how to write an actual program.

But consider step 1 of TRUTH-VALUE CALCULATOR. Suppose the name of the input string is INPUTSTRING. Suppose also that we have already identified the atomic sentences in INPUTSTRING and determined that they are stored in an array ATOMIC(n). For instance, ATOMIC(1) = 'A', ATOMIC(2) = 'B', etc. The truth value of each of these atomic sentences can be stored in a parallel array, TRUTH(n). For example, TRUTH(1) = 1, TRUTH(2) = 0, etc. Naturally, ATOMIC(n) will have just as many elements as TRUTH(n). (If you are working in a language such as Pascal or PL/I, such parallel arrays can be implemented as a single "record" with two "fields.")

It will also be useful to have two string functions:

LENGTH(STRING)

will determine the length of the string STRING—that is, the number of symbols in it— and

MID(STRING, n)

will find the nth symbol in the string STRING. Thus if STRING = 'LOGIC', then

LENGTH(STRING) = 5

because

LENGTH('LOGIC') = 5

And

MID(STRING, 3) = 'G'

since the third symbol in 'LOGIC' is 'G'.

Here is a refinement of step 1 using these arrays and functions:

1.1. INPUT INPUTSTRING.
1.2. Let k = the number of atomic sentences in INPUTSTRING.
1.3. FOR n = 1 to LENGTH(INPUTSTRING)
    (a) FOR m = 1 to k
       i. IF MID(INPUTSTRING, n) = ATOMIC(m)
          THEN OUTPUT TRUTH(m).
      ii. IF MID(INPUTSTRING, n) = (
          or MID(INPUTSTRING, n) =)
          or MID(INPUTSTRING, n) = &
          or MID(INPUTSTRING, n) = v
          or MID(INPUTSTRING, n) = >
        THEN OUTPUT MID(INPUTSTRING, n).

The two OUTPUT statements in steps 1.3(a)i and 1.3(a)ii should be used to create a new string, NEWSTRING, which is exactly like INPUTSTRING, except that it contains truth values in the places of atomic-sentence letters. Where '+' indicates a "concatenation" operation of putting strings together to form longer strings (for example, 'LO' + 'GIC' = 'LOGIC'), these OUTPUT steps can be refined as follows (NEWSTRING must first be initialized to a blank: ' '):

1.3(a)i. IF MID(INPUTSTRING, n) = ATOMIC(m)
        THEN let NEWSTRING be NEWSTRING + TRUTH(m).
1.3(a)ii. IF MID(INPUTSTRING, n) = (
        or MID(INPUTSTRING, n) =)
        or MID(INPUTSTRING, n) = &
        or MID(INPUTSTRING, n) = v
        or MID(INPUTSTRING, n) = >
      THEN let NEWSTRING be NEWSTRING + MID(INPUTSTRING, n).

Although this program sketch might at first appear intimidating, the procedure it describes is not all that difficult. The "outer" FOR-loop in step 1.3 has the effect of looking, symbol-by-symbol, at INPUTSTRING. The "inner" FOR-loop in step 1.3(a) has the effect of checking every atomic-sentence letter, 'A', 'B',.... The test in step 1.3(a)i asks whether the symbol in INPUTSTRING currently under consideration is an atomic-sentence letter.

If it is, then its corresponding truth value is concatenated to NEWSTRING. If it is not (step 1.3(a)ii), then that symbol is copied dutifully into NEWSTRING, unless it is a blank or some other irrelevant symbol. The entire procedure has the desired effect of converting INPUTSTRING into NEWSTRING by copying symbols into NEWSTRING—unless they are sentence letters, in which case their truth values are copied into NEWSTRING.

The first counter described in the refinement of step 5(d) of TRUTH-VALUE CALCULATOR can be implemented as follows. Here, we use our LENGTH and MID functions from before, but now $>$ and $+$ have their normal arithmetical meanings:

1. Let m initially be 0.
2. FOR n = 1 to LENGTH(NEWSTRING)
   (a) IF MID(NEWSTRING, n) = (
       THEN let m be $m + 1$.
   (b) IF MID(NEWSTRING, n) =)
       THEN let m be $m - 1$.
   (c) IF $m > r$
       THEN let r be m.

The FOR-loop sweeps through NEWSTRING from left to right, and step 2(c) stores the highest value of m in variable r.

If we want the program also to decide whether parentheses are correctly used, we might add the following steps:

   2(b)ii. IF $m < 0$
           THEN OUTPUT "Error in parentheses."
   3(a). IF $m > 0$
           THEN OUTPUT "Too many left parentheses."
   3(b). IF $m < 0$
           THEN OUTPUT "Too many right parentheses."

SENTENTIAL LOGIC: Algorithms for Truth Tables and Determining Validity

In Chapters 3 and 4, we frequently used truth tables: extensional characterizations of truth functions. These were two-dimensional displays showing the functional relationship between the truth value of a molecular sentence and the truth values of its parts. In mathematics, such a table would be called a "matrix"; in computer science, it would be called a two-dimensional "array."

For disjunction, we wrote:

V(**P**)	V(**Q**)	V(**P** v **Q**)
0	0	0
0	1	1
1	0	1
1	1	1

The two columns on the left display the possible combinations of truth (1) and falsity (0) that the sentences **P** and **Q** may take in various "situations." We might think of each row as describing a situation. Up until now, the right-most column has displayed the truth values of a single molecular sentence in the situations described by the truth values of the sentences that are its parts. For example, in the above table, the first row describes the situation in which both **P** and **Q** are FALSE; in that situation, the disjunction (**P** v **Q**) is also FALSE.

CHAPTER 6

The second row describes the situation in which the disjunction (**P** v **Q**) is TRUE; and so on for the other rows.

Since we have already fully described in Chapter 5 how to calculate the truth value of a molecular sentence, no matter how complex, given the truth values of its atomic parts, we can now produce truth tables of more complexity, such as:

V(**P**)	V(**Q**)	V(**P** → (**P** → (**P** & **Q**)))
0	0	1
0	1	1
1	0	0
1	1	1

We calculate each of the values in the last column by using the algorithm from Chapter 5. To do so for the first row, we replace each occurrence of **P** with '0' and each occurrence of **Q** with '0' and then calculate the value of the resulting hybrid:

$$(0 \rightarrow (0 \rightarrow (0 \text{ \& } 0)))$$

which will turn out to be 1. We could also have seen that this is the case by observing that $V(0 \rightarrow n) = 1$ no matter what the value of n is.

We can also use a truth table to show how *several* molecular sentences are dependent on the truth values of their atomic parts. This kind of truth table will turn out to be very useful in determining the validity or invalidity of arguments in the logic of sentences, as we shall soon see.

Consider this truth table:

V(**P**)	V(**Q**)	V(**R**)	V(**P** → **Q**)	V(**Q** → **R**)	V(**P** → **R**)
0	0	0	1	1	1
0	0	1	1	1	1
0	1	0	1	0	1
0	1	1	1	1	1
1	0	0	0	1	0
1	0	1	0	1	1
1	1	0	1	0	0
1	1	1	1	1	1

The first row shows that whenever **P** is FALSE, **Q** is FALSE, and **R** is FALSE, then the truth value of (**P** → **Q**) is TRUE, the truth value of (**Q** → **R**) is TRUE, and the truth value of (**P** → **R**) is TRUE. In the whole truth table, we have a display of the truth values of (**P** → **Q**), (**Q** → **R**), and (**P** → **R**) as functions of all the combinations of truth values of their atomic parts.

TRUTH TABLES AND VALIDITY

General Truth Tables

The previous large table suggests the following generalization of the format of a truth table.

Truth Values of Atomic Sentences	Truth Values of Sentences Dependent on These Atomic Sentences
Situations: All Possible Combinations of Truth Values for the Atomic Sentences	

There are some general observations that can be made about truth tables:

1. The atomic sentences in which we are interested—displayed in the *left* columns—are just those that are contained in the dependent sentences. Thus if the sentences we are considering are $(P \rightarrow Q)$, $(Q \rightarrow R)$, and $(R \rightarrow S)$, then the atomic sentences to be displayed are **P, Q, R,** and **S.**

2. If there are n atomic sentences in which we are interested, then there are $2 ** n$ possible combinations of truth values for these atomic sentences. The reason for this is that there are only *two* possible values that *each* atomic sentence can have. So for two atomic sentences, there are $2 ** 2 = 2 \times 2 = 4$ combinations (00, 01, 10, 11); for three, there are $2 ** 3 = 2 \times 2 \times 2 = 8$; and so on. (We use '$a ** n$' for a raised to the nth power.)

3. An orderly way to place truth values in the rows under each atomic sentence, so as to exhaust all $2 ** n$ combinations, is as follows. In row 1, place the binary numeral for 0, beginning at the far right. In row 2, place the binary numeral for 1, also at the far right. In general, in row k, place the binary numeral for $k - 1$ at the far right. The last row will be a string of n '1's. Finally, fill in all remaining blanks under the atomic sentences with '0's.

As an example, suppose we have three atomic sentences, **P, Q,** and **R.** We thus need $2 ** 3 = 8$ rows for our truth table. The first row has '0' squeezed as far right as possible, the second has '1', the third has '10', the fourth has '11', and so on. The result is:

V (**P**)	V (**Q**)	V (**R**)	
		0	
		1	
	1	0	
	1	1	
1	0	0	
1	0	1	
1	1	0	
1	1	1	

We then complete the procedure by filling in the blanks with '0's, obtaining:

V (P)	V (Q)	V (R)
0	0	0
0	0	1
0	1	0
0	1	1
1	0	0
1	0	1
1	1	0
1	1	1

We finish the truth table by displaying the sentences whose truth values we are interested in at the top of other columns to the right. We then fill in the rows under these sentences with the results of our calculations of their truth values (using TRUTH-VALUE CAL-CULATOR), using the truth values of the atomic sentences indicated at the beginning of each row.

The Algorithm: Truth-Table Generator

Having just informally described the construction of a truth table, we can now give an algorithm for generating one.

ALGORITHM TRUTH-TABLE GENERATOR

1. INPUT the sentences whose truth-functional relationships we are investigating.
2. Let m = the number of these sentences. (For an argument, m will be the number of premises plus one (for the conclusion).)
3. Let n = the number of distinct atomic sentences occurring in these sentences.
4. Create a table with $n + m$ columns and $2 ** n$ rows.
5. FOR each atomic sentence S

   (a) Write 'V(S)' at the top of the columns, beginning at the left.

6. FOR each sentence S whose truth-functional relationships we are investigating

   (a) Write 'V(S)' at the top of the remaining columns, beginning with column $n + 1$.

7. (a) Count in the binary system from 0 to $(2 ** n - 1)$.
    (b) Place these binary numerals, one to each row, squeezed right under the first n columns, one digit to a box. (That is, in the first row, the nth column will have '0'. In the second row, the nth column will have '1'. In the third row, the $(n - 1)$th column will have '1' and the nth column will have '0'—and so on.)
    (c) When the last row has been filled, return to earlier rows, placing '0' in any of the spaces in the first n columns that were left blank.

8. FOR each column **c** from $n + 1$ to $n + m$

    (a) FOR each row **r** from 1 to $2 ** n$

        i. OUTPUT the truth value produced by TRUTH-VALUE CALCULATOR, using as input the sentence at **c** and the truth values at **r**.

9. STOP.

For example, if our three initial sentences are $(P \rightarrow Q)$, $(Q \rightarrow R)$, and $(P \rightarrow R)$, this algorithm will output the following truth table:

V (P)	V (Q)	V (R)	V (P → Q)	V (Q → R)	V (P → R)
0	0	0	1	1	1
0	0	1	1	1	1
0	1	0	1	0	1
0	1	1	1	1	1
1	0	0	0	1	0
1	0	1	0	1	1
1	1	0	1	0	0
1	1	1	1	1	1

Determining Validity

Truth tables can be used in the logic of sentences for determining the validity or invalidity of an argument. To see this, you should recall what an argument is and what a *valid* argument is. An argument is a set of sentences, one sentence of which is identified as the conclusion—which is claimed to follow from the other sentences (the premises). An argument is valid iff

In every situation where the premises are all TRUE, the conclusion is also TRUE.

CHAPTER 6

or, equivalently,

There is no situation where the premises are all TRUE and the conclusion is FALSE.

An argument is *in*valid iff

There *is* some situation where the premises are all TRUE and the conclusion FALSE.

The "situations" in the logic of sentences are just different combinations of the truth and falsity of *atomic* sentences (as described by the first n columns). Our truth tables have been constructed to exhaust all possible situations: Each row represents a different situation, and, all together, the different rows exhaust all possible situations.

If we had reserved the right-most columns except for the last—that is, the $(n + 1)$th through the $(n + m - 1)$th columns—for the *premises* of an argument and the *last,* or $(n + m)$th, column for the *conclusion,* then we could use this truth table to decide whether that argument is valid or invalid. Our reasoning would be as follows:

> If there is any row containing a '1' (TRUE) in every premise-column and a '0' (FALSE) in the conclusion-column, then the argument is invalid.
> If there are no such rows, then the argument is valid.

Consider the following argument:

1. If the Soviet Union rejects the proposed treaty, then a final agreement will be postponed.
2. The Soviet Union rejects the proposed treaty.
   So,
3. A final agreement will be postponed.

We could symbolize this argument as follows:

1. $(A \rightarrow B)$
2. A
$\therefore$ 3. B

We use $\therefore$ as a sign for 'So' or 'Therefore', standard conclusion indicators.

Is this argument valid? Using the truth-table method we have just proposed, we answer this question as follows. We construct a truth table, using some of the procedures described in TRUTH-TABLE GENERATOR.

> Step 1: There are three sentences in the argument: two premises and a conclusion. So, $m = 3$.
> Step 2: These sentences contain just two atomic sentences (A, B). So, $n = 2$.
> Step 3: Thus our table will have $n + m = 2 + 3 = 5$ columns, and $2 ** n = 2 ** 2 = 4$ rows.
> Steps 4–7: Labeling the columns and filling in the rows, we have:

TRUTH TABLES AND VALIDITY

V (A)	V (B)	V (A → B)	V (A)	V (B)
0	0	1	0	0
0	1	1	0	1
1	0	0	1	0
1	1	1	1	1

This display contains a great deal of information. The first row tells us that in the situation where the sentences 'The Soviet Union rejects the proposed treaty' and 'A final agreement will be postponed' are both FALSE, the sentence 'If the Soviet Union rejects the proposed treaty, then a final agreement will be postponed' is TRUE. In this situation, the first premise is TRUE, the second premise is FALSE, and the conclusion is FALSE. Each of the last three rows describes a different situation and indicates whether the premises and conclusion are TRUE or FALSE in that situation.

We can use this information to determine whether the argument is valid or invalid. If there is a row where both premises are TRUE and the conclusion is FALSE, then the argument is invalid; if there is no such row, then the argument is valid. Inspection of the above truth table will show that there are *no* rows where the premises are TRUE and the conclusion is FALSE. Hence, the argument is valid.

In fact, not only is *this* argument (involving a treaty and the Soviet Union) valid, but any argument of the same *form* is also valid. That is, any argument of the form

If <Sentence 1> then <Sentence 2>
<Sentence 1>
∴ <Sentence 2>

is valid. Arguments of this form are said, in traditional Latin terminology going back to the Middle Ages, to have used the inference pattern *modus ponens*. Any instance of *modus ponens* is valid.

Let us consider another argument:

1. If Harry uses heroin, then Harry once smoked marijuana.
2. Harry once smoked marijuana.
   Therefore,
3. Harry uses heroin.

Symbolized, the argument becomes:

1. (H → M)
2. M
∴ 3. H

Before continuing, you should notice the difference between the pattern in this example and the pattern in the previous example. In this example, the second premise is the *consequent* of the conditional (the first premise). And the conclusion is the *antecedent* of that conditional. That is, the pattern of this new argument is:

If <Sentence 1> then <Sentence 2>
<Sentence 2>
∴ <Sentence 1>

Fallacies are patterns of invalid arguments that unfortunately are often used in everyday life. This particular fallacy is called "affirming the consequent." In the earlier example, the second premise was the *antecedent* of the conditional, and the conclusion was the *consequent* of the conditional.

Our truth table for this new argument would be:

V (H)	V (M)	V (H → M)	V (M)	V (H)
0	0	1	0	0
0	1	1	1	0
1	0	0	0	1
1	1	1	1	1

Here, we can see that there *is* a row in which the premises are both TRUE but the conclusion FALSE: the second row. The second row describes the situation in which Harry does smoke marijuana but does not use heroin. In this situation, both premises are TRUE, but the conclusion is FALSE. Since there is such a row, the argument is *invalid*. In a valid argument, the truth of the premises "guarantees" the truth of the conclusion. However, as we have just seen, the truth of the premises of this argument does not guarantee the truth of the conclusion.

The Algorithm: Validity/Invalidity Determiner

The truth-table method we have just been exploring provides the basis for an algorithm for determining whether or not an already symbolized argument in the logic of sentences is valid. Applied properly, it will always yield the correct answer in a finite amount of time, and applying it requires no guesswork or special imagination.

Described in full, our method for evaluating the validity of an argument in the logic of sentences would consist of the following steps:

ALGORITHM VALIDITY/INVALIDITY DETERMINER

1. INPUT a symbolized argument.
2. Apply TRUTH-TABLE GENERATOR.
   (*Note:* In step 6 of TRUTH-TABLE GENERATOR, the $(n + m)$th column should contain the truth values of the conclusion.)

TRUTH TABLES AND VALIDITY

3. IF there is a row in which each box in a premise column (that is, the $(n + 1)$th through $(n + m - 1)$th columns) contains '1' and the box in the last column contains '0'
      THEN OUTPUT "Argument invalid" and STOP.
4. IF there is no such row
      THEN OUTPUT "Argument valid" and STOP.

Step 3 is, of course, the critical step, since it is here that we actually obtain the result of whether the argument is, or is not, valid. It can be refined as follows:

3.1. FOR each row
   (a) Let COLUMN = $n + 1$.
   (b) WHILE COLUMN $\leqslant n + m - 1$ and '1' occurs in this row and column
         Let COLUMN be COLUMN + 1.
   (c) IF COLUMN = $n + m$
         THEN IF '0' occurs in this row and column
         THEN OUTPUT "Argument invalid" and STOP.

This procedure begins by scanning across the first row (step 3.1), starting in the first premise-column, $n + 1$ (step 3.1(a)). As long as there are still premises and each one is TRUE, the scanning continues (step 3.1(b)). If a FALSE premise is found, then the next row is scanned from the first premise. If all premises are TRUE, then the conclusion (in column $n + m$) is examined (step 3.1.(c)). If the conclusion is FALSE, then the argument is invalid (step 3.1(c)i) and the algorithm stops; otherwise, the *next* row is scanned from the first premise. If all rows are examined and a row with all TRUE premises and a FALSE conclusion is not found, then the argument is valid (step 4).

Alternative Methods

If the number of atomic sentences involved in our premises and conclusion is relatively large, the resulting truth table may approach awesome proportions. For the following straightforward—and invalid—argument:

   1. $(A \rightarrow B)$
   2. $(B \rightarrow C)$
   3. $(C \rightarrow D)$
   4. $(D \rightarrow E)$
   5. E
∴ 6. A

the truth table has 2 ** 5, or 32, rows, and 11 columns are required. Since the truth table has 32 × 11 boxes, there are 352 truth values to be written into them. In other cases, some molecular sentences may be quite complex, such as:

((A → (~B v (C & ~D))) v ~(~D → A))

The truth value of each such sentence must be recalculated for every row, using TRUTH-VALUE CALCULATOR. In short, the truth-table method may consume large amounts of paper, ink, and our valuable time.

If we program a computer to perform this procedure, then TRUTH-VALUE CAL-CULATOR presents no serious difficulties. The computer will not use paper and ink in its calculations; instead it will use electrical states in memory locations as its "truth table." And even arguments containing many atomic sentences or having long, complicated sentences would not consume *our* time—although they would consume *computer* time.

So, in principle, we could use a computer to apply the truth-table method of determining validity to arguments of normally intimidating size or complexity. Of course, we may not always have a computer available, or we might not have the skill or patience to program it properly. Furthermore, the full truth-table method, with its maze of truth values, seldom resembles the way we actually reason. It is unlikely that a person proposing an argument used the truth-table method to devise it. And it is very unlikely that most people hearing the argument—even logicians—would think it to be valid (or invalid) because of a full truth table they were doing in their heads. Are there, we might ask, quicker, easier, or more natural ways of determining whether an argument is valid or invalid?

There are indeed such ways, but they are not as powerful as we might desire. We can, in what is called a "formal deduction system," construct a "proof" of a valid argument. If we can find a correct proof, we then know that the argument is valid. Unfortunately, if we cannot find a proof, we cannot conclude that the argument is invalid. Our failure to find a proof might have been due to our own inability, or perhaps we didn't try hard enough. In this case, the argument might still be valid; we could then fall back on the full truth-table method to determine if it is valid or invalid. In Chapters 8 and 9, we shall discuss the method of showing an argument to be valid by giving a proof.

WANG'S ALGORITHM

Another algorithm to determine whether or not a symbolized argument is valid is WANG'S ALGORITHM, named after the logician Hao Wang (1921–). WANG'S ALGORITHM, like the truth-table algorithm VALIDITY/INVALIDITY DETERMINER, will always determine whether a symbolized argument in the logic of sentences is valid or invalid. But unlike the truth-table algorithm, it does not require us to create large tables.

The idea behind WANG'S ALGORITHM is very simple. In constructing a truth table to determine the validity of an argument, we are searching for a situation in which the premises are all TRUE but the conclusion is FALSE. If there is such a situation, then the argument is invalid. If there is no such situation, then the argument is valid. In terms of the truth table, we look for the *row* where the premises are all TRUE and the conclusion FALSE. WANG'S ALGORITHM is designed to find this situation (row) *without* having to examine all situations. The algorithm will also tell us if there exists no such situation.

Before we introduce WANG'S ALGORITHM in full detail, we shall look at some examples showing the principles that lie behind it. Consider this argument:

       1. A
       2. B
    ∴ 3. A

Let us consider an attempt to make the premises TRUE and the conclusion FALSE. To do so, we shall write the sentences of this argument in a new way. On the left, we shall write a list of the sentences we are trying to make TRUE, and on the right, we shall write a list of the sentences we are trying to make FALSE. We shall draw a vertical line to separate the two columns. In the case of this argument, we write:

       A   │   A
       B   │

In other words, we are trying to make the sentences A and B TRUE and, in the same situation, make A FALSE. But it should be easy to see that we cannot make the same sentence both TRUE and FALSE in the same situation. Since sentence A appears on both the list of sentences we are trying to make TRUE and the list of sentences we are trying to make FALSE, it should be clear that this attempt will fail. This result leads us to our first observation about these lists:

> If the same sentence occurs on both the left and right lists of sentences, then we shall fail in the attempt to make the sentences in the left list TRUE and those in the right list FALSE. When this occurs, we shall say that this attempt has *failed.*

Let us consider another, more unusual argument:

       1. C
       2. ~C
    ∴ 3. D

Using the technique of left and right lists of sentences, we would now write:

       C   │   D
      ~C   │

meaning that we are trying to make C and ~C TRUE and D FALSE. But trying to make ~C TRUE is the same as trying to make C FALSE. A situation in which ~C is TRUE is the same situation as one in which C is FALSE. So, we could transform the lists in the following way. We could move ~C from the left to the right list, removing its outer negation sign as we do so. The result would be:

```
C  |  D
   |  C
```

But this is a case we have seen before: The same sentence occurs on *both* lists. We have already seen that such an attempt fails. Seeing what occurred to the negation sign, we can make a second observation:

> If a negated sentence occurs on a list, move it to the other list and drop its outer negation sign.

Now consider this argument:

> 1. (A & B)
> ∴ 2. B

Transformed into our pair of lists, the argument becomes:

> (A & B) | B

But how could '(A & B)', the first sentence on the left list, be made TRUE? It is a conjunction, and there is only one way. The two conjuncts, A and B, must both be TRUE. In other words, the above lists can be transformed into:

```
A  |  B
B  |
```

We then see that this attempt, too, fails, because the same sentence occurs on both lists. What we just saw happen to a conjunction leads us to our third observation:

> If a conjunction appears on the *left* list, then remove that conjunction and add its two conjuncts separately to the left list.

There is a similar operation that we may perform on a sentence on the right list:

> If a disjunction appears on the *right* list, then remove that disjunction and add its two disjuncts separately to the right list.

The justification for this operation is not difficult to find. The right list contains the sentences we are trying to make FALSE. But how can we make a *disjunction* FALSE? There is only one way: both of its disjuncts must be made FALSE.

We are accumulating rules for manipulating our pair of lists. We have three rules so far for creating new list-pairs from old ones. They are:

1. If a negated sentence occurs on a list, then move it from that list to the other list and drop its outer negation sign.
2. If a conjunction occurs on the *left* list, then replace that conjunction with its two conjuncts, listed separately.

TRUTH TABLES AND VALIDITY

3. If a disjunction occurs on the *right* list, then replace that disjunction with its two disjuncts, listed separately.

We also have made a generalization that "passes judgment" on a pair of lists:

If there is a sentence that occurs on both lists, then the attempt has failed.

Before we go further, let's apply these principles to another argument:

1. ~~(A & (B v C))
∴ 2. (A v D)

The first list-pair we form is:

~~(A & (B v C)) | (A v D)

Since '~~(A & (B v C))' on the left list is a negation, we move it to the right side, being careful to drop only its outer negation sign. The result is:

| (A v D)
| ~(A & (B v C))

The left list is temporarily empty. But '~(A & (B v C))' on the right list is also a negation, so applying rule 1 again, we have:

(A & (B v C)) | (A v D)

The sentence now on the left list is a conjunction, so we can apply rule 2, which deals with conjunctions on the left list. The result is:

A | (A v D)
(B v C) |

The sentence on the right list, '(A v D)', is a disjunction. According to rule 3, we obtain:

A | A
(B v C) | D

At this point, we should see that one sentence, A, occurs on both lists. Employing our generalization that passes judgment on list-pairs, we see that our attempt to make the sentences on the left list TRUE and on the right list FALSE has failed. Because we began by trying to make the premises of the argument TRUE and the conclusion FALSE, and because making these successive list-pairs is the only way to do so, we can conclude that this argument must be valid. That is, there is no situation where the premises are each TRUE and the conclusion is FALSE.

So far, we have looked only at valid arguments. Consider this argument:

  1. (A & ~B)
∴ 2. (B v C)

Our first list-pair is:

  (A & ~B) | (B v C)

Because '(A & ~B)' is a conjunction on the left list, we get:

  A   (B v C)
  ~B

And because '(B v C)' on the right list is a disjunction, we obtain:

  A   B
  ~B   C

Finally, since '~B' on the left list is a negation, applying rule 1 produces:

  A   B
             C
             B

No sentence occurs on both lists. Furthermore, all the sentences on both lists are *atomic* sentences.

When all the sentences on each list are atomic, and when no atomic sentence occurs on both lists, we shall say that we have *succeeded* in our attempt to make the sentences on the left list TRUE and on the right FALSE. Whenever this occurs, we know that the original argument is invalid. When each list is composed of only atomic sentences, and when no sentence occurs on both lists, we have found the situation in which the premises are TRUE but the conclusion FALSE. Looking at the last pair of lists for the preceding argument, we note that that situation is:

  V(A) = TRUE
  V(B) = FALSE
  V(C) = FALSE

since A is on the "Make TRUE" list and B and C are on the "Make FALSE" list.

Let us consider another argument:

  1. ~A
  2. (A v B)
∴ 3. B

The first list-pair based on the argument is:

  ~A   B
  (A v B)

TRUTH TABLES AND VALIDITY

Applying rule 1, we obtain these lists:

(A v B) | B
A

But now what do we do? Rule 2 applies only to conjunctions on the left list, and rule 3 applies only to disjunctions on the right list. Here we have a disjunction on the left list.

The occurrence of a sentence on the left list means that we are trying to make it TRUE. In order to make a disjunction TRUE, at least one of the disjuncts must be TRUE. But we have a choice of which one. In the above example, '(A v B)' must be made TRUE, and this can be accomplished in either of two ways: either one disjunct, 'A', is made TRUE, or the other disjunct, 'B', is made TRUE.

In other words, there are at least two ways to make '(A v B)' TRUE. This means that we should now create two new pairs of lists. To do this, we duplicate the original pair and then replace each disjunction with a disjunct—a different one for each duplicate:

1.   (A v B) | B
                                                   A

2(a). (A v B) | B   (A v B)   B
                 A   A

2(b).   A   B   B | B
                   A   A

Our attempt to make '(A v B)' TRUE "branches" into two new attempts. One of these new attempts makes '(A v B)' TRUE by making A TRUE, the other by making B TRUE.

But notice that both of these two attempts have a sentence occurring on both lists. On the new left branch, the sentence letter 'A' occurs on both lists. On the new right branch, the sentence letter 'B' occurs on both lists. So *both* of these attempts fail, and the argument is therefore valid.

We now add four new rules for transforming lists:

4. If a disjunction occurs on the *left* list, create two new list-pairs by duplicating the original pair. On one of the new pairs, replace the disjunction with its first disjunct. On the other new pair, replace the disjunction with its second disjunct.

5. If a conjunction occurs on the *right* list, create two new list-pairs by duplicating the original pair. On one of the new pairs, replace the conjunction with its first conjunct. On the other new pair, replace the conjunction with its second conjunct.

6. If a conditional occurs on the *left* list, create two new list-pairs by duplicating the original pair. On one of the new pairs, replace the conditional with the negation of its antecedent. On the other new pair, replace the conditional with its consequent.

7. If a conditional occurs on the *right* list, replace it with two sentences: the negation of its antecedent and also its consequent.

Rule 6 is based on the idea that for a conditional to be made TRUE, either the antecedent must be made FALSE or the consequent made TRUE. On the other hand, if a conditional appears on the *right* list (rule 7), for it to be made FALSE, its antecedent must be made

TRUE and its consequent FALSE. To make its antecedent TRUE, we make the negation of that antecedent FALSE.

Whenever we encounter a rule that requires us to "branch" into two attempts, we shall always continue working on the first attempt. We shall put the second attempt "on hold" and turn to it later. In the terminology of computer science, we place these other list-pairs resulting from branching onto a "stack." WANG'S ALGORITHM is now virtually complete. We need only to add two generalizations for evaluating these lists. These two generalizations are:

If every attempt to make the sentences on the left lists TRUE and those on the right lists FALSE *fails*—including all branched attempts—then the argument is valid.
If a single attempt succeeds, then the argument is invalid.

We have already described what it is for an attempt to "fail" or "succeed." An attempt has failed when a sentence occurs on both lists. An attempt has succeeded when only atomic sentences occur on each list and no sentence occurs on both lists.

We are now in a position to give the full algorithm.

WANG'S ALGORITHM

1. INPUT a symbolized argument.
2. Create two lists: Place the premises of the argument on the left list and the conclusion on the right list.
3. FOR every sentence on both lists:

(i) IF the sentence is a negation
THEN

(a) Move it from that list to the other list, and drop its outer negation sign.
(b) TEST the lists. (TEST is a procedure described below.)

(ii) IF the sentence is a conjunction on the left list
THEN

(a) Replace that conjunction with its two conjuncts, listed separately.
(b) TEST the lists.

(iii) IF the sentence is a disjunction on the right list
THEN

(a) Replace that disjunction with its two disjuncts, listed separately.
(b) TEST the lists.

(iv) IF the sentence is a disjunction on the left list
THEN

- (a) Create two new list-pairs by duplicating the original pair.
- (b) On one of the new pairs, which will remain the current attempt, replace the disjunction with its first disjunct.
- (c) TEST the lists.
- (d) On the other new pair, to be put on the "stack" for later manipulation, replace the disjunction with its second disjunct.
- (e) TEST the lists.

(v) IF the sentence is a conjunction on the right list
   THEN

- (a) Create two new list-pairs by duplicating the original pair.
- (b) On one of the new pairs, which will remain the current attempt, replace the conjunction with its first conjunct.
- (c) TEST the lists.
- (d) On the other new pair, to be "stacked," replace the conjunction with its second conjunct.
- (e) TEST the lists.

(vi) IF the sentence is a conditional on the left list
   THEN

- (a) Create two new list-pairs by duplicating the original pair.
- (b) On one of the new pairs, which will remain the current attempt, replace the conditional with the negation of its antecedent.
- (c) TEST the lists.
- (d) On the other new pair, to be "stacked," replace the conditional with its consequent.
- (e) TEST the lists.

(vii) IF the sentence is a conditional on the right list
   THEN

- (a) Replace it with two sentences: the negation of its antecedent and also its consequent.
- (b) TEST the lists.

4. STOP.

The output and the use of the stack are handled by the procedure TEST:

PROCEDURE TEST

1. IF the current attempt has a sentence on both lists
   THEN

- (a) Mark that attempt "failed."
- (b) IF there is a list-pair remaining in the stack

THEN

    (i) Consider the last such pair that was added to be the current attempt.

    (ii) Delete it from the stack.

    (iii) Proceed to the next step in the main procedure.

  (c) IF there is not such a list-pair remaining in the stack
      THEN OUTPUT "Argument valid" and STOP.

2. IF an attempt does not have a sentence occurring on both lists
   THEN

    (a) IF the sentences on both lists are all atomic
       THEN OUTPUT "Argument invalid" and STOP.

    (b) IF the sentences on both lists are not all atomic
       THEN proceed with the next step in the main procedure.

Main Connectives

One idea used in step 3 of WANG'S ALGORITHM is the notion of a sentence being a negation, a disjunction, a conjunction, or a conditional. How can this be determined in a mechanical way? A sentence is a conditional if its "main connective" is → (and so on for the other connectives).

The *main connective* of a sentence is the connective that is surrounded by the *fewest* parentheses. This makes the notion of a main connective almost the opposite of the notion of an "innermost subformula" (see Chapter 5).

The following procedure can be used to find what the main connective of a sentence is:

PROCEDURE MAIN-CONNECTIVE

1. INPUT a sentence.

2. IF the sentence consists of only one character
   THEN
    (a) The sentence is atomic and has no main connective.
    (b) STOP.

3. IF the first character is ~
   THEN
    (a) The main connective is ~.
    (b) STOP.

4. Let $n = 0$.

> 5. FOR every character in the sentence:
>   (a) IF that character is '('
>   THEN let n be $n + 1$.
>   (b) IF that character is ')'
>   THEN let n be $n - 1$.
>   (c) IF that character is v and $n = 1$
>   THEN
>   (i) The main connective is v.
>   (ii) STOP.
>
>   (d) IF that character is & and $n = 1$
>   THEN
>
>   (i) The main connective is &.
>   (ii) STOP.
>
>   (e) IF that character is → and $n = 1$
>   THEN
>
>   (i) The main connective is →.
>   (ii) STOP.

Observe that steps 5(a) and 5(b) of this procedure are just the "first counter" of TRUTH-VALUE CALCULATOR from Chapter 5. The "first counter" measures how deeply a character is buried in parentheses. If the sentence is neither atomic nor a negation, then the *least* deeply a character can be buried is 1. So the '$n = 1$' clauses in step 5 tell us when a character is surrounded by the fewest parentheses.

Some Examples

Let's apply WANG'S ALGORITHM to several arguments.
Consider this argument:

1. A
2. (A → (B & C))
∴ 3. C

Applying WANG'S ALGORITHM, after steps 1 and 2, we have:

A   C
(A → (B & C))

Note that step 3 does not modify atomic sentences, such as A and C, so the next step to take action is step 3(vi). The result is that we "branch" to two attempts. Here, and in later examples, we duplicate list pairs and replace in one step.

```
    A  |  C          A          |  C
   ~A  |            (B & C)     |
```

We continue work on the first pair of lists, applying now step 3(i):

```
    A  |  C
       |  A
```

FAILED

That is, applying TEST, we see that a sentence occurs on both lists. We then return to the other branch, which we had temporarily put aside:

```
           A        |  C
        (B & C)      |
```

Applying step 3(ii):

```
           A        |  C
           B        |
           C        |
```

FAILED
ARGUMENT VALID

That is, the test of this list-pair shows that the attempt has failed. Since there are no more attempts to consider (that is, no more list-pairs in the stack), the argument is shown to be valid.

Consider another argument:

    1. $\sim A$
    2. $(A \to B)$
$\therefore$ 3. $\sim B$

We first have:

```
   ~A        |   ~B
 (A → B)     |
```

Then:

```
              |   ~B
 (A → B)      |    A
```

But now we branch to:

~A | ~B   B | ~B
    | A | A

Continuing work on the first branch:

| ~B
| A
| A

Then:

B | A
  | A

But since only atomic sentences occur on each list, and no sentence occurs on both lists, TEST tells us the argument is invalid.

Summary

This chapter began with a review of truth tables, showing how to construct them for any molecular sentence, no matter how complex. We gave an algorithm for doing this—TRUTH-TABLE GENERATOR (which calls on TRUTH-VALUE CALCULATOR as one of its procedures). We then showed how to use a truth table to determine whether or not an argument is valid. The key ideas here are (1) to generate a truth table whose left-most columns are for the atomic sentences occurring in the argument and whose right-most columns are for the premises and conclusion, and (2) that the rows of this truth table provide the information needed to determine the situations, if any, in which the premises are TRUE and the conclusion FALSE. The algorithm VALID-ITY/INVALIDITY DETERMINER (which calls on TRUTH-TABLE GENERATOR as one of *its* procedures) does this. While efficient enough for computers, this latter algorithm can rapidly get out of hand (by growing quite large). WANG'S ALGORITHM is an elegant and more efficient procedure for determining validity.

Exercises

A. For each of the arguments given below:
   (a) State how many rows are required for a truth table for the argument.
   (b) State the truth values in the columns for each of the atomic sentences.

CHAPTER 6

Example:

    (A → (B & ~C))

    (~B & ~C)

∴ ~A

Answer:

(a) Eight rows are necessary.

    [There are three distinct atomic sentences, A, B, and C, and 2 ** 3 = 8.]

(b)

V(A)	V(B)	V(C)	
0	0	0	
0	0	1	
0	1	0	
0	1	1	
1	0	0	
1	0	1	
1	1	0	
1	1	1	

1.   ~(A → B)

     ~B

  ∴ A

2.   (C v D)

     (~C & (D → B))

  ∴ (D & B)

3.   (A & ~A)

     B

  ∴ ~B

4.   A

     B

  ∴ (C v ~C)

5.   (A → (B & C))

     (B → D)

     A

  ∴ D

6.   (A → B)

     (~B v C)

     ~A

  ∴ ~C

7.   (~D & (B v ~C))

     (~D → B)

  ∴ C

8.   (B → ~(C & D))

     (C & D)

  ∴ ~~~B

9.　(A → B)
　　(B → C)
　∴ (A → C)

10.　(A → B)
　∴ (~B → ~A)

11.　(A → B)
　　(A → C)
　∴ (B → C)

12.　(A v B)
　　~A
　∴ B

B. Examine the following right-hand fragments of truth tables. Answer these questions: (1) Is the argument valid or invalid? (2) If the argument is invalid, which row(s) show it to be so?

1. | Prem. 1 | Prem. 2 | Conclusion |
|---|---|---|
| 0 | 1 | 1 |
| 1 | 1 | 1 |
| 0 | 0 | 0 |
| 1 | 1 | 0 |
| 1 | 0 | 0 |

2. | Prem. 1 | Prem. 2 | Prem. 3 | Conclusion |
|---|---|---|---|
| 1 | 0 | 1 | 1 |
| 0 | 0 | 0 | 0 |
| 1 | 1 | 1 | 1 |
| 0 | 1 | 1 | 1 |

3. | Prem. 1 | Prem. 2 | Conclusion |
|---|---|---|
| 0 | 1 | 1 |
| 1 | 1 | 0 |
| 0 | 1 | 1 |
| 0 | 0 | 0 |
| 1 | 1 | 1 |
| 0 | 1 | 0 |
| 1 | 1 | 0 |
| 0 | 1 | 0 |

4. | Prem. 1 | Prem. 2 | Prem. 3 | Prem. 4 | Conclusion |
|---|---|---|---|---|
| 0 | 1 | 1 | 1 | 0 |
| 1 | 1 | 1 | 0 | 0 |
| 1 | 1 | 1 | 1 | 0 |

C. Apply TRUTH-TABLE GENERATOR to the arguments given in Exercise A. Indicate whether each argument is valid or invalid.

D. Steps 2 and 3 of TRUTH-TABLE GENERATOR tell us that the size of the truth table needed to test an argument is a function of (1) the number of premises and (2) the number of distinct atomic sentences in the premises and conclusion. Calculate the size of the truth table, measured in rows and columns, needed for arguments that have:

1. 3 premises, 2 atomic sentences
2. 2 premises, 3 atomic sentences
3. 4 premises, 3 atomic sentences
4. 3 premises, 5 atomic sentences

E. In the algorithm VALIDITY/INVALIDITY DETERMINER, we first filled in *all* the blanks in a truth table (as part of step 2) and only then examined each row to see if it showed the argument to be invalid (step 3). We might, however, consider an alternative that first fills in only the first row of truth values and then immediately examines this row to see if it shows the argument to be invalid. If it does, the procedure outputs "Invalid" and stops. If it doesn't, the procedure goes to the next row and repeats the process.

What are the advantages and disadvantages to this method?

F. Apply WANG'S ALGORITHM to the following arguments to determine which are valid and which are invalid.

1.   (A & (C v D))
    ~C
    (D → E)
  ∴ E

2.   (B → ~C)
    (A v (D & B))
  ∴ (D v A)

3.   (A & C)
    (D → A)
    (D → E)
  ∴ (D & E)

4.   ~(A → ~B)
    ~(C v E)
  ∴ (C → A)

5.   (~A & (C → D))
    (D → A)
    ((F & E) → C)
  ∴ (~F v ~E)

G. Determine a formula for calculating how large the left and right lists might become for a given argument. (*Hint:* Consider the number of atomic sentences.)

H. Determine a formula for calculating the maximum number of branches an application of WANG'S ALGORITHM might take.

I. Write a program to apply WANG'S ALGORITHM to a list-pair that contains & and ~ as main connectives on the left list and →, ~, and v on the right list. (You will not have to consider branching and the resulting stacks.)

J. Write a program that applies WANG'S ALGORITHM in its entirety to an input argument and prints out all the list-pairs, such that every branch of this "tree" ultimately ends with either "ATTEMPT FAILS" or "ATTEMPT SUCCEEDS, ARGUMENT INVALID."

Suggestions for Computer Implementation

The design of a program to implement WANG'S ALGORITHM requires the following considerations. First, something must be created to store the main list-pair ("the current attempt"). Provisions must also be made for the list-pairs that are put "on hold"—that is, for the stack. Second, a procedure, or function, must be created to input a sentence and determine whether the sentence is atomic, a negation, a conditional, a conjunction, or a disjunction. We might call this procedure MAIN-CONNECTIVE, since its principal task is to determine the main connective in a sentence. And third, a procedure must be designed to test the list-pairs: the procedure TEST.

In most programming languages, the list-pairs would be stored in string arrays. (In languages that accept genuine lists, such as LISP and LOGO, the list-pairs can be stored as lists.) LLIST and RLIST would be convenient names for the left and right lists currently under consideration. It might also prove convenient to have a variable that remembers how many sentences are stored in LLIST and RLIST at any given time: we might call these two variables LCOUNT and RCOUNT.

The procedure MAIN-CONNECTIVE inputs a string and might output:

A   If the input sentence is atomic.
~   If a negation.
v   If a disjunction.
&   If a conjunction.
>   If a conditional.

For the manipulation of strings, we would also need to construct some functions or procedures to perform the following tasks:

1. Remove the first character (usually a negation sign) from a string. We can call this 'NEGOFF' for "NEGation OFF."
2. Generate from an input sentence the sentence to the left of the main connective. We might call this the 'LEFTSEN' function.
3. Generate from an input sentence the sentence to the right of the main connective. We might call this the 'RIGHTSEN' function.

Here are some examples of the way these three functions work:

NEGOFF [~~(A & B)]   = ~(A & B)
LEFTSEN [((A & B) v (C v D))]   = (A & B)

RIGHTSEN [((A & B) v (C v D))] = (C v D)

Using these procedures, and using our program design language in a very detailed way, the program might begin:

    1. INPUT LLIST [the premises].
    2. INPUT RLIST [the conclusion].
    3. Let LCOUNT be the number of sentences on LLIST.
    4. Let RCOUNT be 1 [since only the conclusion is initially on RLIST].
    5. FOR every sentence on LLIST, from I = 1 to LCOUNT:
      (a) IF MAINCONNECTIVE(LLIST(I)) = ~
          THEN
            (i) Let RLIST(RCOUNT + 1) be NEGOFF(LLIST(I)).
            (ii) Let LLIST(I) be " " [a space, which serves as a placeholder].
            (iii) Let RCOUNT be RCOUNT + 1.
            (iv) TEST the list-pair.
      (b) IF MAINCONNECTIVE(LLIST(I)) = &
          THEN
            (i) Let LLIST(LCOUNT + 1) be LEFTSEN(LLIST(I)).
            (ii) Let LLIST(I) be RIGHTSEN(LLIST(I)).
            (iii) Let LCOUNT be LCOUNT + 1.
            (iv) TEST the list-pair.

and so on for the RLIST as well.

The branching that results from disjunctions or conditionals on LLIST and conjunctions on RLIST requires some special considerations. One list-pair at a time is put on a stack. Two stacks are needed; we can call them 'LSTACK' and 'RSTACK'. LSTACK will store the stacked left lists, and RSTACK will store the stacked right lists. It is extremely handy if both LSTACK and RSTACK are two-dimensional arrays whose first index indicates *when* a list was stacked (first, second, and so on) and whose second index indicates the sentence on the list. For example, LSTACK (2,3) would refer to the third sentence on the second left list that was previously stacked. We shall put the lists onto the stacks in the order of when we branch, and we shall take them off and make them the "main attempt" in reverse order. That is, we shall first take the last list-pair that was stacked. This is called the "last in, first out" method. A good reason for using stacks rather than, say, a "first in, first out" organization (a queue) is that the last list-pair put on the stack is probably more highly "digested"—that is, broken into simpler strings—than the first and so might allow us to reach a "failed" attempt with minimal manipulation. It is also useful to have counters to keep track of how many sentences are in each "level" of each stack.

TRUTH TABLES AND VALIDITY

One advantage of WANG'S ALGORITHM is that its implementation does not require the sometimes huge arrays that VALIDITY/INVALIDITY DETERMINER does. If there are not too many premises (no more than, say, 6) and not too many atomic sentences (no more than, say, 10), then the arrays LLIST and RLIST need not be larger than 10, or LSTACK and RSTACK larger than 10 × 10.

SENTENTIAL LOGIC: Logical Equivalence, Normal Forms, and Polish Notation

Having answered one major question in sentential logic, namely, how one can mechanically determine whether an argument is valid or invalid, we now turn to other topics of importance to logical theory. Some molecular sentences are so constructed that they always have the truth value TRUE. These logically true sentences are important in their own right, but they also permit us to develop additional ways of determining when arguments are valid or invalid.

We shall also in this chapter examine sentences that, from the point of view of sentential logic, have the same "meaning." Because of the huge range of patterns that even these truth-functionally synonymous sentences can exhibit—especially when we permit so many different connectives—we might wonder if there are any "standard" ways to express a proposition with certain sentences. This question takes us to the topic of "normal forms," which are very useful for the computerized analysis of properties of sentences such as validity (as we shall see in Chapter 14).

Finally, a very different system of notation from the one we have been using is examined. This notational system, Polish notation, cleverly avoids the use of all parentheses and has widespread use in computer applications. Moreover, it enormously simplifies some of the string-processing tasks we have considered earlier (although it complicates others).

CHAPTER 7

Tautologies and Arguments

We have been assuming—and shall continue to assume—that sentences can have one of two truth values, either TRUE or FALSE; that is, if **P** is a sentence, then either V(**P**) = TRUE or V(**P**) = FALSE. To decide whether a molecular truth-functional sentence **P** is TRUE or FALSE, we usually need to find out the truth values of its atomic constituents. However, two kinds of truth-functional sentences are such that we can determine their truth value without knowing the actual truth values of their atomic constituents; they are called "tautologies" and "contradictions."

A sentence **P** is a *tautology* if and only if V(**P**) = TRUE for all possible combinations of truth values of its atomic constituents. A sentence is a *contradiction* if and only if it is a conjunction of a sentence **P** and its negation, ~**P**. It is evident that V(**P** & ~**P**) = FALSE in all situations. So, a tautology is a sentence that is always TRUE, and a contradiction is a sentence that is always FALSE.

The third kind of sentence—the kind whose truth value varies with the particular truth values of its atomic constituents—is called a *contingent* sentence.

Since the truth value of a tautology is TRUE and the truth value of a contradiction is FALSE no matter what truth values their atomic constituents have, it follows that the truth value of a tautology or a contradiction does not vary with the truth values of its atomic constituents.

For example, 'It is raining or it is not raining' is a tautology. If we symbolize it as

(A v ~A)

and look at its truth table,

V(A)	V(~A)	V(A v ~A)
FALSE	TRUE	TRUE
TRUE	FALSE	TRUE

we see that V(A v ~A) = TRUE no matter what V(A) and V(~A) are. That is, 'It is raining or it is not raining' is TRUE whether or not it is, in fact, raining. It is always TRUE no matter what the weather is; hence, it gives us no information about the weather.

Consider, next, the sentence 'It is raining and it is not raining'. This is a contradiction, and an examination of its truth table shows that it is always FALSE:

V(A)	V(~A)	V(A & ~A)
FALSE	TRUE	FALSE
TRUE	FALSE	FALSE

This sentence is FALSE, whether or not it is raining. Thus it also gives us no information about the weather.

In general, it is claimed that no tautologies or contradictions provide any information. Only contingent sentences do. The sentence 'It is raining and I have an umbrella' is contingent. If we symbolize it as

(A & H)

its truth table is:

V(A)	V(H)	V(A & H)
FALSE	FALSE	FALSE
FALSE	TRUE	FALSE
TRUE	FALSE	FALSE
TRUE	TRUE	TRUE

Thus sometimes it is TRUE (when it *is* raining *and* I *have* an umbrella), and sometimes it is FALSE (when it is *not* raining *or* when I *don't* have an umbrella).

Since whether a sentence is a tautology or a contradiction depends on its structure and the behavior of the logical truth functions, it is evident that no atomic sentence is either a tautology or a contradiction. In the logic of sentences all atomic sentences are contingent.

Arguments and Corresponding Conditionals

One important use of tautologies is in determining whether an argument is valid or invalid. Any argument has a set of premises and a conclusion. First, consider an argument with one premise, **P,** and a conclusion, **Q**:

   1. **P**
∴   2. **Q**

This *argument* is *valid* iff it is impossible for **Q** to be FALSE while **P** is TRUE. But those are precisely the circumstances under which the *sentence*

   (**P → Q**)

is a *tautology.*
   Next, consider an argument with two premises, **P** and **Q,** and conclusion **R**:

   1. **P**
   2. **Q**
∴   3. **R**

This argument is valid iff it is impossible for **R** to be FALSE while **P** and **Q** are both TRUE. In other words, this argument is valid iff the sentence

   ((**P & Q**) → **R**)

is a tautology.

CHAPTER 7

In general, for every argument with n premises (P_1, P_2, . . . ,P_n) and conclusion Q:

    1. P_1
    2. P_2
       .
       .
       .
    n. P_n
$\therefore n + 1$. Q

there corresponds a conditional sentence, **R**, whose antecedent is the conjunction of the argument's premises and whose consequent is the argument's conclusion:

    (R) $(((\ldots ((P_1 \mathbin{\&} P_2) \mathbin{\&} P_3) \mathbin{\&} \ldots) \mathbin{\&} P_n) \to Q)$

An argument and its corresponding conditional sentence satisfy the following principle:

    An argument is valid iff its corresponding conditional is a tautology.

Logical Equivalence

Often, two different sentences will be TRUE or FALSE in precisely the same situations. That is, for any combination of truth values of their atomic constituents, both sentences will have the same truth value. As a simple example, consider an atomic sentence **P** and its double negation ~~**P.** They both have the same atomic constituent, **P,** and $V(P) = $ TRUE if and only if $V(\sim\sim P) = $ TRUE. We say that **P** and ~~**P** are "logically equivalent."

As another example, consider a conditional, $(P \to Q)$, and its "contrapositive," $(\sim Q \to \sim P)$. Let us look at their truth tables (using 1 and 0 for TRUE and FALSE, respectively):

$V(P)$	$V(Q)$	$V(P \to Q)$
0	0	1
0	1	1
1	0	0
1	1	1

$V(P)$	$V(Q)$	$V(\sim P)$	$V(\sim Q)$	$V(\sim Q \to \sim P)$
0	0	1	1	1
0	1	1	0	1
1	0	0	1	0
1	1	0	0	1

EQUIVALENCES AND POLISH NOTATION

We see that $V(P \rightarrow Q) = V(\sim Q \rightarrow \sim P)$ for all possible combinations of truth values of **P** and **Q**. So $(P \rightarrow Q)$ and $(\sim Q \rightarrow \sim P)$ are logically equivalent.

In general, a sentence **P** is *logically equivalent* to a sentence **Q** if and only if $V(P) = V(Q)$ for all possible combinations of truth values of their atomic constituents.

What about '(A v ~A)' and '(B v ~B)'? Are they logically equivalent? They share no atomic constituents, so you might think that they couldn't be. Yet they are both tautologies, so they are both always TRUE. Hence $V(A \vee \sim A) = V(B \vee \sim B)$ for all possible combinations of truth values of their atomic constituents. So they *are* logically equivalent. So are '(A & ~A)' and '(B & ~B)', since they are both contradictions, hence always FALSE. In fact, all tautologies are logically equivalent to each other, and all contradictions are logically equivalent to each other (but, of course, no tautology is logically equivalent to any contradiction).

There is another important relationship between tautologies and logical equivalence. Consider a biconditional, $(P \leftrightarrow Q)$. According to its truth table, $V(P \leftrightarrow Q) = $ TRUE if and only if $V(P) = V(Q)$. That is, a biconditional is TRUE if and only if its left-hand side has the same truth value as its right-hand side. This suggests the following principle:

> A sentence **P** is logically equivalent to a sentence **Q**
> if and only if $(P \leftrightarrow Q)$ is a tautology.

As an example, consider $(P \rightarrow Q)$ and $(\sim Q \rightarrow \sim P)$ again. Instead of constructing two *separate* truth tables to show that they are logically equivalent, we could, in effect, combine the tables by constructing a single truth table for their biconditional:

$$((P \rightarrow Q) \leftrightarrow (\sim Q \rightarrow \sim P))$$

and show that this sentence is a tautology.

There are a number of important logical equivalences. We shall leave many of these as exercises, but three will be singled out for discussion here.

The first two are known as *De Morgan's laws:*

1. $(\sim(P \& Q) \leftrightarrow (\sim P \vee \sim Q))$
2. $(\sim(P \vee Q) \leftrightarrow (\sim P \& \sim Q))$

Sentences (1) and (2) are tautologies, so their respective left- and right-hand sides are logically equivalent. It is important to see what this means. Consider De Morgan's law 1. It says that the negation of a conjunction is logically equivalent to a disjunction—in particular, the disjunction of the negations of the original conjuncts. Similarly, De Morgan's law 2 says that the negation of a disjunction is logically equivalent to a conjunction—in particular, the conjunction of the negations of the original disjuncts.

The left-hand side of law 1 is also logically equivalent to (**P** NAND **Q**). Thus (**P** NAND **Q**) is logically equivalent to a disjunction. You should check each of these facts by constructing appropriate truth tables.

Another important logical equivalence is called *exportation*. The sentence

$$(((P \& Q) \rightarrow R) \leftrightarrow (P \rightarrow (Q \rightarrow R)))$$

is a tautology, so the two sides of the biconditional are logically equivalent.

When you are writing computer programs, these rules can be especially helpful in finding efficient ways of expressing conditions that need to be tested. For instance, some computers will not allow you to use a conditional instruction of the form

IF **P** and **Q**
    THEN do X

If **P** is FALSE and **Q** has not been assigned a value yet, it may give you a run-time error. This can be avoided by using the logically equivalent command

IF **P**
    THEN IF **Q**
            THEN do X

Since **P** is FALSE, the command is not executed, and so the illegal value for **Q** is never encountered.

Normal Forms

Suppose you wanted to prove some claim about *all* sentences. It would be helpful if there were some uniform way to express them. Such a uniform method of expressing sentences is called a *normal form*. In particular, we devise normal forms so that every sentence is logically equivalent to a sentence in a normal form. In this section, we shall describe one kind of normal form: *conjunctive normal form*. Another important kind, *disjunctive normal form,* is dealt with in Exercise G.

To define conjunctive normal form, it will prove helpful first to define another kind of sentence called a *basic disjunction:*

1. If **P** is an atomic sentence or the negation of an atomic sentence,
        then **P** is a basic disjunction.
2. If **P** and **Q** are each basic disjunctions,
        then (**P** v **Q**) is a basic disjunction.
3. Nothing else is a basic disjunction.

So, for example,

A
~A
~B
(A v B)
(A v ~A)
((A v B) v C)
((A v B) v (D v ~E))

are all basic disjunctions.

EQUIVALENCES AND POLISH NOTATION

We can now define what it means for a sentence to be in *conjunctive normal form* (CNF):

1. If **P** is a basic disjunction,
   then **P** is in CNF.
2. If **P** and **Q** are each in CNF,
   then (**P** & **Q**) is in CNF.
3. Nothing else is in CNF.

So, for example, all the basic disjunctions listed above, as well as

((A v B) & (~A v B))
(A & ~A)
(((A v B) & (A v C)) & ~B)

are in CNF. You will note that a sentence in CNF is always a multiple conjunction of disjunctions (if you include atomic sentences and their negations standing alone as trivial cases of conjunctions and disjunctions).

There are several algorithms for turning any sentence **P** into an equivalent sentence **Q** in CNF. One requires the use of truth tables:

ALGORITHM CNF-1

1. INPUT sentence **P**.
2. Apply TRUTH-TABLE GENERATOR to construct a truth table for **P**.
3. IF **P** is a tautology
   THEN let **Q** = (**R** v ~**R**), where **R** is the alphabetically first atomic sentence in **P**.
4. IF **P** is not a tautology
   THEN
   (a) FOR each row ROW of the truth table such that V(**P**) = 0
       (i) Form a set NEG-ATOM(ROW) of atomic sentences and their negations as follows:
           (1) FOR each atomic constituent **R**
               (a) IF V(**R**) = 1
                   THEN put ~**R** in the set.
               (b) IF V(**R**) = 0
                   THEN put **R** in the set.
       (ii) Let BASIC-DISJ(ROW) = the disjunction of the members of NEG-ATOM(ROW). (Note that BASIC-DISJ(ROW) is a basic disjunction.)
   (b) Let **Q** = the conjunction of all the BASIC-DISJ(ROW)s.
5. OUTPUT CNF sentence **Q**.
6. STOP.

CHAPTER 7

Another method for transforming a sentence into a CNF does not require the use of truth tables:

ALGORITHM CNF-2

1. INPUT sentence **P**.
2. Replace all subformulas of the form (**R** ↔ **S**) with sentences of the form ((**R** → **S**) & (**S** → **R**)). (*Question:* What principle allows you to do this?)
3. Replace all subformulas of the form (**R** → **S**) with sentences of the form (~**R** v **S**).
4. Repeat the following until the only negated sentences are atomic sentences:
   (a) Replace all subformulas of the form ~(**R** & **S**) with sentences of the form (~**R** v ~**S**).
   (b) Replace all subformulas of the form ~(**R** v **S**) with sentences of the form (~**R** & ~**S**).
   (c) Replace all subformulas of the form ~~**R** with sentences of the form **R**.
5. Repeat the following until a sentence in CNF is reached:
   (a) Replace all subformulas of the form (**R** v (**S** & **T**)) with sentences of the form ((**R** v **S**) & (**R** v **T**)).
   (b) Replace all subformulas of the form ((**R** & **S**) v **T**) with sentences of the form ((**R** v **T**) & (**S** v **T**)).
6. Call the result **Q**.
7. OUTPUT CNF sentence **Q**.
8. STOP.

One useful feature of CNF is that it makes it easy to identify tautologies. In fact, if you use Algorithm CNF-2 to transform a sentence into a logically equivalent CNF sentence, you can decide whether it is a tautology *without using truth tables.* The principle is:

A sentence in CNF is a tautology if and only if each conjunct contains both an atomic sentence and its negation.

For example, consider the sentence

((A & (A → B)) → B)

We shall find logically equivalent CNF sentences using both algorithms, and we shall also check for tautologousness.

Algorithm CNF-1: First, we construct the truth table (you should be sure to do this!). You should see right away that the sentence is a tautology, so

EQUIVALENCES AND POLISH NOTATION

(A v ~A)

is an equivalent CNF sentence.

Algorithm CNF-2:

Step 2 is inapplicable.
Step 3:   We transform the sentence first into
                 ((A & (~A v B)) → B)
              and then into
                 (~(A & (~A v B)) v B)
Step 4(a): ((~A v ~(~A v B)) v B)
Step 4(b): ((~A v (~~A & ~B)) v B)
Step 4(c): ((~A v (A & ~B)) v B)
Step 5(a): (((~A v A) & (~A v ~B)) v B)
Step 5(b): (((~A v A) v B)) & ((~A v ~B) v B))

This is in CNF, since it is a conjunction of basic disjunctions. (Each conjunct is a basic disjunction, since each is a disjunction of atomic sentences and negations of atomic sentences.) Moreover, since each conjunct contains both an atomic sentence and its negation, we see that our original sentence is a tautology.

You might be puzzled about why the two algorithms produced different CNF sentences. In general, there are infinitely many CNF sentences equivalent to a given sentence. (Can you prove this?) All that matters is that the sentence be in CNF and be logically equivalent to the original sentence.

Consistency and Satisfiability

Let us say that a sentence whose truth value is TRUE in some situation (that is, for some values of its atomic constituents) is a *satisfiable* sentence.

A contradiction is a sentence whose truth value is always FALSE, regardless of the truth values of its atomic components. Because of this, contradictions are *not* satisfiable. Because tautologies and contingent sentences can have the value TRUE, they are satisfiable. The notion of satisfiability enables us to investigate some important properties of sets of sentences, and it also gives us another powerful tool for determining the validity of arguments.

Let us explore some simple examples before we discuss the general notion of satisfiability. Consider:

(A) 1. The car starts only if it has gas in its tank.
     2. It has gas in its tank, but the car doesn't start.

We can see this more clearly by symbolizing with obvious abbreviations:

(A) 1. (C → G)
     2. (G & ~C)

Now it is easy to show that (A1) is satisfiable [take V(C) = FALSE], and it is almost as easy to show that (A2) is also. We now raise a new question: Are they "simultaneously" satisfiable? By this we mean: Is there a *single* assignment of truth values to all the atomic components such that *both* molecular sentences have the truth value TRUE? In this case, V(C) = FALSE and V(G) = TRUE results in both (A1) and (A2) having the truth value TRUE.

Here is an example where the sentences are each satisfiable, but the two of them are not simultaneously satisfiable.

(B) 1. If the fish are biting, then it's not the time to swim.
    2. It's time to swim, and the fish are biting.

We can symbolize this as:

(B) 1. $(F \rightarrow \sim H)$
    2. $(H \ \& \ F)$

In this example, notice that

$V(F \rightarrow \sim H)$ = TRUE when V(F) = FALSE, and
$V(H \ \& \ F)$ = TRUE when V(H) = V(F) = TRUE

so each sentence is satisfiable. But there is no single value for V(F) and for V(H) for which $V(F \rightarrow \sim H)$ and $V(H \ \& \ F)$ are both TRUE simultaneously.

We can easily generalize this for any number of sentences.

If there is a single assignment of truth values to all the atomic components of all the sentences in a set such that each of the sentences in the set has the truth value TRUE, then the set of sentences is *simultaneously satisfiable.*

Here is how we can use this notion to investigate the validity of arguments. Remember that if an argument is valid, then whenever all the premises are TRUE, the conclusion *must* be TRUE. Thus if we add the *negation* of the conclusion to the premises, we shall have a set of sentences that is *not* simultaneously satisfiable, if the argument is valid. And in some ways it is easier to show that a set of sentences (especially a finite one) is not simultaneously satisfiable than it is to show that an argument is valid.

One simple way of showing that a set of sentences is not simultaneously satisfiable is to conjoin all the sentences in the set into a gigantic conjunction. Then transform this conjunction into *disjunctive* normal form (see Exercise G). If each of the disjuncts contains a contradiction, then the original set was not simultaneously satisfiable.

So far, we have used the notion of simultaneous satisfiability (or its absence) to show the validity of arguments. Can we reverse this? That is, can we use the notion of a valid argument to show that a set of sentences is (or is not) simultaneously satisfiable? Again, we return to the notion of a valid argument: when the premises are TRUE, the conclusion must be TRUE. But what if the conclusion of a valid argument can't be TRUE? What if the conclusion of a valid argument is a contradiction? In this case, we can reason

EQUIVALENCES AND POLISH NOTATION

"backward" and claim that not all the premises can be TRUE or, more precisely, that the set of premises is not simultaneously satisfiable.

With a little more terminology, we can put all this together.

> If the sentences in a set are used as the premises of a valid argument whose conclusion is a contradiction, then that set of sentences is called *inconsistent*.
> If there is no such valid argument using the sentences in this set as premises, then the set is *consistent*.

If we put the negation in different places, we can say that if no contradiction is a valid conclusion from a set of premises, then this set is consistent.

The key notions we have used in this section are those of a (sentence that is a) contradiction, a consistent set of sentences, an inconsistent set of sentences, a set of sentences that is simultaneously satisfiable (or that is not simultaneously satisfiable), and a valid argument. Let us consider some ways in which these notions are related.

1. A valid argument can have a conclusion that is a contradiction
   iff
   The premises are inconsistent
   iff
   The premises are not simultaneously satisfiable.
2. The premises of an argument *and* the negation of the conclusion are not simultaneously satisfiable
   iff
   This enlarged set is inconsistent
   iff
   The original argument is valid.
3. The set of premises of an argument is inconsistent
   iff
   The set of premises is not simultaneously satisfiable
   iff
   Any argument with these premises is valid.

This last claim requires some comment. If a set of premises of an argument is not simultaneously satisfiable, there will be no occasion when the premises are each TRUE and the conclusion FALSE. Hence the argument is valid.

For practical problem solving, the most important relation is 2 above. For instance, to show that

   1. (A v B)
   2. ~A
∴ 3. B

is a valid argument, conjoin each of the premises and then the negation of the conclusion:

   (((A v B) & ~A) & ~B)

Transforming this to disjunctive normal form (using the techniques of Exercise G), we get:

((((A & ~A) v (B & ~A)) & ~B)

and then:

((((A & ~A) & ~B) v ((B & ~A) & ~B))

We now see that each disjunct contains a contradiction, and so the original argument was valid.

Polish Notation

The use of parentheses, while needed in order to avoid ambiguities, is cumbersome. Often, by the adoption of conventions about "precedence" of logical connectives, the number of parentheses can be reduced, making formulas more readable. A somewhat different system of notation avoids the use of parentheses altogether.

The notation we have been using is sometimes called "infix" notation, since the two-place, truth-functional connectives (&, v, →, ↔, NAND, NOR, XOR) are written "in" between the sentence letters. The negation sign, however, is "prefixed" to its sentence. If "prefix" notation is used for *all* the connectives, then parentheses are not needed, as we shall see.

The most common kind of prefix notation for logic is called *Polish notation*. Instead of using the symbols we have been using for connectives, Polish notation uses certain capital italic letters, as shown below:

~	*N* (for "*N*egation")
v	*A* (for "*A*lteration")
&	*K* (for "*K*onjunction")
→	*C* (for material "*C*onditional")
↔	*E* (for "is *E*quivalent to")

We can define a well-formed sentence in Polish notation as follows:

1. Any atomic sentence is well-formed in Polish notation.
2. If **P** and **Q** are each well-formed in Polish notation, then so are
   NP
   APQ
   KPQ
   CPQ
   EPQ
3. Nothing else is well-formed in Polish notation.

EQUIVALENCES AND POLISH NOTATION

The five sentence-forms in clause 2 of the definition correspond to

~**P**
(**P** v **Q**)
(**P** & **Q**)
(**P** → **Q**)
(**P** ↔ **Q**)

in infix notation.

Let's look at some other sentences in both notations:

Infix	Polish
(1) (**P** & (**Q** & **R**))	*KPKQR*
(2) ((**P** & **Q**) & **R**)	*KKPQR*

In (1), the first and second occurrences of *K* correspond to the first and second occurrences of &, respectively. The string in Polish notation may be read as follows: The conjunction of **P** with (the conjunction of **Q** with **R**).

In (2), the first occurrence of *K* corresponds to the *second* occurrence of &, and the second occurrence of *K* corresponds to the *first* occurrence of &. The Polish-notation string may be read as follows: The conjunction of (the conjunction of **P** with **Q**) with **R**.

As you can see, parentheses are not needed in Polish notation (although they can sometimes be useful) because the Polish-notation strings are not ambiguous. Perhaps this can be made clearer with the following examples:

Infix	Polish
(3) (**P** v (**Q** & **R**))	*APKQR*
(4) ((**P** v **Q**) & **R**)	*KAPQR*

To test your understanding of Polish notation, make sure you can see why the following strings are equivalent:

(**P** v (**Q** → **R**))   *APCQR*
(~(**P** & **Q**) ↔ (~**P** v ~**Q**))   *ENKPQANPNQ*

A simple and elegant algorithm for determining if a string in Polish notation is well-formed illustrates the fact that to solve some problems you need not always pay attention to the usual meanings of symbols.

ALGORITHM WFP

1. INPUT string **P** in Polish notation.
2. FOR each sentence letter **Q** in **P**
   (a) Let RANK(**Q**) = 1.
3. Let RANK(*N*) = 0.
4. Let RANK(*A*) = −1.
5. Let RANK(*K*) = −1.
6. Let RANK(*C*) = −1.
7. Let RANK(*E*) = −1.
8. Let SUM = 0.
9. FOR each symbol S in **P,** beginning at the right and moving to the left,
   (a) Let SUM = SUM + RANK(S).
   (b) IF SUM ⩽ 0
       THEN OUTPUT "Not well-formed."
10. IF SUM = 1
    THEN OUTPUT "Well-formed."
11. IF SUM > 1
    THEN OUTPUT "Not well-formed."
12. STOP.

Two other useful algorithms would be the ones for translating from infix to Polish notation and from Polish to infix. Let us consider the former. As a rough beginning, we want to replace all occurrences of ~**P** with *N***P, (P v Q)** with *A***PQ,** etc. Consider ((**P & Q**) v (**R & S**)). Where do we begin? We could work from the inside out; that is, we could begin with the innermost subformulas, first getting the hybrid (*K***PQ** v *K***RS**), then getting *AK***PQ***K***RS.**

Or we could proceed by identifying the main connective (in this case: v), forming, first, the hybrid *A*(**P & Q**)(**R & S**), and then taking each remaining molecular sentence and repeating the process: identifying the main connective and translating into Polish notation. The result is *AK***PQ***K***RS.**

An algorithm for the second way proceeds as follows:

ALGORITHM INFIX-TO-POLISH

1. INPUT a sentence **P** in infix notation.
2. IF **P** is atomic
   THEN OUTPUT **P** and STOP.
3. IF **P** is not atomic
   THEN
   (a) Apply ALGORITHM MAIN-CONNECTIVE (from Chapter 6).
   (b) Let ☆ be the main connective of **P.**

EQUIVALENCES AND POLISH NOTATION

4. IF **P** has the form ~**Q** (that is, IF ☆ = ~)
   THEN transform **P** into *N***Q.**
5. IF **P** has the form (**Q** ☆ **R**)
   THEN transform **P** into *A***QR,** *K***QR,** *C***QR,** or *E***QR,** as appropriate.
6. Repeat steps 3 to 5 for each subformula of the transformed sentence until there are no more occurrences of infix connectives.
7. OUTPUT the result.
8. STOP.

One other advantage of Polish notation, besides the elimination of parentheses, is that it becomes extremely easy to identify the main connective of a sentence, hence extremely easy to apply WANG'S ALGORITHM. The ease with which the main connective can be identified also makes it easy to figure out the structure of a sentence in Polish notation. Consider, for instance,

(5) *CKNBCGBNG*

The main connective is always the *first* one, so sentence (5)'s main connective is *C.* Since *C* is a two-place connective, sentence (5) has the form *C***PQ.** What are **P** and **Q**? Since **P** must immediately follow *C,* it must begin with *K.* Similarly, since *K* is a two-place connective, **P** must be of the form *K***RS,** for some sentences **R** and **S.** Also, **R** must begin with *N.* But *N* is a one-place connective; hence **R** must be *N*B. Hence **S** must be *C*GB; hence **Q** must be *N*G. Using parentheses to clarify this, we get

C(*K*(*N*B) (*C*GB)) (*N*G)

or, in infix notation,

((~B & (G → B)) → ~G)

Summary

We began this chapter by considering sentences that are TRUE in all situtations (tautologies), sentences that are FALSE in all situations (contradictions), and sentences whose truth values vary from one situation to another (contingent sentences). This enabled us to point out an interesting relationship between an argument and its corresponding conditional sentence (a conditional sentence whose antecedent is the conjunction of the premises of the argument and whose consequent is the conclusion of the argument): An argument is valid iff its corresponding conditional is a tautology.

Many sentences have the same truth values as other sentences in the same situations. Such pairs of sentences are logically equivalent. Thus any two tautologies are logically equivalent, and any two contradictions are logically equivalent. Two other important logical equivalences that we covered are De Morgan's laws and Exportation.

A third important logical equivalence is the one between any sentence and its conjunctive normal form (CNF): a sentence whose form is a conjunction of disjunctions. We gave two algorithms for finding a CNF sentence that is logically equivalent to a given non-CNF sentence.

We then used these concepts to explore sets of sentences. When there is a situation in which all the sentences in some set are TRUE, we say that they are simultaneously satisfiable. If the sentences in a set are taken as the premises of an argument, then the set is consistent if no contradiction can be validly concluded from it.

Finally, we looked at Polish notation, which uses different symbols for the connectives and has a different way of representing molecular sentences. Polish notation completely eliminates the need for parentheses, and it facilitates such procedures as identifying the main connective of a sentence.

Exercises

A. Determine whether each of the following sentences is tautologous, inconsistent, or contingent:
1. $(((A \rightarrow B) \& A) \rightarrow B)$
2. $(((A \rightarrow B) \& A) \rightarrow \sim B)$
3. $(((A \rightarrow B) \& \sim B) \rightarrow \sim A)$
4. $(((A \rightarrow B) \& \sim B) \rightarrow A)$
5. $(((A \rightarrow B) \& \sim A) \rightarrow \sim B)$
6. $(((A \rightarrow B) \& B) \rightarrow A)$
7. $(((A \lor B) \& \sim A) \rightarrow B)$
8. $(((A \lor B) \& \sim A) \rightarrow \sim B)$
9. $(((A \rightarrow B) \& (B \rightarrow C)) \rightarrow (A \rightarrow C))$
10. $(((A \rightarrow B) \& (A \rightarrow C)) \rightarrow (B \rightarrow C))$
11. $((A \& \sim A) \rightarrow B)$
12. $((A \& \sim A) \rightarrow \sim B)$
13. $(((A \rightarrow B) \& A) \& \sim B)$
14. $((A \lor B) \& (\sim A \& \sim B))$
15. $(A \& (\sim A \& B))$
16. $(A \& (\sim A \& \sim B))$
17. $(A \leftrightarrow A)$
18. $(A \leftrightarrow \sim A)$
19. $(((A \leftrightarrow B) \& A) \leftrightarrow B)$
20. $((A \text{ NAND } A) \lor A)$
21. $((A \text{ NAND } B) \text{ NAND } (A \text{ NAND } B))$
22. $((A \text{ NOR } A) \text{ NOR } (B \text{ NOR } B))$
23. $(A \text{ NAND } (B \text{ NAND } B))$
24. $((A \text{ NOR } A) \& A)$
25. $((A \& (A \text{ NAND } (B \text{ NAND } C))) \rightarrow C)$
26. $((A \& (A \text{ NAND } (B \text{ NAND } B))) \rightarrow B)$

27. ((A NAND B) NOR A)
28. ((A NOR B) NAND A)
29. (A XOR A)
30. ((A XOR B) & ~A)
31. (((A XOR B) & ~A) → B)
32. ~(A XOR ~A)

B. Construct the truth table for
$$((A \rightarrow B) \leftrightarrow (\sim B \rightarrow \sim A))$$
and show that it is a tautology.

C. Corresponding Conditionals
1. What are the conditional sentences corresponding to the following arguments?
   a.   1. A
        2. B
        3. C
        4. D
     ∴ 5. E
   b.   1. (A v B)
        2. C
     ∴ 3. D
   c.   1. A
        2. B
        3. C
     ∴ 4. ~(D & C)
   d.   1. (A & B)
        2. C
     ∴ 3. D

2. Determine whether the following arguments are valid or invalid by determining whether their corresponding conditionals are tautologies.
   a. If Sally goes to the zoo, she will see an elephant. Sally saw an elephant today, so she must have gone to the zoo.
   b. If Sally goes to the zoo, she will see an elephant. Sally went to the zoo today, so she must have seen an elephant.

3. What are the arguments that correspond to the following conditional sentences?
   a. (A → B)
   b. (((A & B) & C) → D)
   c. ((A & (B & C)) → D)
   d. (((A v B) & C) → D)
   e. ((A v (B & C)) → D)

D. Decide which of the following pairs of sentences are logically equivalent:
1. (~A v B), (A → B)
2. ~(A & ~B), (A → B)
3. A, (A & A)
4. A, (A v A)
5. (A & (B & C)), ((A & B) & C)

  6. (A ∨ (B ∨ C)), ((A ∨ B) ∨ C)
  7. ~(A → B), (~A & ~B)
  8. ~(A & B), (~A & ~B)
  9. ~(A ∨ B), (~A ∨ ~B)
10. (A → B), (B → A)

11. (A ↔ B), ((A → B) & (B → A))
12. (A ↔ B), ((A & B) ∨ (~A & ~B))
13. (A ∨ (B & C)), ((A ∨ B) & (A ∨ C))
14. (A & (B ∨ C)), ((A & B) ∨ (A & C))
15. ~~A, ~~~~A

16. ((A ∨ ~A) & C), ((B ∨ ~B) & C)
17. ((A ∨ ~A) & C), C
18. ((A & ~A) ∨ C), C
19. (A xor B), ~(A ↔ B)
20. ~(A ↔ B), (A ↔ ~B)

21. (A xor B), ((A ∨ B) & ~(A & B))
22. (A nand A), (A nor A)
23. ((A nand A) nand (B nand B)), (A & B)
24. (A → B), (((A nor A) nor B) nor ((A nor A) nor B))
25. ((A nor B) nor (A nor B)), (A ∨ B)

E. Let **P** be a sentence. Construct another sentence **Q** as follows:
  1. Replace all occurrences of (**S** → **T**) in **P** by (~**S** ∨ **T**), and all occurences of (**S** ↔ **T**) by ((~**S** ∨ **T**) & (~**T** ∨ **S**)).
  2. Replace all atomic sentences in **P** with their negations.
  3. Interchange all occurrences of ∨ and &.
  4. Negate the result.
  5. Eliminate double negations (that is, replace all occurrences of ~~**R** with **R**). For instance, if **P** = '~(~A & B)', then steps 1 to 4 yield '~~(~~A ∨ ~B)', and so, by step 5, **Q** = '(A ∨ ~B)'. For any sentence **P,** we call **Q** constructed as above the *dual* of **P.**
  1. Construct the dual of each of the following:
    a. ~(A & B)
    b. (A ∨ B)
    c. ((A ∨ B) → C)
    d. (~A → (B & C))
  2. Show that for any sentence **P, P** is logically equivalent to its dual.

F. Using either ALGORITHM CNF-1 or CNF-2, find sentences in conjunctive normal form (CNF) that are logically equivalent to:
  1. (A ∨ A)
  2. (A & A)
  3. (A → B)
  4. ((A & B) ∨ (A & C))
  5. ((A ∨ B) & (A & C))

6. $((A \& (A \rightarrow B)) \rightarrow B)$
7. $((A \& B) \vee (A \& C) \vee (A \& B \& {\sim}C))$
8. $((A \vee B) \& (A \vee C) \& (A \vee B \vee {\sim}C))$
9. $((A \& B) \& ({\sim}A \vee {\sim}B))$
10. $(({\sim}A \& B) \& (A \vee {\sim}B))$
11. $(({\sim}A \& B) \vee (A \& {\sim}B))$

G. Disjunctive Normal Form
1. Define disjunctive normal form (DNF). (*Hint:* Just as a sentence in CNF is a conjunction of disjunctions, so a sentence in DNF will be a disjunction of conjunctions.)
2. Write an algorithm for finding an equivalent DNF sentence for any given sentence.
3. Turn the following sentences into DNF:
    a. $(A \& A)$
    b. $(A \rightarrow B)$
    c. $((A \vee B) \rightarrow C)$
    d. $(A \& {\sim}(B \vee C))$
    e. $(A \rightarrow (B \& C))$

H. Polish Notation
1. Translate these sentences from infix to Polish notation:
    a. $(((D \rightarrow B) \& D) \rightarrow B)$
    b. $(((D \rightarrow B) \& (B \rightarrow E)) \rightarrow (D \rightarrow F))$
    c. $((D \rightarrow B) \leftrightarrow ({\sim}B \rightarrow {\sim}D))$
    d. $(D \& (B \& (F \& G)))$
    e. ${\sim}(D \& (B \vee ({\sim}F \& G)))$
    f. $(((D \& B) \& F) \& G)$
2. Translate each of the following from Polish into infix notation:
    a. *ABCDEFG*
    b. *CKCBDBD*
    c. *CBABD*
    d. *CKBDKBD*
    e. *ENNBB*
    f. *EBNNB*
3. Write an algorithm for translating from Polish to infix notation.
4. Postfix notation (also called reverse Polish notation, or RPN) can be defined as follows:
    I. Any atomic sentence is well-formed in RPN.
    II. If **P** and **Q** are each well-formed in RPN, then so are
        P*N*
        PQ*K*
        PQ*A*
        PQ*C*
        PQ*E*

III. Nothing else is well-formed in RPN.

Here, **P**N = ~**P**

PQK = (**P** & **Q**)

PQA = (**P** v **Q**)

PQC = (**P** → **Q**)

PQE = (**P** ↔ **Q**)

a. Write an algorithm for translating from infix to RPN.

b. Write an algorithm for translating from RPN to infix notation.

c. Apply your algorithm for translating from infix to RPN to the sentences in Exercise H-1.

SENTENTIAL LOGIC: A Natural Deduction System

The methods and procedures for deciding whether an argument is valid are complete and workable—as the algorithms show. They can be used to determine in a finite amount of time whether any symbolized argument in the logic of sentences is valid or invalid.

However, we might have some reservations about these methods. First, they require us to busy ourselves with the truth or falsity of sentences in quite explicit terms. We must calculate when all the relevant sentences are TRUE in various situations. The result is a table showing when certain sentences are TRUE and when they are FALSE. Second, it is especially difficult by these methods to show that an argument is *valid.* That is, the truth-table method takes the longest time to apply when the argument is a valid one, and a shorter time if the argument is invalid. Finally, it is unlikely that anyone actually reasons explicitly using the complicated relationships between truth and falsity that we have investigated. It would be nice to have an easier way to reason and to check reasoning for validity—a way, for example, which requires fewer calculations and less writing.

For these and many other historical reasons, most practicing logicians, mathematicians, and computer scientists prefer to do their reasoning, and to demonstrate the validity of reasoning, in what are called "formal deduction systems." A formal deduction system has its main mission in showing an argument to be valid; it is usually not concerned with showing an argument to be invalid.

A formal deduction system shows an argument to be valid in a way that does not require a use of the concepts TRUE and FALSE. Instead, a formal deduction system deals with the "form" or "pattern" of an argument without considering, even temporarily, whether the sentences involved are TRUE or FALSE, or to what things in the real world these sentences refer. It is in this sense that a formal deduction system is *formal*. It deals only with the form (pattern) of an argument, not with its subject matter.

The main vehicle of a formal system is a *derivation*. A derivation is often called a "deduction" or, slightly misleadingly, a "proof." A derivation shows that certain strings of symbols *follow from* other strings according to permitted *rules*. A derivation in a formal deduction system is a deduction of logical consequences from premises. It does not consider the meaning of the terms in a sentence or even the truth values of the sentences. The sole question in a derivation is whether a sentence, considered as a pattern of symbols, follows from other sentences by permitted rules. In deductive logic, these rules are usually called *rules of inference,* because their task is to change some sentences into others that can be validly inferred. We can think of the rules of any formal system as preestablished ways for transforming some strings into others.

Because a formal system has rules that must be followed, it is natural to think of a deduction or derivation as being much like a game. The pieces, cards, plays, or moves of a game do not usually have any significance outside of the game, but a game must be played according to certain rules. So, too, the "playing pieces" of a derivation do not have any clear meaning—or, rather, it is not worthwhile in constructing the derivation to *consider* their meaning—but they must be handled according to preestablished rules.

A Simple Formal System:
The Game of Stars and Slashes

To begin, let us consider some games that can be played with four kinds of symbols as playing pieces. The available symbols will be the two letters 'A' and 'B', stars, and slashes:

A   B   ☆   /

These symbols can be combined, or "strung together," in many ways, and we may use as many copies of these symbols as we wish. For example,

AB☆/
///☆AA
/A☆B/

are all strings of these symbols. To create a game, some of these strings will be called "winning" strings, and the others will all be "losing" strings. The object of one game might be to construct as many winning strings as possible. (To make this game more interesting, you might want to add some constraints, such as a time limit, but we won't do that here.) Another game might be to decide whether a given string is a winning string or a losing string. For instance, an opponent might challenge you to decide whether

S /////A☆B/☆A/☆A/☆B/☆B//

is a winning string.

Of course, as in any other game, there will have to be some rules, and clearly, we'll need rules that precisely specify which strings are winning strings and which are losing strings. For both the "construction" game and the "decision" game, there will be three rules:

1. The symbol
   A
   by itself is a winning string.
2. The symbol
   B
   by itself is a winning string.
3. If S_1 and S_2 are winning strings, then
   /S_1☆S_2/
   is a winning string. That is, to make a new winning string, we connect one winning string to another with the symbol '☆' and sandwich the result between a pair of slashes.

It is usually understood that nothing else is a winning string except the strings that result from applying rules 1 to 3.

To see how these rules work, we can start playing the first, "construction," game. According to the first two rules, the string

A

and the string

B

are winning strings—they have been "given" to us by rules 1 and 2. Now that we have two winning strings, rule 3 can be applied. To apply it, we just have to consider the special case where S_1 is 'A' and S_2 is 'B'. Then, according to rule 3,

/A☆B/

is a winning string. According to another application of rule 3, this time taking S_1 as 'B' and S_2 as 'A',

/B☆A/

is a winning string. We now have four winning strings, and it is clear that we can continue to apply the third rule to produce many more of them. For instance, letting S_1 be 'A' and S_2 be '/B☆A/', we see that

/A☆/B☆A//

is a winning string. But

/A☆/B☆A/

is a losing string: it is understood that if a string is not producible by rules 1, 2, and 3, then it is a losing string.

How can we show that '/A☆/B☆A/' is a losing string? Unfortunately, it's not enough to try to produce it from the rules but fail, because—especially with longer, more complex strings—there are always two possible reasons for failure: the string is indeed a losing string, or else it really is a winning string, but we just didn't try hard enough (or weren't clever enough) to produce it.

To show that '/A☆/B☆A/' is a losing string, notice that all winning strings either consist only of the symbol 'A' or 'B' or else have the following structure:

1. The first and last symbols are slashes.
2. If you remove the first and last symbols, you will have a star between two winning strings.

Now, the string we are considering fails to satisfy the second of these two conditions. To see that it fails, remove the outer pair of slashes, leaving

A☆/B☆A

We can see that this is not a string formed by joining two winning strings with a star. The string to the right of the first star is

/B☆A

which violates the first condition. And the string to the left of the second star is

A☆/B

which also violates the first condition. Since there is no other way to analyze the string, it must be a loser: there is no way to analyze it such that it consists of two winners joined by a star.

NATURAL DEDUCTION

Formal Systems

The game of stars and slashes illustrates the basic components of the simplest kind of formal system. A *formal system* consists of three features:

1. A set of symbols out of which strings may be formed, together with rules specifying what constitutes a well-formed string. (In our game, the symbols were 'A', 'B', ☆, and /. Any string was considered well-formed, so long as it was some string of these symbols.)
2. A set of "winning" strings that is given to you. This set is called the set of axioms. (In our game, the axioms were given by rules 1 and 2.)
3. A set of methods for constructing new winning strings. This set is called the set of rules of inference. (Our game had only one rule in this sense.)

A winning string is then understood to be a well-formed string, such that the string is an instance of an axiom or comes from previous winning strings by applications of any of the rules.

A more common name for a winning string in mathematics and logic is *theorem.* In our game,

/A☆B/

was a theorem. It can be seen to be a winning string from rule 1, rule 2, and one application of rule 3.

The formal deduction system we shall develop in the next sections will look much like the game of stars and slashes—at least in its broad outline. It will have well-formed strings, and it will have rules for generating new winning strings. And it will be understood that there are no winning strings except those that arise from the rules. But there will be no axioms. That is, no strings will be given that are automatic winners. A deduction system without axioms is called a *natural* deduction system.

A Natural Deduction System

Our game of stars and slashes is a good example of a formal system. It has rigorous rules for generating winning strings, and it has procedures for constructing derivations using the rules. But it is not a formal *deduction* system. A formal deduction system has two additional features. First, all the strings of a formal deduction system are *sentences.* Second, the rules by which we derive some sentences from others are not arbitrary. A proper rule of inference should allow us to derive only those sentences that logically follow from earlier sentences. Additionally, a formal *natural* deduction system has no axioms.

The special quality a rule in a deduction system must have is that of being *truth-preserving.* Truth-preserving rules never lead us from TRUE sentences to FALSE ones.

The quality of being truth-preserving is the central concern of logic, as we saw in Chapter 1. It is also the idea that is so perfectly captured by the concept of "validity." A good argument is first and foremost an argument that is truth-preserving. If the premises are all TRUE, then the conclusion cannot help but be TRUE too.

All the rules of a formal deduction system should, then, be truth-preserving. It should never be the case that we could begin with TRUE sentences and move, using correct applications of our rules, to a FALSE sentence. Note that there is nothing at all wrong with having rules that might take us from FALSE sentences to TRUE ones. Similarly, perhaps, we would frown upon a machine that turned gold into mud, although we would be quite happy with one that turned mud into gold!

As we mentioned before, and saw demonstrated in the game of stars and slashes, the most important application of a formal system is in producing a derivation. A derivation is a sequence of steps, all of which are legitimate according to the rules of the formal system. To help someone reading a derivation see that it is correct, we shall number each step in the derivation and state whatever justifies our making that step.

Conjunction Introduction

Let us consider the first rule of our formal deduction system for sentential logic which we shall call "conjunction introduction," or &INTRO for short:

&INTRO   If **P** and **Q** are any two previous sentences in a derivation,
              then you may derive their conjunction:
              (P & Q)

In other words, if sentence **P** had been permitted by the rules earlier in a derivation, and so had sentence **Q,** then you may "put them together," so to speak, joined by the conjunction connective.

Most deductions have the task of showing that a sentence (the conclusion) follows from other sentences by the permitted rules of inference. Accordingly, the premises are "given" to you, and you may accept them as permitted sentences, without being disturbed by the fact that they are not otherwise justified.

A deduction will then typically begin with sentences that have no justification other than their being the premises of the argument given to you. When we write the justification for such sentences in a deduction, we shall say, simply, PREMISE. For example, if an argument had the premises

A
(B → C)

then the natural start of a deduction using these premises might look like this:

1. A   :PREMISE
2. (B → C)   :PREMISE

But how can the deduction continue? Aside from listing the premises of the argument, which we have now exhausted, we only have one rule so far, &INTRO. The rule &INTRO permits us to combine any two previous sentences with &. We should see that 'A' and '(B → C)' are two previous sentences, the first corresponding to the **P** of the rule, the second corresponding to the **Q**. We could then continue our deduction:

```
1. A                :PREMISE
2. (B → C)          :PREMISE
3. (A & (B → C))    :&INTRO applied to lines 1 and 2
```

In fact, the rule &INTRO can be applied over and over again:

```
1. A                        :PREMISE
2. (B → C)                  :PREMISE
3. (A & (B → C))            :&INTRO,1,2
4. ((B → C) & A)            :&INTRO,2,1
5. (A & A)                  :&INTRO,1,1
6. ((A & A) & (A & (B → C)))  :&INTRO,5,3
```

It should be clear that we could keep on going, applying &INTRO to any two of our accumulating sentences. Notice also that the "two" previous lines to which the rule &INTRO is applied can even be the same line. In the above deduction, we have:

```
1. A        :PREMISE

        .

        .

        .

5. (A & A) :&INTRO,1,1
```

The main quality we aim for in formulating our rules in a formal deduction system is that they are truth-preserving. Is the rule &INTRO truth-preserving? That is, if previous sentences in a derivation were all TRUE, then does the rule &INTRO allow us to derive only other TRUE sentences?

A way to see that &INTRO is truth-preserving is to look at the pattern of the sentences in an application of &INTRO and compare it with the truth table for &.

```
1. P        :PREMISE
2. Q        :PREMISE
3. (P & Q) :&INTRO,1,2
```

Is there any possible way sentences **P** and **Q** could be true and yet in the same situation sentence (**P** & **Q**) be FALSE? This is, of course, impossible, as we have seen in Chapter 3. Looking at the truth table, we find:

V(P)	V(Q)	V(P & Q)
0	0	0
0	1	0
1	0	0
1	1	1

There is no situation where both **P** and **Q** are TRUE but (**P & Q**) is FALSE. So the rule &INTRO is truth-preserving.

If a rule such as &INTRO is truth-preserving, then we can apply it over and over again to TRUE sentences without being afraid that a FALSE sentence could somehow creep in. If &INTRO preserves truth once, it will do it twice, or any number of times. If the premises are all TRUE, then applying truth-preserving rules any number of times and in any order never allows a FALSE sentence to creep in. This fact lies behind the security we should feel with derivations. If a derivation uses only truth-preserving rules, then the derivation as a whole will be truth-preserving. The derivation will never allow us to go from TRUE premises to a FALSE conclusion.

The Format of a Derivation

Observe carefully that we shall always present a derivation in a certain format. We shall, for example, *number* the lines of the derivation, write a *sentence* on each line, and then explain why we are permitted to write that sentence. The explanation of why we are permitted to write a sentence will be called the *justification* for that sentence.

So far, we have only two possible justifications for writing a sentence in a derivation:

1. The sentence was given to us by the terms of the original argument and so has the justification PREMISE.
2. The sentence was derived from the sentences in two previous lines by the rule &INTRO.

More generally, every line of a derivation will have the following features:

1. The line will begin with a number (a positive integer) followed by a period. We shall call the number of a line the *line number.* No two distinct lines of a derivation begin with the same line number. (We shall shortly modify this requirement slightly and allow certain symbols to be written before the line number.)
2. Next in the line must appear a *sentence,* that is, a string that is well-formed according to the rules developed in Chapters 3 to 5.
3. Last in the line must appear a colon (:) followed by a *justification* for the sentence. This justification is either PREMISE or a rule of the deduction system according to which we are permitted to write the sentence. If the justification is the result of applying a rule to previous lines of the derivation, then we must also identify

NATURAL DEDUCTION

the line numbers of these previous lines. Thus we can have as a justification of a line

    :PREMISE

which does not require us to cite previous lines of the derivation, or (for example)

    :&INTRO,1,2

which cites lines 1 and 2.

Conjunction Elimination

Let us now introduce the companion rule to &INTRO: *conjunction elimination,* or &ELIM for short:

    &ELIM   If (**P** & **Q**) is a previous sentence in a derivation, then you may derive either the first conjunct:

            P

        or the second conjunct:

            Q

The following short derivation shows a correct application of this new rule.

    1. (A & B) :PREMISE
    2. C   :PREMISE
    3. A   :&ELIM,1

Here, the sentence, 'A' plays the role of **P**, and 'B' plays the role of **Q**. Sometimes the derived sentence may be more complex. Consider this derivation:

    1. (D & (E → F)) :PREMISE
    2. E   :PREMISE
    3. (E → F)   :&ELIM,1

Here, the sentence 'D' plays the role of **P** in the rule, and the molecular sentence '(E → F)' plays the role of **Q**. In other words, the rule &ELIM says, "From any conjunction

    (<sentence 1> & <sentence 2>)

you may derive

    <sentence 1>

by itself or, if you wish,

    <sentence 2>

by itself." These derived sentences may be atomic or molecular. The single requirement is that the original sentence must be a *conjunction,* a sentence whose main connective is &.

It is easy to see that &ELIM is truth-preserving. If

(P & Q)

is TRUE, then

P

is also TRUE, as well as

Q

We can consult our truth tables in Chapter 3 to see this. So the rule &ELIM, like the rule &INTRO, will never take us from TRUE sentences to FALSE ones.

Observe that the rule &INTRO converts *two* previous sentences into *one* new sentence, while the rule &ELIM converts one sentence into another sentence. (Although the &ELIM rule says that you are permitted to derive *either* conjunct, you must in every application derive just one of these conjuncts.) This means that the justification for a sentence using the &ELIM rule must refer only to one previous line number, while a sentence justified by &INTRO must cite two previous line numbers. Here are some sample justifications:

    :&ELIM,3
    :&INTRO,2,4
    :&INTRO,1,1
    :&ELIM,7

But the following "justifications" would always be mistaken.

    :&ELIM,1,2   [Incorrect, because &ELIM must cite one and only one previous
                   line.]
    :&INTRO,3   [Incorrect, because &INTRO must cite two previous lines.]
    :PREMISE,3   [Incorrect, because with the justification PREMISE, we do not cite
                   any previous lines.]

The two rules &INTRO and &ELIM have a certain symmetry, as their names suggest. The rule &INTRO introduces a new conjunction, a sentence whose main connective is &. The rule &ELIM, on the other hand, takes us from a sentence that is a conjunction to one that has one less conjunction sign in it.

The names of these two rules provide some clues to when they should be applied. The rule &INTRO should usually be applied when we want to obtain a sentence with an & in it. And the rule &ELIM should usually be applied if we want to eliminate an & or reduce the number of &'s in our earlier sentences. Most of our rules will, in fact, have

NATURAL DEDUCTION

this symmetry of either introducing a connective or eliminating one. Each rule will thus come with some advice on when it might wisely be applied.

Demonstrating the Validity of an Argument with a Derivation

We are now in a position to relate a derivation to an argument. The derivation of the conclusion of an argument from the premises of that argument will have these features:

1. Every sentence of every line is justified by either (*a*) its being a premise of the given argument or (*b*) its having been correctly derived from previous lines by the application of permissible rules.
2. The sentence in the last line of the derivation is the conclusion of the given argument.

So, if you are given the valid argument

```
   A
   B
∴ (A & B)
```

a correct derivation of the conclusion from the premises would be:

```
1. A        :PREMISE
2. B        :PREMISE
3. (A & B) :&INTRO,1,2
```

The last line of this derivation is the conclusion of the given argument. And the only justifications are PREMISE and a permissible rule. We shall speak of "deriving the conclusion," or "showing the argument to be valid."

If you were given the valid argument

```
   (C & D)
∴  C
```

then a correct derivation of the conclusion from the premises would be:

```
1. (C & D) :PREMISE
2. C        :&ELIM,1
```

For the first argument [A, B, ∴(A & B)], it should be easy to see that &INTRO *must* be used, since the conclusion contains an ampersand, but the premises do not. And for the second argument [(C & D), ∴C], it should be easy to see that &ELIM must be used, since the premise contains an ampersand, but the conclusion does not.

We now give several more examples of derivations.

Argument 1.
  (A & B)
∴ (B & A)
Derivation
  1. (A & B)   :PREMISE
  2. A   :&ELIM,1
  3. B   :&ELIM,1
  4. (B & A)   :&INTRO,3,2

Observe carefully that the correct application of &INTRO in line 4 requires us to cite where the first conjunct, 'B', comes from (line 3) and then where the second conjunct, 'A', comes from (line 2).

Argument 2.
  A
∴ A
Derivation
  1. A   :PREMISE

This is admittedly a strange proof, but it conforms to the requirements for a correct derivation: we have used only the justification PREMISE, and the "last" line—which is also the first line—is the conclusion.

Argument 3.
  (A & B)
  C
∴ (C & A)
Derivation
  1. (A & B)   :PREMISE
  2. C   :PREMISE
  3. A   :&ELIM,1
  4. (C & A)   :&INTRO,2,3

Argument 4.
  ((A & B) & C)
∴ (A & C)
Derivation
  1. ((A & B) & C)   :PREMISE
  2. (A & B)   :&ELIM,1
  3. A   :&ELIM,2
  4. C   :&ELIM,1
  5. (A & C)   :&INTRO,3,4

Argument 5.
  (A & (C → D))
  (~A v B)

NATURAL DEDUCTION

Derivation
1. (A & (C → D)) :PREMISE
2. (~A v B) :PREMISE
3. (C → D) :&ELIM,1

Before continuing with the introduction of the next pair of rules, you should reflect on what a derivation shows. A derivation shows that a sentence—the last line of the derivation—can be derived from earlier sentences by the application of rules of inference. These rules are known to have the property of being truth-preserving. Consequently, we know that *if* the sentences introduced by the only justification other than a rule (namely, PREMISE) were all TRUE, then the last line of the derivation would also be TRUE. But then, the argument is valid. So a correct derivation of a conclusion from premises shows that the argument is valid. In most cases, this will be a far easier way to show an argument to be valid than constructing a truth table. A derivation will also usually give us a clearer understanding of *why* an argument is valid than does a cluttered truth table.

Subproofs and Negation Introduction

Consider the following argument.

I can't both look at TV all night and get my homework done. I will watch TV all night. Therefore, I won't get my homework done.

When symbolized, this argument becomes:

Argument 6.
~(L & H)
L
∴ ~H
where

L = 'I will look at TV all night.'
H = 'I will get my homework done.'

As reasoning to defend the validity of my argument I might offer:

I can't both look at TV all night and get my homework done.
I will watch TV all night.
 But suppose I do get my homework done too.
 Then I would watch TV all night *and* (somehow) get my homework done.
 But this contradicts my first statement that I *cannot* do both of these things.
 So my supposition that I do get my homework done must be mistaken.
That is, I will *not* get my homework done.

If we had used symbolized sentences, we might have reasoned:

~(L & H)   :PREMISE
L   :PREMISE
  Suppose H.
  Then (L & H).
  But ~(L & H) is the first premise.
  So the supposition H must be mistaken.
Therefore, ~H.

The steps going from "Suppose H" to "Therefore, ~H" have the effect of introducing a negation sign. They exhibit the central reasoning behind the new rule, *negation introduction,* or ~INTRO for short. In this reasoning, which is not quite in our required form for derivations, there are two new, important ideas. One is the idea of "supposing" something. A supposition such as 'I will get my homework done' is not a PREMISE. We are not told to accept it as TRUE by the given argument. But neither is it derivable from previous lines by a rule like &ELIM or &INTRO. Instead, we are introducing this sentence *as if* it were legitimate in order to see what follows from it. We shall call these suppositions "assumptions." Because assumptions are "trial balloons"—neither given as PREMISES nor derivable from previous lines—they must be used with extraordinary care.

Subproofs

A *subproof* is a digression from the main proof. A subproof is also a proof within a proof. The supposition that begins a subproof may be thought of as a "temporary premise." This assumption is a "premise" only for the duration of the subproof—not for the entire derivation.

    We shall require subproofs to be distinguished from the rest of the proof by two features:

1. Subproofs have asterisks before their line numbers to indicate that these lines depend on an assumption.
2. The sentences in a subproof will be indented proportionally to the number of asterisks.

Thus our full proof of '~H', with some gaps in the justifications, would be:

```
  1.  ~(L & H)      :PREMISE
  2.  L             :PREMISE
* 3.    H           :ASSUMPTION
* 4.    L
* 5.    (L & H)     :&INTRO,4,3
* 6.    ~(L & H)
* 7.    ~H          :~INTRO,3,5,6
  8.  ~H
```

Lines 3 to 7 are the subproof in this derivation. A subproof can be identified because each line will have the same number of asterisks, and that section of the derivation will not be broken by a line with fewer asterisks. A subproof will also always begin with the justification ASSUMPTION, which we have in line 3. The main proof, containing lines without any asterisks, includes lines 1, 2, and 8.

Negation Introduction

What follows in Argument 6 from the assumption of 'H' is a sentence that could not possibly be TRUE, namely

(L & H)

It could not be TRUE if the premises are all TRUE, because its negation,

~(L & H)

was also asserted as the first premise. When one sentence is the exact negation of another sentence, we shall say that the sentences *contradict* one another. This is the second new idea introduced in this reasoning. In the language of Chapter 7, these two sentences are not "simultaneously satisfiable" and thus are "inconsistent." More important, since our rules are truth-preserving, when contradictory sentences are derived from premises and an assumption, the premises plus the assumption are not simultaneously satisfiable either. And this means that *if* the premises are satisfied, then the assumption is not satisfied. Thus, finally, if the premises are satisfied, then the *negation* of the assumption is also satisfied.

Therefore, when we have derived two sentences that contradict one another, such as '(L & H)' and its negation, '~(L & H)', in a subproof that begins with an assumption, we are then permitted to derive the negation of that assumption, the justification being ~INTRO. The reasoning behind this rule has been frequently employed in philosophy, mathematics, theology, and other fields such as law and the natural sciences. Its traditional Latin name is *reductio ad absurdum,* or, translating the expression, "reduction to an absurdity." The *reductio ad absurdum* principle is that if we correctly reason to two sentences that cannot *both* be TRUE, then at least one of our earlier claims must be mistaken.

The use of the new rule ~INTRO in line 7 is our special concern at this point.

~INTRO   If from an assumption **P** both a sentence **Q** and its negation ~**Q** can be derived in the same subproof, then
   ~**P**
may be derived in that subproof.

Notice that the rule refers to *three* previous lines, all in the same subproof: line 3 (the assumption) is cited first, then line 5, and finally line 6, which contains the negation of the sentence on line 5.

The missing elements in this derivation are the justifications for lines 4, 6, and 8. We can see that the sentence of line 4 in the subproof is the same as the sentence of line 2. And the sentence of line 6 is the same as that of line 1. Furthermore, the sentence of line 8 is the same as that of line 7.

SEND and RETURN

We require that a subproof be a proof in its own right (with ASSUMPTION serving a role much like that of PREMISE) and that the subproof be distinct from the main proof and from other subproofs. Because they are independent sections of the derivation, the subproof and the main proof must "communicate" with each other. The flow of information between a subproof and the main proof can be in one of two directions. Information can be sent from the main proof into the subproof—as we seem to have in the derivation for Argument 6 from line 2 to line 4 and from line 1 to line 6. Or information can be returned from the subproof to the main proof, as occurs between lines 7 and 8.

We shall justify information legitimately flowing *into* a subproof with a new rule SEND plus the citation of the earlier line number outside of the subproof. The justification SEND can be used, provided:

1. We are in a subproof with more asterisks than the cited line.
2. The sentence being "sent" is exactly the sentence in the cited line.
3. Every line between the SEND line and the cited line has at least as many asterisks as the cited line.

We shall justify information legitimately flowing *out* of a subproof with a new rule RETURN plus the citation of a line in the subproof. The justification RETURN can be used, provided:

1. We are outside of the subproof, with one less asterisk than the cited line.
2. The sentence being returned is exactly the sentence in the cited line.
3. There is no line between the present line and the cited line with fewer asterisks than the cited line.
4. The cited line has the justification ~INTRO.

This last proviso is to ensure that the returned information is not "contaminated" with any specific information stemming from the assumption.

With these newly available justifications, our proof of '~H' becomes a complete, correct derivation of '~H' from premises '~(L & H)' and 'L'.

```
  1.   ~(L & H)      :PREMISE
  2.   L             :PREMISE
* 3.   H             :ASSUMPTION
* 4.   L             :SEND,2
* 5.   (L & H)       :&INTRO,4,3
* 6.   ~(L & H)      :SEND,1
* 7.   ~H            :~INTRO,3,5,6
  8.   ~H            :RETURN,7
```

NATURAL DEDUCTION

The lines 3 to 7 are the subproof of this derivation. The subproof begins with an assumption, as all subproofs do. Information is "sent into" the subproof at lines 4 and 6. Information is "returned from" the subproof to the main proof in line 8.

Rules such as SEND and RETURN are little more than "repetition" rules, which allow us to repeat a sentence that occurs earlier in a proof. But these repetitions have a twist: They are really communications between sections of the proof that are at different "levels"—between a main proof and a subproof, or between a subproof and a more deeply nested subproof.

The rules SEND and RETURN, which allow communication between different levels of a derivation, are included in our formal deduction system for several reasons. One is that the communication between a main proof and a subproof is very much like the communication that occurs between a main procedure and a subprocedure in an algorithm or a computer program. Recent developments in good programming style have emphasized the importance of explicitly declaring what information is being transferred into and out of subprocedures.

The information contained in sentences of the main proof is much like the information stored in so-called "global" variables in a program. A *global variable* is the name for information that can be accessed or changed at any point in the entire program. Hence it is "global" information. Analogously, the information contained in the sentences of the main proof of a derivation—the lines without asterisks—can be used anywhere in a proof, in a subproof, in sub-subproofs, and so on, provided that it is first sent. On the other hand, so-called "local" variables are names for stored information which can only be used in restricted sections of an algorithm. Outside of these restricted sections, the variables cannot be used at all; if they are used, they may have undesirable values. The information contained in our assumptions and the sentences dependent on them are much like local variables. The information such sentences contain cannot, in general, be used outside of the subproofs that contain the sentences. The only exceptions to this are those situations that allow the use of the RETURN rule.

More metaphorically, we can think of the information in subproofs as being "impounded" because it is known to be "contaminated" by a dubious sentence, the assumption. Because of these suspicions, information in a subproof is not allowed to "leak out" to the outside world. The restrictions on communication with the outside world are policed by the rules SEND and RETURN.

Using Subproofs

Before we continue, several observations must be made. First, if you are attempting to show that the conclusion of an argument can be derived from the premises, then the conclusion must be in the main proof. That is, the conclusion must be the sentence on the last line of the derivation, and that line cannot have any asterisks. This condition is necessary to ensure that the conclusion is not dependent on any assumption we might have made.

Second, no rule except SEND or RETURN is permitted to cite a line in another subproof or outside of that subproof. In practice, this implies that no line can ever cite a line that has more or fewer asterisks—unless the justification is SEND or RETURN. In the above example, we might have been tempted to create this "derivation":

```
1.  ~(L & H)       :PREMISE
2.  L              :PREMISE
* 3.  H            :ASSUMPTION
* 4.  (L & H)      :&INTRO,2,3 [Incorrect]
* 5.  ~H           :~INTRO,3,4,1 [Incorrect]
6.  ~H             :RETURN,5
```

Lines 4 and 5 are incorrect for the following reason. The &INTRO rule cannot cite a line which is outside of its own subproof. (In line 4 it is used incorrectly to cite line 2.) The information concerning 'L' must be sent into the subproof. Similarly, the information concerning '~(L & H)' must also be sent into the subproof before the ~INTRO rule can refer to it.

Finally, notice two facts about asterisks. An asterisk is added to a line only by the justification ASSUMPTION. And an asterisk is removed from a line only by the justification RETURN.

Using ~INTRO

Is the ~INTRO rule truth-preserving? Suppose that the premises of a derivation are all TRUE. Suppose further that ~INTRO is used to derive ~**P** but that ~**P** is somehow FALSE. If ~**P** is FALSE, then the assumption **P** of the subproof for ~INTRO must be TRUE. But if the assumption **P** is TRUE, then how could the contradictory sentences arise? There are only two ways that two contradictory sentences can arise if the assumption is TRUE:

1. SEND is not truth-preserving.
2. The other available rules, &INTRO and &ELIM, are not truth-preserving.

But SEND is surely the most truth-preserving of all our rules: it merely copies a previous sentence. And we have already seen that &INTRO and &ELIM are truth-preserving.

So two contradictory sentences cannot arise in a subproof if all previous sentences are TRUE, unless the assumption is FALSE. And if the assumption **P** is FALSE, then its negation, ~**P**, must be TRUE. Thus with premises that are TRUE, the subproof using ~INTRO results in a sentence ~**P** that is also TRUE. So, the ~INTRO rule is truth-preserving.

Before introducing the next rule, let us consider some applications of ~INTRO, SEND, and RETURN.

Argument 7
  A
∴ ~~A
Derivation
```
  1.  A           :PREMISE
* 2.  ~A          :ASSUMPTION
* 3.  A           :SEND,1
* 4.  ~~A         :~INTRO,2,3,2
  5.  ~~A         :RETURN,4
```

NATURAL DEDUCTION

This is a proof that from a sentence, **P**, its double negation, ~~**P**, can be derived. Notice that the ~INTRO rule requires us to *add* a negation sign to the assumption. This results in **P**'s acquiring two negation signs. Notice also that line 4 cites line 2 twice: once because it must cite the assumption, and again because the sentence in line 2 is the negation of the sentence in line 3. Check carefully, and you will see that asterisks, indenting, the SEND rule, the RETURN rule, and the ~INTRO rule are all correctly used.

Argument 8
 A
∴ ~(~A & B)
Derivation
  1. A   :PREMISE
* 2. (~A & B)   :ASSUMPTION
* 3. ~A   :&ELIM,2
* 4. A   :SEND,1
* 5. ~(~A & ~B) :~INTRO,2,4,3
  6. ~(~A & ~B) :RETURN,5

Negation Elimination

The rule *negation elimination,* or ~ELIM, enjoys an even closer relationship to ~INTRO than &ELIM does to &INTRO. As a result, there are virtually no ideas in ~ELIM that we have not seen in ~INTRO.

~ELIM If from an assumption ~**P** both a sentence **Q** and its negation ~**Q** can be derived in the same subproof, then
     P
  may be derived in that subproof.

The parallelism between the two rules, ~INTRO and ~ELIM, can be seen when we compare the steps to be used in applying each.

~**INTRO**	~**ELIM**
In a subproof:	In a subproof:
Assume **P**.	Assume ~**P**.
Derive a sentence, **Q**.	Derive a sentence, **Q**.
Derive the negation	Derive the negation
of that sentence, ~**Q**.	of that sentence, ~**Q**.
Derive, by ~INTRO,	Derive, by ~ELIM, the
the negation of the	assumption without
assumption, ~**P**.	its negation, **P**.

In other words, ~INTRO adds (*intro*duces) a negation sign to the assumption, while ~ELIM removes (*elim*inates) a negation sign from the assumption. The names of the rules give us a hint about when they are appropriately applied. If we wanted to derive a sentence that has a negation sign in front of it, we might consider assuming the sentence without its negation sign, then use ~INTRO. If we want to derive *any* sentence, we might consider assuming the sentence with a negation, then use ~ELIM.

The same conditions governing subproofs, SEND, and RETURN that applied to ~INTRO also apply to ~ELIM. In particular, the rule RETURN must be modified to allow citation of a ~ELIM line as well as a ~INTRO one. So, there is very little new in ~ELIM.

Let us consider some examples.

Argument 9
  ~~A
∴ A
Derivation
```
  1.  ~~A         :PREMISE
* 2.  ~A          :ASSUMPTION
* 3.  ~~A         :SEND,1
* 4.  A           :~ELIM,2,2,3
  5.  A           :RETURN,4
```

Notice carefully what our strategy was. We wanted to derive the conclusion, 'A', using ~ELIM. So we assumed '~A' and searched for two contradictory sentences.

Argument 10
  ~(~A & ~B)
  ~A
∴ B
Derivation
```
  1.  ~(~A & ~B)      :PREMISE
  2.  ~A             :PREMISE
* 3.  ~B             :ASSUMPTION
* 4.  ~A             :SEND,2
* 5.  (~A & ~B)      :&INTRO,4,3
* 6.  ~(~A & ~B)     :SEND,1
* 7.  B              :~ELIM,3,5,6
  8.  B              :RETURN,7
```

Notice again our strategy. We wanted to derive the conclusion, 'B'. So we assumed its negation, '~B', and sought two contradictory sentences.

Comment Lines in a Derivation

In longer proofs such as the one above, we will occasionally write notes to ourselves on what we are trying to do. These notes will help enormously in the creation of proofs. These notes to ourselves will be called *comments* and will look like the following:

NATURAL DEDUCTION

/BEGIN: ~ELIM to derive B/
/END: ~ELIM to derive B/

These lines are not "officially" part of the derivation, and so they do not have line numbers. Comments will start and finish with slashes (/). With comments added, the previous derivation would look like this:

```
1.  ~(~A & ~B)        :PREMISE
2.  ~A                :PREMISE
      /BEGIN: ~ELIM to derive B/
* 3.  ~B              :ASSUMPTION
* 4.  ~A              :SEND,2
* 5.  (~A & ~B)       :&INTRO,4,3
* 6.  ~(~A & ~B)      :SEND,1
* 7.  B               :~ELIM,3,5,6
      /END:    ~ELIM to derive B/
8.  B                :RETURN,7
```

Because these comments are very useful, we should develop some guidelines, or suggestions, for when they are properly used.

1. Every /BEGIN . . ./ comment should have a corresponding /END . . ./ comment.
2. Such comments are strongly recommended when rules using subproofs are applied, such as ~INTRO and ~ELIM. They remind us of our target, or goal, when we begin a subproof.
3. When these comments are used to state the goal of a subproof, indent them the same amount the subproof would be indented.
4. In creating a derivation, one should always work toward the goal of the last /BEGIN . . ./ comment that lacks a matching /END . . ./ comment.

The purpose of such comments should always be to help us keep in mind where we are going and what rule we are about to apply. For this reason, a few such comment lines are helpful, but too many would obscure the goal of our derivation.

The following derivation shows an elaborate use of ~INTRO and ~ELIM, as well as of our optional comments.

Argument 11
   ~(~A & ~B)
   ~(A & ~C)
   ~(B & ~C)
∴ C
Derivation
```
1.  ~(~A & ~B)        :PREMISE
2.  ~(A & ~C)         :PREMISE
3.  ~(B & ~C)         :PREMISE
```

```
        /BEGIN:   ~ELIM to derive C/
 *4.    ~C                      :ASSUMPTION
          /BEGIN: Derive ( ~ A & ~ B) and ~ ( ~ A & ~ B)/

          /BEGIN: ~ INTRO to derive ~ A/
 **5.     A                     :ASSUMPTION
 **6.      ~ C                   :SEND,4
 **7.     (A & ~ C)             :&INTRO,5,6
 **8.      ~ (A & ~ C)          :SEND,2
 **9.      ~ A                  : ~ INTRO,5,7,8
          /END:   ~ INTRO to derive ~ A/
 *10.    ~ A                    :RETURN,9

          /BEGIN: ~ INTRO to derive ~ B/
 **11.   B                      :ASSUMPTION
 **12.    ~ C                   :SEND,4
 **13.   (B & ~ C)             :&INTRO,11,12
 **14.    ~ (B & ~ C)          :SEND,3
 **15.    ~ B                  : ~ INTRO,11,13,14
          /END: ~ INTRO to derive ~ B/
 *16.    ~ B                    :RETURN,15
 *17.    ( ~ A & ~ B)          :&INTRO,10,16
 *18.     ~ ( ~ A & ~ B)       :SEND,1
          /END: Derive ( ~ A & ~ B) and ~ ( ~ A & ~ B)/
 *19.    C                      :~ ELIM,4,17,18
          /END: ~ ELIM to derive C/
 20.    C                       :RETURN,19
```

The basic strategy here, as our first comment tells us, was to apply ~ELIM in the hope of deriving the conclusion, 'C'. But once we have assumed '~C', we must then look for our two contradictory sentences. An early guess was made that these two might be

   (~A & ~B)

and

   ~(~A & ~B)

The second sentence is, of course, just the first premise. But to derive '(~A & ~B)' we might first derive '~A', then derive '~B'—and then put them together later with &INTRO. We can use our comments alone to sketch our strategy.

```
/BEGIN:~ELIM to derive C/
/BEGIN: Derive (~A & ~B) and ~(~A & ~B)/
   /BEGIN:  &INTRO to derive (~A & ~B)/
     /BEGIN: ~INTRO to derive ~A/
     /END:    ~INTRO to derive ~A/
```

NATURAL DEDUCTION

```
/BEGIN:  ~INTRO to derive ~B/
/END:    ~INTRO to derive ~B/
/END:    &INTRO to derive (~A & ~B)/
/END:    Derive ( ~ A & ~ B) and ~ ( ~ A & ~ B)./
/END:    ~ELIM to derive C/
```

Completeness

There is a sense in which the formal deduction system we have given so far, with only the justifications or rules

PREMISE	&INTRO
ASSUMPTION	&ELIM
SEND	~INTRO
RETURN	~ELIM

is complete. First, notice that any sentence using the sentence connectives &, ~, v, →, NOR, NAND, and so on, is logically equivalent to a sentence using only the connectives ~ and &. For example:

(**P** v **Q**) is logically equivalent to ~(~**P** & ~**Q**).
(**P** → **Q**) is logically equivalent to ~(**P** & ~**Q**).

So we can translate any sentence using these connectives into a logically equivalent sentence that contains only ~ and & as connectives. There is even an algorithm to make this translation—although we will not give it here. (See Exercise F.)

Furthermore, our paired rules

&INTRO
&ELIM

and

~INTRO
~ELIM

are sufficient to derive any conclusion that validly follows from a set of premises, so long as the premises and conclusion are expressed using only ~ and &, though we shall not prove that here.

But because the derivations using only these rules would often be very long and difficult to construct—mainly because of the cumbersome ~INTRO and ~ELIM rules—we shall proceed in the next chapter to introduce additional rules of inference which apply directly to sentences containing v, →, and ↔.

Summary

The notion of a *formal system* was introduced. Then we said that a *natural deduction system* is a formal system whose elements are sentences and whose rules are truth-preserving. The natural deduction system developed so far has the following rules. (We list the names of the rules with a brief, informal statement of each rule.)

> PREMISE—Premises are placed at the beginning of a derivation.
> ASSUMPTION—Any sentence may be assumed as the first line of a subproof.
> &INTRO—If **P** and **Q** are earlier lines,
> > then (**P** & **Q**) is derivable.
> &ELIM—If (**P** & **Q**) is an earlier line,
> > then **P** and **Q** are each derivable.
> ~INTRO—If the assumption **P** leads to a contradiction,
> > then ~**P** is derivable.
> ~ELIM—If the assumption ~**P** leads to a contradiction,
> > then **P** is derivable.
> SEND—Any earlier line in a proof may be sent to a subproof.
> RETURN—The last line of a subproof may be returned out of the subproof
> > under certain restrictions.

A derivation in our system is a numbered sequence of lines containing sentences and justifications. We distinguish between the *main proof* and *subproofs*. Finally, we use *comments* to help ourselves to structure the derivation, but such comments are not formally a part of the derivation.

Exercises

A. Stars and Slashes
   1. Why is '/B☆A' a losing string?
   2. Why is 'A☆B' a losing string?
   3. Is string S on page 155 a winning string? If so, how can it be constructed? If it's a losing string, why is it a losing string?
B. Formal Systems
   1. Suppose that we describe a new game, Left and Right, where we want to distinguish left and right slashes. In this game, winning strings with a '/' on the left will now have '(', and those with a '/' on the right will now have ')'.
      a. What would be an appropriate modification of rule 3?
      b. Construct two winning strings and two losing strings in the game of Left and Right. Show how the winning strings can be derived and why the losing strings cannot be derived.
   2. a. Write down a complete set of rules for a further modification in which the

NATURAL DEDUCTION

symbol ✰ is replaced by symbols for addition, multiplication, subtraction, and division. (Call the new system the game of Arithmetical Formulas.)

b. Construct two winning strings and two losing strings in the game of Arithmetical Formulas. Show how the winning strings can be derived and why the losing strings cannot be derived.

3. Modify the system still further by adding a new symbol that represents a "prefix" operation (for instance, a symbol $\sqrt{}$ to represent the square-root operation, or a symbol $-$ to represent the "forming the negative of" operation).

C. Natural Deduction System

Use the natural deduction system developed in this chapter to give derivations of the conclusions of the following arguments:

1.   (A & B)
    ~(A & ~C)
∴ C

2.   A
  ∴ ~(~B & B)

3.   ~(A & ~B)
   ~B
∴ ~A

4.   (A & ~A)
  ∴ B

5.   ~(A & ~B)
   A
∴ B

D. Symbolize the following arguments, and give derivations of them:

1. It's not the case that both Alfred is an artist and Carol is a scientist. Since Alfred is an artist, Carol isn't a scientist.

2. It's not the case that both David is hungry and Evelyn isn't. But Evelyn isn't hungry. So David isn't hungry.

E. A conclusion of a derivation with no premises is a theorem. To show that a sentence is a theorem, begin with an assumption, so that the only line of the main proof is the last one. Give derivations of the following theorems.
[Hint: Use ~INTRO for each of these.]

1. ~(A & ~A)
2. ~((A & B) & ~(A & B))
3. ~((~(A & ~B) & A) & ~B)

F. Logical Equivalences

1. Give an algorithm for replacing each of the following sentences with a logically equivalent sentence whose only connectives are ~ and &.

(**P → Q**)

(**P v Q**)

(**P ↔ Q**)

(**P** NOR **Q**)

(**P** NAND **Q**)

CHAPTER 8

2. Consider an arbitrary sentence whose only connectives are (possibly) ~, &, v, →, and ↔. Construct an algorithm for finding a logically equivalent sentence whose only connectives are ~ and &.

3. a. Show how (**P** & **Q**) can be expressed using only NOR.
   b. Show how ~**P** can be expressed using only NOR.
   c. Show how (**P** & **Q**) can be expressed using only NAND.
   d. Show how ~**P** can be expressed using only NAND.

In view of the fact (shown in 1, above) that all sentences can be expressed in terms of ~ and &, and in view of the fact (shown in 3) that all sentences that use only ~ or & can be expressed using only NOR or using only NAND, you should be able to see that *all* sentences can be expressed using only *one* two-place connective, namely, NOR, or else NAND.

SENTENTIAL LOGIC: Additional Rules of Inference

In the previous chapter, we studied two pairs of rules for deriving sentences from other sentences. As we mentioned, these four rules—&INTRO, &ELIM, ~INTRO, and ~ELIM—are sufficient to derive all sentences that can be validly inferred from given premises. There are, however, two factors that make using only these four rules somewhat inconvenient. One factor is that two of the rules, ~INTRO and ~ELIM, require us to discover contradictory sentences, but there does not seem to be any easy way of finding out in advance what these contradictory sentences will be. Consequently, in applying ~INTRO and ~ELIM, we must make guesses concerning what these contradictory sentences might be—or we might even have to wade into a subproof hoping accidentally to run across two contradictory sentences.

The second factor is even more of a hindrance, if we were to apply just the four rules we have so far studied. These four rules are sufficient for deriving other sentences *if* these sentences are expressed only as negations and conjunctions. As we saw in Chapters 3 and 4, it is useful to have other connectives, such as v, →, ↔, and even others. We could translate any sentences containing these additional connectives into logically equivalent sentences containing only the negation and conjunction connectives. But this is not so handy as, say, permitting the symbols v and → to have their own rules. In this chapter we shall broaden our deduction system to include additional rules. These rules are not really needed, but they will often make the job of constructing a derivation considerably easier than trying to work only with the four rules of Chapter 8.

Conditional Introduction and Elimination

One of the most frequently used patterns of reasoning has this form:

If **P,** then **Q.**
P.
Therefore, **Q.**

For example:

If the butler had a motive, then the butler committed the crime.
The butler did have a motive.
Therefore, the butler committed the crime.

This pattern of correct reasoning was recognized as such from earliest times. Its Latin name is *modus ponens.* When symbolized, the pattern of such arguments is:

$(P \rightarrow Q)$
P
∴ Q

Because the sentence $(P \rightarrow Q)$ is logically equivalent to the sentence $\sim(P \& \sim Q)$, the above argument is valid iff the argument

$\sim(P \& \sim Q)$
P
∴ Q

is valid. In the previous chapter, we gave a derivation of an argument having just this pattern. It is:

ADDITIONAL RULES

```
1. ~(P & ~ Q)              :PREMISE
2. P                       :PREMISE
    /BEGIN: ~ ELIM to derive Q/
*3. ~Q                     :ASSUMPTION
*4. P                      :SEND,2
*5. (P & ~ Q)              :&INTRO,4,3
*6. ~ (P & ~ Q)            :SEND,1
*7. Q                      :~ ELIM,3,5,6
    /END: ~ ELIM to derive Q/
8. Q                       :RETURN,7
```

Since $(P \rightarrow Q)$ is logically equivalent to $\sim(P \ \& \ \sim Q)$, and since the argument pattern $\sim(P \ \& \ \sim Q)$, $P \therefore Q$ is truth-preserving, then the pattern $(P \rightarrow Q)$, $P \therefore Q$ must also be truth-preserving. This observation forms the basis of our next rule: *conditional elimination,* or $\rightarrow$ELIM for short.

$\rightarrow$ELIM   From a sentence of the form
            $(P \rightarrow Q)$
        and a sentence of the form
            P
        you may derive the sentence
            Q

A more direct way of seeing that this rule is truth-preserving would be to examine the truth table for $(P \rightarrow Q)$. There will be no situation where **P** and $(P \rightarrow Q)$ are both TRUE but **Q** is FALSE.

Let us now look at several applications of the $\rightarrow$ELIM rule in derivations.

Argument 1

    $(A \rightarrow (B \rightarrow C))$
    A
$\therefore (B \rightarrow C)$

Derivation

```
1. (A → (B → C))     :PREMISE
2. A                 :PREMISE
3. (B → C)           :→ELIM,1,2
```

Here, the conclusion is itself a conditional, '$(B \rightarrow C)$'.

Be sure that the two sentences have the required pattern before applying the rule $\rightarrow$ELIM. That pattern is:

    (<sentence 1> $\rightarrow$ <sentence 2>)
    <sentence 1>
    Therefore, <sentence 2>

That is, the derived sentence is the *consequent* of the conditional. And the antecedent of that conditional must also be a distinct sentence on a separate line.

It is quite easy to become momentarily confused and to think of this pattern:

(<sentence 1> → <sentence 2>)
<sentence 2>
Therefore, <sentence 1>

As we saw in Chapter 6, this argument pattern is not valid, and a rule based upon it would not be truth-preserving. This non-truth-preserving pattern of reasoning is so often employed that it is termed a *fallacy*, specifically, the fallacy of "affirming the consequent."

The companion rule of →ELIM is the rule *conditional introduction,* or →INTRO for short.

>→INTRO   If from an assumption of the form
>   **P**
>   a sentence
>   **Q**
>   can be derived in the same subproof, then you may derive
>   **(P → Q)**

The rule →INTRO, like the earlier rules ~INTRO and ~ELIM, requires a subproof beginning with an assumption. The intuitive reasoning behind the rule is not difficult to understand. Suppose a sentence, **P**, were TRUE. Consider a sentence, **Q,** that can be derived from the assumption of **P.** If **Q** can be derived from the assumption of **P,** then we have shown **Q** on condition that **P**—that is, if **P** then **Q**.

The rule →ELIM is used when we wish to reduce the number of conditional connectives. The rule →INTRO, however, is used when we wish to derive a sentence whose main connective is →.

Here are some applications of the rule:

Argument 2

   (A → B)
   (B → C)
∴ (A → C)

Derivation

```
    1. (A → B)        :PREMISE
    2. (B → C)        :PREMISE
  *3.  A              :ASSUMPTION
  *4.  (A → B)        :SEND,1
  *5.  (B → C)        :SEND,2
  *6.  B              :→ELIM,4,3
  *7.  C              :→ELIM,5,6
  *8.  (A → C)        :→INTRO,3,7
    9. (A → C)        :RETURN,8
```

ADDITIONAL RULES

Before beginning the derivation, we observe that the conclusion, '(A → C)', is a conditional. Normally, when we wish to derive a conditional, we should proceed so that →INTRO can be applied. In order to apply →INTRO, we must first begin with an *assumption,* and this assumption should be the *antecedent* of the conditional we are trying to derive. Once a subproof is begun with this assumption, our goal should then be to derive the consequent of the desired conditional. Once we have an assumption and the consequent of this conditional, we may then apply →INTRO—and the result will be exactly what we wanted. Note that →INTRO cites two previous line numbers, which must both be in the same subproof: first the assumption, then another sentence (the consequent of the desired conditional). Observe also that the rule RETURN is now expanded to permit the citation of a line where →INTRO was applied.

We can perhaps better see the strategy in this derivation if we add our comments:

```
 1. (A → B)          :PREMISE
 2. (B → C)          :PREMISE
      /BEGIN: →INTRO to derive (A → C)/
*3.  A               :ASSUMPTION
      /BEGIN: →ELIM to derive C/
*4.  (A → B)         :SEND,1
*5.  (B → C)         :SEND,2
*6.  B               :→ELIM,4,3
*7.  C               :→ELIM,5,6
      /END:  →ELIM to derive C/
*8.  (A → C)         :→INTRO,3,7
      /END:  →INTRO to derive (A → C)/
 9. (A → C)          :RETURN,8
```

Let's consider another example.

Argument 3

   (A & B)
∴ (C → A)

Here, it should be clear that →INTRO should be used. The conclusion contains an →, while the only premise does not. To apply →INTRO and have the result turn out correctly, we must assume the sentence 'C', then work toward the sentence 'A' in that subproof.

Derivation

```
 1. (A & B)          :PREMISE
      /BEGIN: → INTRO to derive (C → A)/
*2.  C               :ASSUMPTION
*3.  (A & B)         :SEND,1
*4.  A               :&ELIM,3
```

*5.   (C → A)   : → INTRO,2,4
      /END: → INTRO to derive (C → A)/
 6.   (C → A)   :RETURN,5

We observe that the conclusion is a conditional, probably to be reached by →INTRO. If we are to apply →INTRO to obtain '(C → A)', we must assume 'C', then (somehow) derive 'A'. In line 2, we assume 'C'. Practically the only reasonable step open to us at this point is to "send" the single premise into the subproof. Once we do this, it is, of course, easy to derive 'A'.

Argument 4

   A
∴(B → (C → A))

Derivation

 1. A   :PREMISE
        /BEGIN: → INTRO to derive (B → (C → A))/
*2.   B   :ASSUMPTION
        /BEGIN: → INTRO to derive (C → A)/
**3.   C   :ASSUMPTION
**4.   A   :SEND,1
**5.   (C → A)   : → INTRO,3,4
        /END: → INTRO to derive (A → A)/
*6.   (C → A)   :RETURN,5
*7.   (B → (C → A))   :→INTRO,2,6
        /END: → INTRO to derive (B → (C → A))/
 8. (B → (C → A))   :RETURN,7

This derivation uses two applications of →INTRO, with the result that there is a subproof within a subproof. The desired conclusion is '(B → (C → A))'. Since the conclusion is a conditional, the appropriate rule to use seems to be →INTRO. To arrive at this conclusion we must assume

   B

which is the antecedent of the conclusion, and work toward

   (C → A)

But '(C → A)' is itself a conditional, which suggests another use of →INTRO. To reach '(C → A)', we again apply →INTRO, beginning with the assumption of sentence 'C' and working toward sentence 'A'. The overall strategy is:

/BEGIN: →INTRO to derive (B → (C → A))/
  /BEGIN: →INTRO to derive (C → A)/
  /END: →INTRO to derive (C → A)/
/END: →INTRO to derive (B → (C → A))/

This plan of attack virtually dictates the final form of our derivation. For example, the remark

/BEGIN: →INTRO to derive (B → (C → A))/

dictates that the next step should be the assumption of the antecedent, 'B'.

Disjunction Introduction and Elimination

We have two paired rules for dealing with sentences involving disjunctions. They are *disjunction introduction,* or vINTRO for short, and *disjunction elimination,* or vELIM for short.

The first rule, vINTRO, is a rule of deceptive simplicity.

vINTRO   From any sentence of the form
      P
you may derive
    (P v Q)
or you may also derive
    (Q v P)

It states that from any sentence, **P,** you may derive a sentence that has another sentence, **Q,** "added" to **P.** For this reason the rule is occasionally called "addition." The sentence added to the sentence we already have may be *any sentence whatever.* Thus lines 2 to 5 are all legitimate applications of vINTRO:

1. A   :PREMISE
2. (A v B)   :vINTRO,1
3. (A v (C & D))   :vINTRO,1
4. ((E → (F v G)) v A)   :vINTRO,1
5. ((A v B) v (A v B))   :vINTRO,2

In the second line, 'B' is the added sentence. In the third line, it is the molecular sentence '(C & D)'. In the fourth line, the molecular sentence

(E → (F v G))

is added to the sentence 'A', but 'A' is the second disjunct. In the fifth line, we added '(A v B)' to itself.

Because the rule vINTRO is extremely generous and can be applied to any sentence whatever, the stumbling block is not in learning what the rule is but rather in learning *when* and *how* to use it and *what* sentence to add. As with our other rules, some hint of when the rule vINTRO should probably be used is given by its name. The rule vINTRO should usually be used when we have a disjunction to derive. For example, consider the following valid argument:

Argument 5

    (A & B)
∴ (C → (A v D))

The desired conclusion is a conditional: (C → (A v D)). This suggests that the major strategy should probably be →INTRO. We would begin by assuming sentence 'C'. But observe that once we have done this, we should then derive '(A v D)'. This sentence is, of course, a disjunction and suggests that vINTRO should then be used. Our strategy, then, is sketched as follows:

    /BEGIN: →INTRO to derive (C → (A v D))/
    /BEGIN: vINTRO to derive (A v D)/
    /END: vINTRO to derive (A v D)/
    /END: →INTRO to derive (C → (A v D))/

The resulting derivation is:

    1. (A & B)   :PREMISE
          /BEGIN: → INTRO to derive (C → (A v D))/
  *2. C   :ASSUMPTION
          /BEGIN: vINTRO to derive (A v D)/
  *3. (A & B)   :SEND,1
  *4. A   :&ELIM,3
  *5. (A v D)   :vINTRO,4
          /END: vINTRO to derive (A v D)/
  *6. (C → (A v D))   :→INTRO,2,5
          /END: → INTRO to derive (C → (A v D))/
    7. (C → (A v D))   :RETURN,6

At step 5, absolutely any sentence could have been "added" to sentence 'A'. But since we were aiming for '(A v D)', the natural addition was the sentence 'D'.

Here is another application of vINTRO:

Argument 6

    ((A v B) → C)
    A
∴ C

Derivation

```
1. ((A v B) → C)    :PREMISE
2. A                :PREMISE
3. (A v B)          :vINTRO,2
4. C                :→ELIM,1,3
```

The rule vELIM is also simply stated:

vELIM   From a sentence of the form

(P v Q)

and one of the form

~P

you may derive

Q

Or, alternatively, from a sentence of the form

(P v Q)

and one of the form

~Q

you may derive

P

In other words, from a disjunction and a sentence that is the negation of one of the disjuncts, you may derive the other disjunct.

The simplest example showing the application of this rule is as follows:

Argument 7

```
  (A v B)
  ~A
∴ B
```

Derivation

```
1. (A v B)    :PREMISE
2. ~A         :PREMISE
3. B          :vELIM,1,2
```

Observe that the rule vELIM cites the line with the disjunction first, and the second citation is the line with the negated sentence.

Here is another application of vELIM:

Argument 8

(B v C)
(A → ~C)
∴ (A → B)

At first, this argument might not look too promising for an application of vELIM. We have a disjunction, '(B v C)', and one conditional, '(A → ~C)'. The desired conclusion is a conditional, and so we might try an →INTRO strategy by assuming 'A'. We now try to derive 'B' in the subproof.

Derivation

1. (B v C)   :PREMISE
2. (A → ~C)   :PREMISE
       /BEGIN: → INTRO to derive (A → B)/
*3. A   :ASSUMPTION
*4. (A → ~C)   :SEND,2
*5. ~ C   : → ELIM,4,3
*6. (B v C)   :SEND,1
*7. B   :vELIM,6,5
*8. (A → B)   : → INTRO,3,7
       /END: → INTRO to derive (A → B)/
9. (A → B)   :RETURN,8

Please note that the next example is an *incorrect* use of vELIM:

Argument 9

1. (Bv ~ C)   :PREMISE
2. C   :PREMISE
3. B   :vELIM,1,2 [Incorrect]

Later in this chapter, we will see how to derive '~~C' from C and so correctly derive the conclusion:

1. (B v ~C)   :PREMISE
2. C   :PREMISE
3. ~~C   :RR DN,2 (see "Rules of Replacement")
4. B   :vELIM,1,3

ADDITIONAL RULES

Truth Preservation

Are the last four rules of inference we have introduced— →ELIM, →INTRO, vINTRO, and vELIM—truth-preserving? There are two methods we can use in answering this question. We might, for example, try to show directly that such a rule will never produce FALSE sentences out of TRUE ones. We could examine a truth table to see if there is a possible situation where the earlier sentences are TRUE but the derived sentence is FALSE. Another, and usually easier, method is to show that the new rule is derivable from rules that we already have and which are known to be truth-preserving. By "derivable from" we mean here that the new rule can only derive sentences that earlier rules could also have derived.

We can readily see that the rule vINTRO is derivable from a combination of other previously introduced rules which are all known to be truth-preserving. The pattern of inference we see with vINTRO is:

$$P$$
$$\therefore (P \vee Q)$$

where **Q** can be any sentence. Is such a rule truth-preserving? If we intend to apply the second method of showing that it is truth-preserving, we ask: Are there steps using previous rules that would get us from **P** to (**P** v **Q**)? The answer is yes, as the following derivation (repeated from the previous chapter) shows:

```
1.  P                    :PREMISE
*2.   ( ~P & ~ Q)        :ASSUMPTION   [ ~ ( ~ P & ~ Q) is
                                          logically equivalent to (P v Q)]
*3.  P                   :SEND,1
*4.  ~ P                 :&ELIM,2
*5.  ~ ( ~ P & ~ Q)      :~ INTRO,2,3,4
 6.  ~ (~ P & ~ Q)       :RETURN,5
```

In other words, wherever we have a derivation that has already reached the sentence, **P**, we could insert the above derivation (with line numbers altered) and arrive at ~(~**P** & ~**Q**), without ever having to use vINTRO.

A similar demonstration is possible to show that vELIM is truth-preserving. To show that →INTRO is truth-preserving is difficult using the second method but rather easy using the first method.

Biconditional Introduction and Elimination

The last of the frequently used connectives for which we have not yet given truth-preserving rules of inference is ↔. One rule for the biconditional is:

↔INTRO   From a sentence of the form
        (P → Q)
    and another of the form
        (Q → P)
    you may derive
        (P ↔ Q)

Note that the application of the ↔INTRO rule requires two previous sentences. Both must be conditionals, and the antecedent of each one is the consequent of the other. The other rule for the biconditional is:

↔ELIM   From a sentence of the form
        (P ↔ Q)
    you may derive either
        (P → Q)
    or
        (Q → P)

These two rules, as their names suggest, are usually applied when we need to derive a sentence containing ↔, or when we need to derive a sentence that does not contain ↔ from sentences which do. The application of these two rules is shown in the following two derivations.

Argument 10

  (A ↔ B)
  A
∴ B

Derivation

  1. (A ↔ B)   :PREMISE
  2. A   :PREMISE
     /BEGIN: ↔ELIM to obtain (A → B)/
  3. (A → B)   :↔ELIM,1
     /END: ↔ELIM to obtain (A → B)/
  4. B   :→ELIM,3,2

Observe that the use of ↔ELIM in a derivation requires citing one previous line, and that line must contain a biconditional. In the above argument, it should be apparent that ↔ELIM would probably have to be applied. One of the premises contains a biconditional, while the conclusion does not—therefore, the ↔ must be "eliminated."

Argument 11

> (A & (B → C))
> (C → B)
> ∴ (A & (B ↔ C))

Derivation

1. (A & (B → C))   :PREMISE
2. (C → B)   :PREMISE
3. A   :&ELIM,1
4. (B → C)   :&ELIM,1
5. (B ↔ C)   :↔INTRO,4,2
6. (A & (B ↔ C))   :&INTRO,3,5

These two rules can easily be shown to be truth-preserving.

Rules of Replacement

All the rules we have seen so far are what might be termed "one-way" rules. They permit us to derive a sentence from earlier sentences:

> <sentence 1>
> <sentence 2>
> .
> .
> .

Derive:
> <sentence 3>

But this does not mean that from <sentence 3> we could have derived <sentence 1>. For example, from (**P & Q**) we can derive **P**; but from **P** alone we cannot derive (**P & Q**). Furthermore, these rules can be applied only when the *entire sentence* on a line has the appropriate form. For example, from

1. (A → B)   :PREMISE
2. A   :PREMISE

we can derive by →ELIM

3. B   :→ELIM,1,2

since the sentences on lines 1 and 2 are of the proper form. But note that the following derivation is not correct:

1. $((A \rightarrow B) \vee C)$:PREMISE
2. A   :PREMISE
3. B   :$\rightarrow$ELIM,1,2   [Incorrect]

The difficulty lies with the fact that even though line 1 *contains* a conditional, '$(A \rightarrow B)$', the *entire* sentence is not a conditional. (It is, in fact, a disjunction.) In brief, then, all our earlier rules can be applied to earlier sentences in a derivation, but not to *parts* of these sentences.

For example, it is quite tempting to try the following derivation:

1. $((A \& B) \rightarrow C)$:PREMISE
2. $(A \rightarrow C)$:&ELIM,1   [Incorrect]

The difficulty here lies in the fact that &ELIM can be applied only to a sentence that is a conjunction, not to one *containing* a conjunction.

In this last section, we shall introduce rules that are "two-way" and which allow us to make alterations in *parts* of previous sentences. The general name for such rules is *rules of replacement,* or RR for short.

RR   From any sentence containing another sentence, **P**, as a part:
      $(\ldots \mathbf{P} \ldots)$
      if you know that **P** is logically equivalent to **Q**, then you may derive the same sentence with **P** replaced by **Q**:
      $(\ldots \mathbf{Q} \ldots)$

In other words, a sentence with a sentence part replaced by a logically equivalent sentence may be derived.

In theory, the application of the replacement rule, RR, would require us always first to show that two sentences are logically equivalent before we derive a sentence in which one is replaced by the other. But there are a handful of logically equivalent pairs that are so frequently used that we can give them names and then appeal to them whenever we wish, without having to demonstrate that they are logically equivalent.

These logically equivalent pairs, along with the names we shall give to them, are:

P	$\sim\sim$**P**	DN (Double-negation)
(P & Q)	**(Q & P)**	CM (&-Commutativity)
(P ∨ Q)	**(Q ∨ P)**	CM (∨-Commutativity)
P	**(P & P)**	ID (&-Idempotency)
P	**(P ∨ P)**	ID (∨-Idempotency)
(P & (Q & R))	**((P & Q) & R)**	AS (&-Associativity)
(P ∨ (Q ∨ R))	**((P ∨ Q) ∨ R)**	AS (∨-Associativity)
(P & (Q ∨ R))	**((P & Q ∨ (P & R))**	DIS (&-over-∨-Distributivity)
(P ∨ (Q & R))	**((P ∨ Q) & (P ∨ R))**	DIS (∨-over-&-DIstributivity)
$\sim$**(P & Q)**	**($\sim$P ∨ $\sim$Q)**	DM (De Morgan)
$\sim$**(P ∨ Q)**	**($\sim$P & $\sim$Q)**	DM (De Morgan)
(P $\rightarrow$ Q)	**($\sim$Q $\rightarrow$ $\sim$P)**	CN (Contraposition)
(P $\rightarrow$ Q)	**($\sim$P ∨ Q)**	EQ ($\rightarrow$/∨Equivalence)
(P $\rightarrow$ Q)	$\sim$**(P & $\sim$Q)**	EQ ($\rightarrow$/&Equivalence)
((P & Q) $\rightarrow$ R)	**(P $\rightarrow$ (Q $\rightarrow$ R))**	EXP (Exportation)

ADDITIONAL RULES

When applying one of these replacement rules in a derivation, you should write 'RR' (for "rule of replacement"), then the abbreviation for the particular rule (listed above), then the line number of the previous line undergoing a replacement.

The following short derivations show the correct application of several of these rules.

Argument 12

(A & (B ∨ C))
∴ (A & (C ∨ B))

Derivation

1. (A & (B ∨ C))   :PREMISE
2. (A & (C ∨ B))   :RR CM,1

The only difference between the premise and the conclusion is the second conjunct: the second conjunct of the premise is '(B ∨ C)', while the second conjunct of the conclusion is '(C ∨ B)'. Since '(B ∨ C)' is logically equivalent to '(C ∨ B)', we may replace one with the other in the premise, directly obtaining the conclusion.

Argument 13

(~A → B)
∴ (B ∨ A)

Derivation

1. (~A → B)   :PREMISE
2. (~~A ∨ B)   :RR EQ,1
3. (A ∨ B)   :RR DN,2
4. (B ∨ A)   :RR CM,3

Argument 14

(A & ~(B → ~C))
∴ ((A & B) & C)

Derivation

1. (A & ~(B → ~C))   :PREMISE
2. (A & ~(~B ∨ ~C))   :RR EQ,1
3. (A & (~~B & ~~C))   :RR DM,2
4. (A & (B & ~~C))   :RR DN,3
5. (A & (B & C))   :RR DN,4
6. ((A & B) & C)   :RR AS,5

Argument 15

((A v ~B) → ~E)
(A v (~B & C))
∴ ~E

Derivation

1. ((A v ~B) → ~E)   :PREMISE
2. (A v (~B & C))   :PREMISE
3. ((A v ~B) & (A v C)) :RR DIS,2
4. (A v ~B)   :&ELIM,3
5. ~E   :→ELIM,1,4

Throughout all these lines, the main justification for a sentence is "rule of replacement." We then cite how we know the replacement sentence is logically equivalent to the original sentence. One way is to cite by abbreviation one of the logically equivalent pairs given in the above list.

Is the rule RR truth-preserving? That is, if we begin with TRUE sentences, will we derive only TRUE sentences, even if we use RR repeatedly? The truth value of a compound sentence is a function of the truth values of its parts. This fact was made abundantly clear in Chapters 3 through 6. If one of these parts is replaced by a sentence having the same truth value, the truth value of the entire sentence will not be changed. If the sentence was TRUE before, then replacing a part of that sentence with a part known to have the same truth value will result in a sentence which is also TRUE. Logically equivalent sentences are just sentences that have the same truth value in all situations. Thus the rule RR is truth-preserving: replacing a subformula of a sentence with a sentence logically equivalent to the part will not change its truth value.

Sometimes we might not have available the list of logically equivalent sentences given above. Or perhaps we might have good reason to believe that two sentences are logically equivalent, even though they aren't on the list, and wish to use them in RR. What do we do?

We could demonstrate that the two sentences are logically equivalent by constructing a truth table off to the side of the derivation, showing that the two sentences have the same truth values in all situations. But this would often be very paper- and time-consuming; we would clutter our otherwise neat derivation with a long digression into what derivations are supposed to avoid: considerations of the truth and falsity of sentences.

Instead of writing a truth table, we shall make use of an earlier observation. Two sentences, **P** and **Q,** are logically equivalent if and only if the biconditional (**P** ↔ **Q**) is a tautology. Furthermore, a sentence is a tautology if and only if it can be RETURNed from a section of a derivation that does not use SEND on any premises or any lines outside of that section. When ↔INTRO is used on two tautologies, the resulting biconditional is a tautology.

In other words, a biconditional can be shown to be a tautology if we can construct a section of the derivation with this structure:

/BEGIN: ↔INTRO to derive (**P** ↔ **Q**)/
  /BEGIN: →INTRO to derive (**P** → **Q**)/
  /END: →INTRO to derive (**P** → **Q**)/
    /BEGIN: →INTRO to derive (**Q** → **P**)/
    /END: →INTRO to derive (**Q** → **P**)/
/END: ↔INTRO to derive (**P** ↔ **Q**)/

and within this section no SEND line is ever applied to lines before this section of the derivation.

Consider the following argument:

Argument 16

  (B & ((A ∨ A) & A))
∴ (B & A)

We might begin by observing that if we could replace ((A ∨ A) & A) with A, the derivation would be very simple. Furthermore, we might suspect that the sentences

  ((A ∨ A) & A)

and

  A

are logically equivalent, which would allow their replacement by RR. We might proceed as follows:

  1. (B & ((A ∨ A) & A))   :PREMISE
    /BEGIN: ↔INTRO to derive
        (A ↔ ((A ∨ A) & A)) for RR/

       /BEGIN: →INTRO to derive (A → ((A ∨ A) & A))/
*2.   A   :ASSUMPTION
*3.   (A ∨ A)   :∨INTRO,2
*4.   ((A ∨ A) & A)   :&INTRO,3,2
*5.   (A → ((A ∨ A) & A))   :→INTRO,2,4
    /END: →INTRO to derive (A → ((A ∨ A) & A))/
  6. (A → ((A ∨ A) & A))   :RETURN,5

       /BEGIN: →INTRO to derive (((A ∨ A) & A) → A)/
*7.   ((A ∨ A) & A)   :ASSUMPTION
*8.   A   :&ELIM,7
*9.   (((A ∨ A) & A) → A)   :→INTRO,7,8
    /END: →INTRO to derive (((A ∨ A) & A) → A)/
  10. (((A ∨ A) & A) → A)   :RETURN,9
  11. (A ↔ ((A ∨ A) & A))   :↔INTRO,6,10
    /END: ↔INTRO to derive (A ↔ ((A ∨ A) & A))/
  12. (B & A)   :RR (2–11),1

A careful inspection of lines 2 to 11 will show that no previous lines outside of the section were cited. That section of the derivation is "self-contained." Consequently, it can be used to show that the sentence in line 11 is a tautology and thus that the two sentences are logically equivalent. In line 12 we apply the rule of replacement, RR, using the information garnered in lines 2 to 11 that 'A' and '((A v A) & A)' are logically equivalent. The replacement of '((A v A) & A)' by 'A' was applied to line 1, so we cite it.

Modus Tollens

Another rule for eliminating a conditional is commonly known by its Latin name, *modus tollens,* or MT for short. It deals with sentences that combine → and ~.

> MT From a sentence of the form
> **(P → Q)**
> and a sentence of the form
> **~Q**
> you may derive
> **~P**

In other words, if we have a conditional sentence and the *negation of the consequent* of that sentence, we may derive the *negation of the antecedent.*

Reasoning according to the rule *modus tollens* is quite common in everyday affairs. An example is:

> If this is a pine tree, then it must have pine cones.
> It does not have pine cones.
> Therefore, this is not a pine tree.

One way to show that MT is truth-preserving is to derive the desired conclusion:

```
  1. (P → Q)        :PREMISE
  2. ~Q             :PREMISE
       /BEGIN:  ~INTRO to derive ~P/
 *3.  P             :ASSUMPTION
 *4.  (P → Q)       :SEND,1
 *5.  Q             :→ELIM,4,3
 *6.  ~Q            :SEND,2
 *7.  ~P            :~INTRO,3,5,6
       /END:    ~INTRO to derive ~P/
  8. ~P             :RETURN,7
```

So, MT is truth-preserving, since SEND, →ELIM, ~INTRO, and RETURN are truth-preserving. What we have shown is that any time we have a sentence of the form (P → Q) and a sentence of the form ~**Q**, we can derive a sentence of the form ~**P.**

ADDITIONAL RULES

We shall call such a rule a *derivable* rule, because the validity of this new rule really rests on earlier rules. (In fact, as we mentioned earlier, all the rules in this chapter are derivable from the rules in Chapter 8.)

Thus MT (or any derivable rule) used as a justification of a line in a derivation can be thought of as an abbreviation of its own derivation (given above). In an unabbreviated, or "expanded," derivation, the line whose citation is MT would be replaced by a copy of the above derivation, perhaps slightly altered: Each of the sentences **P** and **Q** would be replaced by appropriate sentences from the abbreviated derivation; the justifications for lines 1 and 2 might have to be replaced by the justifications for (**P** → **Q**) and ~**Q** from the abbreviated derivation; line numbers might have to be changed; and so on.

An example should clarify this:

Argument 17

(~A → B)
~B
∴ A

Abbreviated Derivation

1. (~ A → B)   :PREMISE
2. ~B   :PREMISE
3. ~~A   :MT,1,2
4. A   :RR DN,3

Expanded Derivation

1. (~A → B)   :PREMISE
2. ~B   :PREMISE
*3.   ~A   :ASSUMPTION
*4.   (~A → B)   :SEND,1
*5.   B   :→ELIM,4,3
*6.   ~B   :SEND,2
*7.   ~~A   :~INTRO,3,5,6
8. ~~A   :RETURN,7 [instead of MT,1,2]
9. A   :RR DN,8

There are many other useful derivable rules. Some of these are explored in the exercises. (The "expansion" of an "abbreviated" derivation that uses a derivable rule corresponds to the expansion of "macros" in assembly-language programming: Instead of always spelling out the details of a section of derivation to derive a sentence from earlier rules, we give certain steps a name—such as MT—and use that name to refer to that sequence of steps.)

CHAPTER 9

Summary

To make derivations simpler and more natural, additional derived rules of inference were added to our natural deduction system: introduction and elimination rules for the connectives v, →, and ↔.

vINTRO—From **P**, **(P v Q)** is derivable.
vELIM—From **(P v Q)** and ~**P, Q** is derivable.
→INTRO—With **P** as an assumption of a subproof and **Q** a line of that subproof, **(P → Q)** is derivable in the subproof and may be returned.
→ELIM—From **(P → Q)** and **P, Q** is derivable.
↔INTRO—From **(P → Q)** and **(Q → P)**, **(P ↔ Q)** is derivable.
↔ELIM—From **(P ↔ Q)**, either **(P → Q)** or **(Q → P)** is derivable.

Furthermore, the very powerful rule of replacement (RR) was discussed, along with a number of common logical equivalences:

P	~~**P**	DN (Double-negation)
(P & Q)	**(Q & P)**	CM (&-Commutativity)
(P v Q)	**(Q v P)**	CM (v-Commutativity)
P	**(P & P)**	ID (&-Idempotency)
P	**(P v P)**	ID (v-Idempotency)
(P & (Q & R))	**((P & Q) & R)**	AS (&-Associativity)
(P v (Q v R))	**((P v Q) v R)**	AS (v-Associativity)
(P & (Q v R))	**((P & Q) v (P & R))**	DIS (&-over-v-Distributivity
(P v (Q & R))	**((P v Q) & (P v R))**	DIS (v-over-&-Distributivity)
~**(P & Q)**	**(~P v ~Q)**	DM (De Morgan)
~**(P v Q)**	**(~P & ~Q)**	DM (De Morgan)
(P → Q)	**(~Q → ~P)**	CN (Contraposition)
(P → Q)	**(~P v Q)**	EQ (→/vEquivalence)
(P → Q)	~**(P & ~Q)**	EQ (→/&Equivalence)
((P & Q) → R)	**(P → (Q → R))**	EXP (Exportation)

Also, one additional derived rule was introduced:

MT (*modus tollens*)—From **(P → Q)** and ~**Q**, ~**P** is derivable.

Exercises

A. Natural Deductions
   Give derivations for the following arguments:
   1. (A & B)   2. (A → B)
      (A → C)   (B → C)
      ∴ C   (C → D)
                                    ∴ (A → D)

ADDITIONAL RULES

3. $(A \rightarrow (B \vee C))$
    $(D \, \& \, A)$
    $\sim C$
    $\therefore B$

4. $(A \vee B)$
    $(A \vee \sim B)$
    $\therefore A$

5. A
    $\therefore (B \vee \sim B)$

6. $(A \vee B)$
    $\sim A$
    $(B \rightarrow C)$
    $\therefore C$

7. A
    $(A \rightarrow B)$
    $\sim B$
    $\therefore \sim A$

8. $(A \rightarrow (B \rightarrow C))$
    $(A \rightarrow B)$
    $\therefore (A \rightarrow C)$

9. $(\sim A \vee (B \, \& \, C))$
    $\sim B$
    $\therefore \sim A$

10. $(A \rightarrow B)$
    $\sim (B \vee C)$
    $\therefore \sim A$

B.   Symbolize the following arguments, and give derivations for them.

1. The dean and the chairs are in favor of the regulation, or the dean and the faculty are in favor of it. The faculty are in favor of the regulation only if a majority of students are in favor of it. But a majority of students are not in favor of the regulation. Hence, the chairs are in favor of the regulation.

2. Either my son or my daughter will have the car tonight. If either my son or my daughter has the car tonight, my wife will not be happy. I will be happy if neither has the car tonight. But if my wife is not happy, I will not be happy. And if I am not happy, I am grouchy. Thus I will be grouchy.

3. The sports program will be discontinued unless there is additional money. If it is discontinued, we will attract students if and only if we are well known. But we will attract students and we are not well known. Therefore, there is additional money.

4. If oil supplies run out, then the price of electricity will rise, and the cost of solar energy will increase provided that oil supplies do not run out. If the price of electricity rises, then people will be cold. Thus people will not be cold only if the cost of solar energy increases.

5. Evil cannot exist unless God is unwilling or unable to prevent it. If God is omnipotent, then He is able to prevent evil. If God is omnibenevolent, then He is willing to prevent evil. If God exists, He is both omnipotent and omnibenevolent. Nevertheless, evil exists. Thus God does not exist.

6. If the laws are just and are strictly enforced, there will be fewer crimes. If strictly enforced laws result in fewer crimes, then we can reduce the size of the police force. Therefore, if we cannot reduce the size of the police force, the laws are not just.

7. Neither Albert nor Charlene is a good student. Yet either Albert is a good student if David is, or if David or Elizabeth is a good student, then Charlene is a good student if and only if David is. So David is not a good student.

8. Paul is a philosopher only if Rudolph or Karl is. If Rudolph is a philosopher, then Alfred and Ludwig are philosophers. If Alfred is a philosopher, then Ludwig is one only if Willard is too. But not both Willard and Paul are philosophers. So Paul is a philosopher only if Karl is also.

C. The conclusion of a derivation that has no premises is called a theorem of logic. If the rules of derivation are correct, a theorem is a tautology. To prove a theorem, one must begin the derivation with one or more ASSUMPTIONS, which are subsequently eliminated by RETURN. Hence, the last line of the derivation is in the main proof and has no asterisk. Prove the following theorems:

1. $(A \rightarrow A)$
2. $((A \rightarrow B) \rightarrow ((B \rightarrow C) \rightarrow (A \rightarrow C)))$
3. $((A \rightarrow B) \rightarrow ((C \rightarrow A) \rightarrow (C \rightarrow B)))$
4. $((A \rightarrow (B \rightarrow C)) \rightarrow ((A \rightarrow B) \rightarrow (A \rightarrow C)))$
5. $((A \rightarrow (B \rightarrow C)) \rightarrow (B \rightarrow (A \rightarrow C)))$
6. $((A \rightarrow (A \rightarrow B)) \rightarrow (A \rightarrow B))$
7. $((A \rightarrow B) \rightarrow (\sim B \rightarrow \sim A))$
8. $(A \rightarrow (\sim A \rightarrow B))$
9. $(\sim A \rightarrow (A \rightarrow B))$
10. $((\sim A \rightarrow A) \rightarrow A)$
11. $((A \rightarrow \sim A) \rightarrow \sim A)$
12. $(\sim (A \rightarrow B) \rightarrow A)$
13. $(\sim (A \rightarrow B) \rightarrow \sim B)$
14. $((A \& B) \leftrightarrow (B \& A))$
15. $((A \& (B \& C)) \leftrightarrow ((A \& B) \& C))$
16. $(((A \& B) \rightarrow C) \leftrightarrow (A \rightarrow (B \rightarrow C)))$
17. $((A \rightarrow (B \& C)) \leftrightarrow ((A \rightarrow B) \& (A \rightarrow C)))$
18. $(((A \rightarrow B) \& (C \rightarrow D)) \rightarrow ((A \& C) \rightarrow (B \& D)))$
19. $(((\sim A \vee B) \& A) \rightarrow B)$
20. $((A \rightarrow B) \leftrightarrow \sim (A \& \sim B))$
21. $((A \& B) \leftrightarrow \sim (A \rightarrow \sim B))$
22. $(\sim (A \& B) \leftrightarrow (A \rightarrow \sim B))$
23. $(A \leftrightarrow (A \& A))$
24. $((A \& \sim B) \rightarrow \sim (A \rightarrow B))$
25. $(\sim (A \& B) \leftrightarrow (\sim A \vee \sim B))$
26. $(\sim (A \vee B) \leftrightarrow (\sim A \& \sim B))$
27. $(((A \rightarrow B) \& (C \rightarrow B)) \leftrightarrow ((A \vee C) \rightarrow B))$
28. $((A \vee B) \leftrightarrow (B \vee A))$
29. $((A \vee (B \vee C)) \leftrightarrow ((A \vee B) \vee C))$
30. $((A \rightarrow (B \vee C)) \leftrightarrow ((A \rightarrow B) \vee (A \rightarrow C)))$
31. $((A \rightarrow B) \vee (B \rightarrow C))$
32. $(A \vee \sim A)$
33. $((A \& (B \vee C)) \leftrightarrow ((A \& B) \vee (A \& C)))$
34. $((A \vee (B \& C)) \leftrightarrow ((A \vee B) \& (A \vee C)))$
35. $(A \leftrightarrow ((A \& B) \vee (A \& \sim B)))$
36. $(A \leftrightarrow ((A \vee B) \& (A \vee \sim B)))$
37. $(A \leftrightarrow \sim \sim A)$
38. $((A \rightarrow B) \leftrightarrow (\sim A \vee B))$
39. $(((A \& B) \rightarrow C) \leftrightarrow (A \rightarrow (B \rightarrow C)))$
40. $((A \leftrightarrow B) \leftrightarrow ((A \rightarrow B) \& (B \rightarrow A)))$

ADDITIONAL RULES

D. Define appropriate introduction and elimination rules for NAND, NOR, and XOR, and show that they are truth-preserving.

E. Show that the following rules are derivable:

1. Hypothetical Syllogism (HS):
   From a conditional of the form
   $(P \rightarrow Q)$
   and another of the form
   $(Q \rightarrow R)$
   you may derive a third conditional of the form
   $(P \rightarrow R)$

2. Constructive Dilemma (CD)
   From a disjunction of the form
   $(P \vee Q)$
   and two conditionals of the form
   $(P \rightarrow R)$
   $(Q \rightarrow S)$
   you may derive the disjunction
   $(R \vee S)$

F. Show that the following rules are truth-preserving:

1. Hypothetical syllogism (HS)
2. $\rightarrow$INTRO

SENTENTIAL LOGIC: An Algorithm for Checking Proofs

In Chapter 5, we gave algorithms for calculating truth values and for determining whether a symbolized sentence is well-formed. In Chapter 6, we gave algorithms for producing a truth table for an argument and for using this truth table to determine whether a symbolized argument in the logic of sentences is valid or invalid.

In Chapters 8 and 9, we gave the rules for showing an argument in the logic of sentences to be valid by giving a *derivation.* This method of showing how an argument is valid is considerably less cumbersome than the truth-table method of Chapters 5 and 6; it also reflects a more "natural" way of thinking about *how* an argument is valid. It should, however, be kept in mind that the "proof" method does have its weaknesses: If an argument is valid, we can derive its conclusion. Moreover, the proof shows us *why* it is valid. But if the argument is *in*valid, the proof method is not useful. We would simply get "stuck" and not be able to derive the conclusion. Before even beginning to try to show an argument to be valid using a derivation, we should first have a hunch that it *is* valid.

In applying the "proof" method of Chapters 8 and 9, two important questions arise:

1. If we have written a proof, how do we know it is correct? That is, how can we be sure that it follows the rules for proofs?

2. If we know that the argument is indeed valid (perhaps we have been told that it is valid by a reliable authority), how can we produce a proof?

The first question is one of whether a proof *given* to us is correct. The second question is one of how to create proofs in the first place.

These two questions constitute the topics of the next two chapters. In this chapter we shall address the first question—how to determine when a proof is correct—by describing an algorithm that checks a proof to determine if it is correct. We shall call the algorithm PROOF-CHECKER.

The second question—how to construct a proof given the premises and the conclusion—will be discussed in Chapter 11.

Lines of a Proof

The algorithm for checking a proof should detect *any* error we might make: line numbers out of order, an improperly used rule, or a mistaken subproof. The algorithm must be sensitive to several aspects of a line in a proof. Because a line of a derivation contains organized information, it is customary to speak of a line as a "data structure." A line is the basic and most important data structure in PROOF-CHECKER.

Each line in a proof should have the following structure:

⟨asterisks⟩⟨line number⟩.⟨sentence⟩:⟨rule⟩,⟨line numbers⟩

An example is:

*4. (A & B)   :&INTRO,2,3

Each line has predetermined areas that should contain special information. These areas of the line will be called its *fields*.

The first field contains a string of asterisks—possibly a "null" string, that is, one with *no* asterisks. The number of asterisks indicates the number of assumptions under which we are working in that section of the proof. We shall call this section of a line the *subproof-depth field,* because the number of asterisks indicates the "depth" of the subproofs at that point.

The second field is the *line-number field.* It simply indicates the line number in a proof and should contain a (positive) whole number (1, 2, 3, . . .). For convenience, the line-number field is separated from the next field by a period ('.').

The third field should contain a well-formed sentence, such as '(A & B)', '(C → D)', and so on. We shall call it the *sentence field.* It is separated from the next field by a colon (':').

The fourth field contains whatever justifies our writing the sentence in the sentence field: PREMISE, &INTRO, vELIM, and so on. We shall call this area of the line the *rule field.* We shall call whatever occupies the rule field the *rule* used in that line—in spite of the fact that two justifications (PREMISE and ASSUMPTION) are not actually rules in our earlier terminology. If there are citations to previous lines, then following the rule field is a comma.

Finally, the fifth field will contain the line numbers of any previous lines that might need to be cited according to the rule we are using. Two rules (PREMISE and AS-SUMPTION) do not need such previous lines, so this last field might be empty. We shall call this field the *citation field.* It can contain up to three (positive) whole numbers, separated by commas.

As an example, consider the following line:

***11. (A → (B & C))   : → ELIM,2,4

Occupying each field in this line we have:

Subproof-depth field: ***
Line-number field: 11
Sentence field: (A → (B & C))
Rule field: →ELIM
Citation field: 2,4

You should see that the fields of a line can be uniquely identified; that is, an algorithm could be written to identify them. Although we shall not present such an algorithm (because it largely depends on the particular data structure chosen to represent a line), we shall assume that it is available for use in PROOF-CHECKER.

The Algorithm: Proof-Checker

Errors in a proof can occur in all sorts of ways. But in each case, the error will occur in *some* line of the derivation:

There may be too few, or too many, asterisks.
The line number may not be correct.
What occupies the sentence field might not be a well-formed sentence.
The period ending the line-number field, or the colon ending the sentence field, might be missing.
What occupies the rule field might not be a proper rule, or it might not correctly justify the sentence in the sentence field—that is, the rule might be misapplied.
And, finally, what is in the citation field might not be appropriate for the sentence in the sentence field and the rule in the rule field.

In short, there are lots of mistakes we might make and for which our algorithm must be on the lookout. We shall divide the algorithm PROOF-CHECKER into several parts, or "procedures," each of which corresponds to various types of mistakes in a derivation.

The four procedures in PROOF-CHECKER are:

CHECK-LINE-STRUCTURE: makes sure that every line has the correct format and provides names for the fields of each line.

CHECK-SENTENCE-STRUCTURE: determines whether what occupies the sentence field is a well-formed sentence.

CHECK-RULE: makes sure that every rule in a rule field, together with the accompanying cited lines, correctly justifies the sentence in the sentence field.

CHECK-SUBPROOF: makes sure that every subproof uses the correct number of asterisks and follows the rules for subproofs.

The complete algorithm is shown below.

ALGORITHM PROOF-CHECKER

1. INPUT the derivation to be tested.
2. FOR every line of the derivation
   (a) CHECK-LINE-STRUCTURE.
   (b) CHECK-SENTENCE-STRUCTURE.
   (c) CHECK-RULE.
   (d) CHECK-SUBPROOF.
3. IF there are no errors
      THEN OUTPUT "Derivation is correct; argument is valid."
4. STOP.

We now turn to the task of refining each of the four procedures.

The Procedure CHECK-LINE-STRUCTURE

Let's begin with the simplest and most fundamental of the four procedures: CHECK-LINE-STRUCTURE. What exactly must the structure of every line in a proof be? We shall ignore our "comment" lines, which begin with '/' and end with '/', since these are not part of the proof but just notes to ourselves. Every line must have a *period* (separating the line-number and sentence fields) and a *colon* (separating the sentence and rule fields). Between the beginning of the line and the period, a *number* must occur. But this is only a collection of observations. We now present the algorithm for checking to see if the requirements are met.

Recall that this procedure is repeated for each line of the derivation, so the input for the procedure is a line, which we shall call THISLINE. Such an abbreviation will allow us to refer to what occupies the fields of this line and other lines. For example, SUBPROOF-DEPTH(THISLINE) will be the subproof depth of the current line, and SENTENCE(THISLINE) will be the sentence of the current line. We can also use this system to refer to whatever occupies a field of another line. For example, SENTENCE(line *n*) is whatever occupies the sentence field of line *n*.

Algorithm PROOF-CHECKER, Procedure CHECK-LINE-STRUCTURE

1. IF there is no period in THISLINE
    THEN OUTPUT "Error."
2. IF there is no colon somewhere after the first period in THISLINE
    THEN OUTPUT "Error."
3. Let SUBPROOF-DEPTH(THISLINE) = the number of asterisks in the subproof-depth field of THISLINE.
4. IF the line-number field of THISLINE is empty
    THEN OUTPUT "Error."
5. IF the line-number field of THISLINE is not empty
    THEN
    (a) Let LINENUMBER(THISLINE) = the number in the line-number field of THISLINE.
    (b) IF LINENUMBER(THISLINE) is not a (positive) whole number
        THEN OUTPUT "Error."
    (c) IF this is the first time the procedure CHECK-LINE-STRUCTURE is being applied and LINENUMBER(THISLINE) $\neq$ 1
        THEN OUTPUT "Error."
    (d) IF this is not the first time
        and LINENUMBER(THISLINE) $\neq$ 1 + LINENUMBER (the previous line)
        THEN OUTPUT "Error."
6. IF the sentence field of THISLINE is empty
    THEN OUTPUT "Error."
7. IF the sentence field of THISLINE is not empty
    THEN let SENTENCE(THISLINE) be the sentence in the sentence field of THISLINE.
8. IF the rule field of THISLINE is empty
    THEN OUTPUT "Error."
9. IF the rule field of THISLINE is not empty
    THEN let RULE(THISLINE) be the rule in the rule field of THISLINE.
10. IF the citation field of THISLINE is not empty
    THEN
    (a) Let CIT1(THISLINE) be the first citation in the field.
    (b) IF there is a second citation
        THEN let CIT2(THISLINE) be the second citation.
    (c) IF there is a third citation
        THEN let CIT3(THISLINE) be the third citation.
    (d) IF there is a fourth citation
        THEN OUTPUT "Error."
    (e) IF any one of the citations is not a (positive) whole number
        THEN OUTPUT "Error."
    (f) IF any one of the citations is $\geq$ LINENUMBER(THISLINE)
        THEN OUTPUT "Error."

End of the procedure CHECK-LINE-STRUCTURE

The steps in this procedure make sure that all the basic elements of a line of a proof are in order before a more detailed examination is begun. Steps 3, 5(a), 7, 9, and 10(a) to (c) also give names to the fields of the line for future reference.

The Procedure CHECK-SENTENCE-STRUCTURE

The second procedure of PROOF-CHECKER, CHECK-SENTENCE-STRUCTURE, is, for our purposes in this chapter, very simple. The first procedure, CHECK-LINE-STRUC-TURE, told us which part of the line is *supposed to be* the well-formed string. But in Chapter 5, we gave an algorithm for determining whether a string is well-formed. We need only to insert that algorithm here. So CHECK-SENTENCE-STRUCTURE is just the algorithm SENTENCE-CHECKER from Chapter 5 that examines strings for their well-formedness, using SENTENCE(THISLINE) as its input.

The Procedure CHECK-RULE

The third procedure in PROOF-CHECKER, CHECK-RULE, is the heart of the Algorithm PROOF-CHECKER: It determines if the rule given as a justification in each line was correctly applied. Because of the number of possible rules which could have been used to justify a sentence, this procedure is somewhat lengthy: we must examine the way each rule works. The procedure uses RULE(THISLINE) as its input.

Algorithm PROOF-CHECKER, Procedure CHECK-RULE
0. IF RULE(THISLINE) = PREMISE
   THEN
   (a) IF SUBPROOF-DEPTH(THISLINE) ≠ 0
       THEN OUTPUT "Error."
   (b) IF there is a number in the citation field
       THEN OUTPUT "Error."
1. IF RULE(THISLINE) = &ELIM
   THEN
   (a) IF there is not just one number in the citation field
       THEN OUTPUT "Error."
       [This is because the rule &ELIM refers back to only one previous line.]
   (b) Where SENTENCE(CIT1(THISLINE)) is the sentence in the line whose
       number is CIT1(THISLINE),
       IF SENTENCE(CIT1(THISLINE)) ≠ (SENTENCE(THISLINE) & **P**) or to
       (**P** & SENTENCE(THISLINE)), where **P** is some sentence
       THEN OUTPUT "Error."
       [That is, the previous line cited must be a conjunction—a sentence
       whose main connective is &—and the inferred sentence,
       SENTENCE(THISLINE), must be one of the conjuncts.]

2. IF RULE(THISLINE) = &INTRO
   THEN

(a) IF there are not just two numbers in the citation field
    THEN OUTPUT "Error."
(b) IF SENTENCE(THISLINE) ≠
    (SENTENCE(CIT1(THISLINE)) & SENTENCE(CIT2(THISLINE)))
    THEN OUTPUT "Error."

Step 2 requires that the rule cite two (and only two) previous line numbers. Step 2(b) requires that the sentence in THISLINE consist of '(', followed by the sentence in the *first* line cited, followed by an ampersand (&), followed by the sentence in the *second* line cited, followed by ')'.

Our rule is in fact very exacting, as we have written it. Suppose we encountered the following "proof":

1. A   :PREMISE
2. B   :PREMISE
3. (A & B)   :&INTRO,2,1   [Mistake]

Line 3 contains a mistake (although a small one). In the citation for line 3, we cite *2* before *1*. This indicates that the sentence of line 2 should be the *first* conjunct of the sentence in line 3 and that the sentence in line 1 should be the *second* conjunct. In the example above, they are not.

There are two ways of correcting line 3—that is, two ways of making line 3 correct while retaining its rule as &INTRO. We could keep the rule and citations as they are but correct the *sentence:*

3. (B & A)   :&INTRO,2,1   [Correct]

Or we could change the *citations* and keep the sentence the same:

3. (A & B)   :&INTRO,1,2   [Correct]

This example shows the extraordinary care we must exhibit in using our rules *if* we want to make them subject to algorithms. We *could* allow ourselves more freedom in the expression of a citation, but then our algorithm would be more complicated. For example, if we wanted to allow ourselves the freedom of writing the cited lines in *any* order, we would have to modify step 2(b) to:

2(b) [Experimental]
    IF SENTENCE(THISLINE) ≠ (SENTENCE(CIT1(THISLINE)) & SEN-
    TENCE(CIT2(THISLINE))) and SENTENCE(THISLINE) ≠
    (SENTENCE(CIT2(THISLINE)) & SENTENCE(CIT1(THISLINE)))
    THEN OUTPUT "Error."

This example demonstrates an unfortunate trade-off we often face in writing algorithms. If it is to be convenient and versatile for us humans, then the algorithm must be made more complicated. On the other hand, if the algorithm is to be simple, then the rule is rigid and not always convenient for human users.

Continuing the procedure CHECK-RULE:

3. IF RULE(THISLINE) = →ELIM
    THEN
    (a) IF there are not just two numbers in the citation field
         THEN OUTPUT "Error."
    (b) IF SENTENCE(CIT1(THISLINE)) ≠
         (SENTENCE(CIT2(THISLINE)) → SENTENCE(THISLINE))
         THEN OUTPUT "Error."

Step 3(a) requires the →ELIM rule to cite *two* previous lines. Step 3(b) requires the two cited lines to be "related" in a certain way. The sentence in the second cited line must be the *antecedent* of the sentence in the first cited line. And the sentence in THISLINE must be the *consequent* of the sentence in the first cited line. For this to be true, the sentence in the first cited line must, of course, be a conditional: that is, it must be a sentence whose main connective is →.

This rule, too, has a certain rigidity about it. The cited line numbers must occur in the right order: conditional first, antecedent second. For example, in:

1. (A → B)   :PREMISE
2. A   :PREMISE
3. B   :→ELIM,2,1   [Mistake]

line 3 is mistaken (and would produce an "Error"), because the sentence in line 2 (the first citation of line 3) is *not* identical to:

(SENTENCE(line 1) → SENTENCE(line 3))

This mistake can be corrected by reversing the order of the cited line numbers in line 3:

3. B   :→ELIM,1,2   [Correct]

This is acceptable and would not produce an "Error," because

SENTENCE(line 1) = (SENTENCE(line 2) → SENTENCE(line 3))

is indeed true.

The next step of the procedure CHECK-RULE is:

4. IF RULE(THISLINE) = →INTRO
    THEN
    (a) IF there are not just two numbers in the citation field
         THEN OUTPUT "Error."
    (b) IF CIT2(THISLINE) < CIT1(THISLINE)
         THEN OUTPUT "Error."

    (c) IF RULE(CIT1(THISLINE)) ≠ ASSUMPTION
         THEN OUTPUT "Error."
    (d) IF SENTENCE(THISLINE) ≠
         (SENTENCE(CIT1(THISLINE))) → SENTENCE(CIT2(THISLINE))
         THEN OUTPUT "Error."

This step governs the use of the →INTRO rule. Additional requirements for its proper application will be discussed in the section on CHECK-SUBPROOF, since the use of →INTRO involves the use of a subproof.

Step 4(a) requires that *two* lines be cited. Step 4(b) requires that the consequent of the derived conditional be a line occurring after the assumption. Step 4(c) requires that the rule in the first cited line must have been ASSUMPTION. (Here is where a subproof must begin and an * introduced, if the justification was ASSUMPTION, but this will be discussed later.) Step 4(d) requires that a *conditional* of a certain form be derived on THISLINE.

Continuing with the procedure, we have:

  5. IF RULE(THISLINE) = ~ELIM
      THEN
      (a) IF there are not just three numbers in the citation field
          THEN OUTPUT "Error."
      (b) IF CIT2 or CIT3 < CIT1
          THEN OUTPUT "Error."
      (c) IF SENTENCE(CIT1(THISLINE)) ≠
         the negation of SENTENCE(THISLINE)
          THEN OUTPUT "Error."
      (d) IF RULE(CIT1(THISLINE)) ≠ ASSUMPTION
          THEN OUTPUT "Error."
      (e) IF SENTENCE(CIT3(THISLINE)) ≠
         the negation of SENTENCE(CIT2(THISLINE))
          THEN OUTPUT "Error."
  6. IF RULE (THISLINE) = ~INTRO
      THEN
      (a) IF there are not just three numbers in the citation field
          THEN OUTPUT "Error."
      (b) IF CIT2 or CIT3 < CIT1
          THEN OUTPUT "Error."
      (c) IF SENTENCE (CIT3(THISLINE)) ≠
         the negation of SENTENCE(CIT2(THISLINE))
          THEN OUTPUT "Error."
      (d) IF RULE (CIT1(THISLINE)) ≠ ASSUMPTION
          THEN OUTPUT "Error."
      (e) IF SENTENCE(CIT3(THIS LINE)) ≠
         the negation of SENTENCE(CIT2(THIS LINE))
          THEN OUTPUT "Error."

The steps governing ~INTRO and ~ELIM are identical except for (c). In ~INTRO, the sentence in THISLINE must be the negation of the sentence in the first cited line. In ~ELIM, the sentence in the first cited line must be the negation of the sentence in THISLINE.

Step (a) requires that the rule cite *three* lines. Step (d) requires that the rule have originated with an ASSUMPTION. Step (e) requires that two lines be cited that contradict one another (that is, that could not be TRUE at the same time). And step (b) ensures that these contradictory sentences occur in the derivation *after* the ASSUMPTION.

The next five steps of the procedure are:

7. IF RULE (THISLINE) = vELIM
    THEN
    (a) IF there are not just two numbers in the citation field
        THEN OUTPUT "Error."
    (b) IF SENTENCE(CIT1(THISLINE)) is not a disjunction of the form
        (i) (**P** v SENTENCE(THISLINE)) or
        (ii) (SENTENCE(THISLINE) v **Q**)
        THEN OUTPUT "Error."
    (c) IF SENTENCE(CIT1(THISLINE)) is of form (i)
        and SENTENCE(CIT2(THISLINE)) is not of the form ~**P**
        where **P** is the first disjunct of SENTENCE(CIT1(THISLINE))
        THEN OUTPUT "Error."
    (d) IF SENTENCE(CIT1(THISLINE)) is of form (ii)
        and SENTENCE(CIT2(THISLINE)) is not of the form ~**Q**
        where **Q** is the second disjunct of SENTENCE(CIT1(THISLINE))
        THEN OUTPUT "Error."
8. IF RULE(THISLINE) = vINTRO
    THEN
    (a) IF there is not just one number in the citation field
        THEN OUTPUT "Error."
    (b) IF SENTENCE(THISLINE) ≠ (SENTENCE(CIT1(THISLINE)) v **P**)
        and SENTENCE(THISLINE) ≠ (**P** v SENTENCE(CIT1(THISLINE)))
        where **P** is a well-formed sentence
        THEN OUTPUT "Error."
9. IF RULE(THISLINE) = ↔ELIM
    THEN
    (a) IF there is not just one number in the citation field
        THEN OUTPUT "Error."
    (b) IF SENTENCE(CIT1(THISLINE)) is not a biconditional of the form (**P** ↔ **Q**)
        THEN OUTPUT "Error."
    (c) IF SENTENCE(THISLINE) ≠ (**P** → **Q**)
        and SENTENCE(THISLINE) ≠ (**Q** → **P**)
        THEN OUTPUT "Error."
10. IF RULE(THISLINE) = ↔INTRO
    THEN
    (a) IF there are not just two numbers in the citation field
        THEN OUTPUT "Error."

    (b) IF SENTENCE(CIT1(THISLINE)) and SENTENCE(CIT2(THISLINE)) are not conditionals having the forms
$$(P \rightarrow Q)$$
and
$$(Q \rightarrow P)$$
respectively, where **P** and **Q** are well-formed sentences, and where SENTENCE(THISLINE) is of the form $(P \leftrightarrow Q)$
THEN OUTPUT "Error."

11. IF RULE(THISLINE) is neither one of the above nor ASSUMPTION, SEND, or RETURN
THEN OUTPUT "Error."

Step 11, the final step in CHECK-RULE, requires that the rule be one of the rules discussed in Chapters 8 and 9. The rules ASSUMPTION, SEND, and RETURN will be checked in the next procedure, CHECK-SUBPROOF.

The Procedure CHECK-SUBPROOF

We now turn to the last procedure in PROOF-CHECKER, CHECK-SUBPROOF. This procedure will certify the correctness of certain rules usually involving subproofs.

Algorithm PROOF-CHECKER, Procedure CHECK-SUBPROOF

1. IF SUBPROOF-DEPTH(line 1) > 1
THEN OUTPUT "Error."
2. IF SUBPROOF-DEPTH(line 1) = 1
and RULE(line 1) ≠ ASSUMPTION
THEN OUTPUT "Error."
3. IF SUBPROOF-DEPTH(THISLINE) is more than 1 different from SUBPROOF-DEPTH(the previous line)
THEN OUTPUT "Error."
4. IF SUBPROOF-DEPTH(THISLINE) = 1 + SUBPROOF-DEPTH(the previous line)
and RULE(THISLINE) ≠ ASSUMPTION
THEN OUTPUT "Error."
5. IF SUBPROOF-DEPTH(THISLINE) = SUBPROOF-DEPTH(the previous line) − 1
and RULE(THISLINE) ≠ RETURN
THEN OUTPUT "Error."
6. IF RULE(THISLINE) = ASSUMPTION
THEN
    (a) IF SUBPROOF-DEPTH(THISLINE) ≠
        1 + SUBPROOF-DEPTH(the previous line)
        THEN OUTPUT "Error."
    (b) IF there is a number in the citation field
        THEN OUTPUT "Error."

7. IF RULE(THISLINE) = SEND
   THEN
     (a) IF there is not just one number in the citation field
         THEN OUTPUT "Error."
     (b) IF SENTENCE(THISLINE) ≠ SENTENCE(CIT1(THISLINE))
         THEN OUTPUT "Error."
     (c) IF SUBPROOF-DEPTH(CIT1(THISLINE)) is not less than SUBPROOF-DEPTH(THISLINE)
         THEN OUTPUT "Error."
     (d) IF there is a line number n greater than CIT1(THISLINE) and less than LINENUMBER(THISLINE) such that SUBPROOF-DEPTH(n) < SUBPROOF-DEPTH(CIT1(THISLINE))
         THEN OUTPUT "Error."
8. IF RULE(THISLINE) = RETURN
   THEN
     (a) IF there is not just one number in the citation field
         THEN OUTPUT "Error."
     (b) IF RULE(CIT1(THISLINE)) is not one of →INTRO, ~INTRO, or ~ELIM
         THEN OUTPUT "Error."
     (c) IF SUBPROOF-DEPTH(CIT1(THISLINE)) ≠ SUBPROOF-DEPTH(THISLINE) + 1
         THEN OUTPUT "Error."
     (d) IF SENTENCE(THISLINE) ≠ SENTENCE(CIT1(THISLINE))
         THEN OUTPUT "Error."
     (e) IF LINENUMBER(THISLINE) ≠ CIT1(THISLINE) + 1
         THEN OUTPUT "Error."

Step 1 says that the first line cannot have more than one asterisk. Step 2 says that if the first line does have an asterisk, then the line must be justified by the rule AS-SUMPTION. That is, it must be the *beginning* of a subproof. (The first two steps differ from the remaining steps because they deal with the *first* line of the derivation, not with THISLINE. We shall have more to say on this later.)

Step 3 says that the number of asterisks in a line can change *at most* by one asterisk from the number in the previous line. Step 4 says that the *only* way a line can acquire more asterisks (greater subproof depth) than the previous line is if it uses the rule ASSUMPTION. Step 5 says that the *only* way a line can have fewer asterisks (less subproof depth) than the previous line is if it uses the rule RETURN.

The following error-ridden proof indicates the applications of these conditions.

1. **P	:PREMISE	[Violates step 1]
***2. **Q**	:ASSUMPTION	
3. **(P & Q)	:&INTRO,1,2	[Violates step 5]
***4. **((P & Q) & Q)**	:&INTRO,3,2	[Violates step 4]
5. **(P & Q)	:&ELIM,4	[Violates step 5]
6. **P**	:&ELIM,5	[Violates step 3]

Steps 6 to 8 govern the application of the justifications ASSUMPTION, SEND, and RETURN. They are included as part of CHECK-SUBPROOF rather than as part of CHECK-RULE because they are used exclusively in connection with subproofs. The primary use of SEND and RETURN, as noted in the previous chapters, is to allow us to "send" information into a subproof and to allow us to recover information gained through a subproof (the information is "returned").

If the rule used in a line is SEND, then exactly one previous line must be cited. The sentence in that line must be exactly the sentence in THISLINE: that is, SEND merely copies the sentence. Steps 7(c) and 7(d) are cumbersome to express but have a simple idea behind them: information from a lesser subproof level can be sent into a greater ("deeper") subproof level, but not vice versa. For example, consider the following correct section of a proof:

```
1.  P                    :PREMISE
*2.   Q                  :ASSUMPTION
*3.   P                  :SEND,1
*4.   (Q → P)            :→INTRO,2,3
```

Here, the information given by a premise, **P,** is merely duplicated in line 3 by using the SEND rule. The subproof depth of line 1 is 0, so it is less than the subproof depth of line 3, which is 1. Since **P** was *given* as a premise, it seems harmless to repeat it.

But consider this incorrect section of a proof:

```
1.  Q                    :PREMISE
*2.   P                  :ASSUMPTION
*3.   Q                  :SEND,1
*4.   (P → Q)            :→INTRO,2,3
5.  (P → Q)              :RETURN,4
6.  P                    :SEND,2   [Error—violates step 7 (c)]
```

Line 6 is in error because information in a subproof cannot be sent to a line of less subproof depth—at least not if we're using the SEND rule. We don't, after all, have any reason to believe that **P** is true—except when we *assumed* it in the subproof in lines 2 to 4. But in line 6 we are "out of" this subproof. And thus in the context of line 6 we have no justification for asserting **P.**

Step 8 tells us the restrictions governing the rule RETURN. As we noted, RETURN extracts information from a subproof for use in a section of the proof which is of lesser subproof depth. It "returns" information *out of* a subproof rather than sending it into one. The rule can only be used, as step 8(b) states, when the cited line is justified by →INTRO, ~INTRO, or ~ELIM. Step 8(c) ensures that RETURN moves information from a greater subproof depth to a lesser one. Step 8(d) requires that the line whose justification is RETURN merely repeats, or copies, the sentence of the line it cites. And step 8(e) checks that *new* subproofs occur at a greater subproof depth.

Finally, the last step of CHECK-SUBPROOF ensures that information is not sent into or out of subproofs *except* by the rules SEND and RETURN:

9. FOR each line L:
   (a) IF SUBPROOF-DEPTH(CIT1(L)) or SUBPROOF-DEPTH(CIT2(L)) or
       SUBPROOF-DEPTH(CIT3(L)) < SUBPROOF-DEPTH(THISLINE)
       and RULE(THISLINE) ≠ SEND
         THEN OUTPUT "Error."
   (b) IF SUBPROOF-DEPTH(CIT1(L)) or SUBPROOF-DEPTH(CIT2(L)) or
       SUBPROOF-DEPTH(CIT3(L)) > SUBPROOF-DEPTH(THISLINE)
       and RULE(THISLINE) ≠ RETURN
         THEN OUTPUT "Error."
   (c) FOR any citation in L
       IF there exists an intervening line n such that
       SUBPROOF-DEPTH(n) < SUBPROOF-DEPTH(THISLINE)
       and RULE(THISLINE) ≠ SEND
         THEN OUTPUT "Error."

This completes the last of the four procedures in ALGORITHM PROOF-CHECKER.

Applications and Modifications of Proof-Checker

Here, again, is the complete algorithm:

ALGORITHM PROOF-CHECKER

1. INPUT the derivation to be tested.
2. FOR every line of the derivation

   (a) CHECK-LINE-STRUCTURE.
   (b) CHECK-SENTENCE-STRUCTURE.
   (c) CHECK-RULE.
   (d) CHECK-SUBPROOF.

3. IF there are no errors
     THEN OUTPUT "Derivation is correct; argument is valid."
4. STOP.

Applying this algorithm would result in some unnecessary repetition of the first two steps of the procedure CHECK-SUBPROOF. These steps, it should be recalled, pertain only to the *first* line of the proof. So the examination of the first line would be needlessly repeated for every line of the proof. A more efficient algorithm might be the following:

ALGORITHM PROOF-CHECKER-1

1. INPUT the derivation to be tested.
2. Apply the procedure CHECK-SUBPROOF, steps 1 and 2.
3. FOR every line of the derivation

    (a) CHECK-LINE-STRUCTURE.
    (b) CHECK-SENTENCE-STRUCTURE.
    (c) CHECK-RULE.
    (d) CHECK-SUBPROOF, steps 3 to 9.

4. IF there are no errors
    THEN OUTPUT "Derivation is correct; argument is valid."
5. STOP.

If we are applying this algorithm ourselves, there are several tasks we can use it for. We can follow it for every line of a proof we have written. If we correctly follow the algorithm and never output "Error," then we know that our proof is correct.

Or, we might wonder if only *one line* is correct; we might be reasonably certain that the other lines are correct. It is fairly quick and simple to modify the algorithm to apply it to just one line.

Or, finally, if we are correcting a proof—noting mistakes in it—we might use the steps in the full algorithm as a shorthand to describe *how* a proof goes wrong. We might, for example, write after a mistaken line in a proof "[Error: violates CHECK-RULE 4(b)]."

For example, consider the following "proof," containing several mistakes, some of which are marked:

1. ~A	:PREMISE	
2. (B → (A & C))	:PREMISE	
*3. B	:ASSUMPTION	
*4. ~A	:SEND,1	
*5. (A & C)	:→ELIM,3,2	[Violates CHECK-RULE 3(b) and violates CHECK-SUBPROOF 8 (b)]
*6. A	:&ELIM,5	
*7. ~B	:~INTRO,3,4,6	[Violates CHECK-RULE 6(c)]
8. ~B	:RETURN,7	

CHAPTER 10

The proof can be corrected so that we obtain

```
1.  ~A              :PREMISE
2.  (B → (A & C))   :PREMISE
*3.  B              :ASSUMPTION
*4.  ~A             :SEND,1
*5.  (B → (A & C))  :SEND,2
*6.  (A & C)        :→ELIM,5,3
*7.  A              :&ELIM,6
*8.  ~B             :~INTRO,3,7,4
9.  ~B              :RETURN,8
```

We might want to add several features to the algorithm. One weakness of the algorithm is that when it encounters an error, it outputs only "Error." It does not tell us *in which line* the error occurs, nor does it tell us *how* the line is mistaken. In short, such a message is uninformative and would not be especially useful in improving the proof: We would know only that it is mistaken *somewhere.*

For example, if we input the mistaken proof we just examined into a computer programmed with ALGORITHM PROOF-CHECKER, it would print out:

Error
Error
Error

—and nothing more. We would then have a difficult time determining how to correct our proof. We would know only that there are three errors in it, somewhere. (When applying the algorithm by hand, we *see* where each error is.)

So if we were really interested in turning ALGORITHM PROOF-CHECKER into a computer program, we would surely want to make some additions—unless we were content with it merely to *count* mistakes. The two additions we would probably be most interested in are the following:

A. At every point in ALGORITHM PROOF-CHECKER where we earlier had written
   OUTPUT "Error"
   replace this with
   OUTPUT "Error at" LINENUMBER(THISLINE).
B. In the algorithm, add to every
   OUTPUT "Error"
   some clarification of the nature of the error, such as:
   Sentence not well-formed.
   2d citation is not the negation of the 3d citation.
   Sentence not the correct conjunction.
   Unknown rule.
   Rule &INTRO must have two citations.
   and so on.

Summary

This chapter presented an algorithm, PROOF-CHECKER, that takes as input a purported derivation in the natural deduction system presented in Chapters 8 and 9 and outputs one of two messages: either "Error," if the input did not follow the rules of correct proof, or "Derivation is correct; argument is valid," if the input followed all the rules.

PROOF-CHECKER works by examining the structure of each line of the derivation, since any error will show up as an error in the line structure. A *line* consists of 0 or more *asterisks* (0 for lines of the main proof; 1 or more for lines of subproofs), followed by a *whole number,* followed by a *period,* followed by a well-formed *sentence,* followed by a *colon,* followed by a *rule* of our natural deduction system, followed by a *comma,* followed by 0 to 3 *line numbers* (as citations for the rule).

There are four procedures: CHECK-LINE-STRUCTURE makes sure that each line has the correct format; if a line is incorrectly formatted, the derivation has a "grammatical" mistake. CHECK-SENTENCE-STRUCTURE makes sure that the sentence is well-formed; if a sentence is not well-formed, the derivation has a "grammatical" mistake. CHECK-RULE makes sure that the rule, together with its citations, correctly justifies the sentence; if a rule does not correctly justify the sentence, then the derivation is incorrect. CHECK-SUBPROOF makes sure that every subproof is properly written; if there are improperly written subproofs, then the derivation has a "grammatical" mistake.

Exercises

A. Use PROOF-CHECKER to locate errors in the following derivations.

1. (a)

	1. (A → B)	:PREMISE
	2. (C & ~B)	:ASSUMPTION
	3. ~B	:&ELIM,2
*4.	A	:PREMISE
*5.	B	:→ELIM,4,1
	6. ~B	:SEND,3
*7.	~A	:~INTRO,4,5,6
	8. ~A	:SEND,7

   (b) Taking the first two lines in (a) as premises, construct a correct derivation of '~A'.

2. (a)

	1. (A v (C & D))	:PREMISE
	2. (A → (C & D))	:PREMISE
*3.	~(C & D)	:PREMISE
*4.	~A	:MT,1,3
*5.	(C & D)	:vELIM,4,1
	6. (C & D)	:RETURN

   (b) Taking the first two lines in (a) as premises, construct a correct derivation of '(C & D)'.

3. (a)

	1. B	:&ELIM,1
	2. (B → (A & D))	:PREMISE
*3.	C	:ASSUMPTION
*4.	B	:RETURN,1
*5.	(C → B)	:→INTRO,4,3
	6. (C → B)	:RETURN,5
**7.	(A & D)	:→ELIM,2,1
	8. ((C → B) & (A & D))	:vINTRO,7,6

(b) Taking the first two lines of (a) as premises, construct a correct derivation of '((C → B) & (A & D))'.

4. (a)

	1. (~A ↔ B)	:PREMISE
	2. ((~A → C) & ~C)	:PREMISE
	3. (B → ~A)	:↔ELIM,1,2
*4.	B	:SEND
*5.	(B → ~A)	:SEND,3
*6.	~A	:→ELIM,3,4
*7.	(~A → C)	:SEND,2
*8.	C	:→INTRO,6,7
*9.	~C	:&ELIM,SEND,2
*10.	~B	:~INTRO,8,9,4
	11. ~B	:RETURN,10
	12. (C & ~B)	:&INTRO,8,9

(b) Taking the first two lines of (a) as premises, construct a correct derivation of '~B'.

B. Add steps to PROOF-CHECKER to check for correct use of these derivable rules:
1. *Modus tollens* (MT)
2. Hypothetical syllogism (HS)

Suggestions for Computer Implementation

The conversion of PROOF-CHECKER into a working program could be somewhat difficult, in some languages requiring a dazzling use of string functions (or a complicated use of records, if you are programming in Pascal). PROOF-CHECKER would presumably begin with the input of an entire proof—either from the user or from a file. Each line of the proof would then be checked for correctness.

Preceding this check would be an identification of each field of each line (record) in the proof. If you were to use string functions, this identification would be simplified if we had reserved specific positions in each line for specific information. For example, we might require that asterisks (or blanks) occupy the first five positions of each line— assuming that we never have the need of six nested subproofs. We might further let the line number (without its accompanying period) occupy the next three positions, the sentence positions 9 through 26, the rule positions 27 through 33, and the citations of previous line numbers positions 34 through 40. Making these changes in our format

CHECKING PROOFS

would complicate typing our proofs but would spare us from having to find fields by locating periods, numbers, and colons by string functions.

Another possibly troublesome feature is the use of commas to separate cited line numbers. Some systems perceive a comma as ending a string. Handy replacements might be the slash (/), a plus sign (+), or even a blank.

In Pascal, each line could literally be a record whose record fields are the fields of the line, simplifying CHECK-LINE-STRUCTURE. But this makes it more difficult to input the derivation.

When the proof is input, it should be stored in arrays (or some other data structure) in order to make reference to the parts of the line simpler. For example, SUBPROOF-DEPTH(n) might be a string array. For example, it might be that

SUBPROOF-DEPTH(3) = **

That is, the subproof depth of line 3 is 2 (asterisks). It would be even more convenient to store the subproof depth in a numerical array. Using this technique, it might be that

SUBPROOF-DEPTH(3) = 2

That is, the subproof depth of line 3 is 2: there are two asterisks preceding the line number.

The sentence and rule of each line can be stored in string arrays SENTENCE(n) and RULE(n), and the citations can be stored in three numerical arrays, CIT1(n), CIT2(n), and CIT3(n).

Thus the sample proof

```
1. B           :PREMISE
2. (B → C)     :PREMISE
3. C           :→ELIM,2,1
```

would be "redigested" and stored by the program as

SUBPROOF-DEPTH(1) = 0	SENTENCE(1) = B	RULE(1) = PREM
SUBPROOF-DEPTH(2) = 0	SENTENCE(2) = (B → C)	RULE(2) = PREM
SUBPROOF-DEPTH(3) = 0	SENTENCE(3) = C	RULE(3) = →ELIM

CIT1(1) = 0	CIT2(1) = 0	CIT3(1) = 0
CIT1(2) = 0	CIT2(2) = 0	CIT3(2) = 0
CIT1(3) = 2	CIT2(3) = 1	CIT3(3) = 0

Data structures such as these allow very handy reference to the fields of each line of the proof. For example, because RULE(3) = →ELIM, it should be the case that

SENTENCE(CIT1(3)) = (SENTENCE(CIT2(3)) → SENTENCE(3))

or, in English, that the sentence referred to by the first citation of line 3 should be identical to the string composed of the sentence referred to by the second citation of line 3, followed by an arrow, followed by the sentence in line 3.

Exercises

Those who are familiar with programming might want to attempt the following exercises.

A. Choose an appropriate data structure for a line (for example, a string, a list, a record, or an array), and write an algorithm that takes a line as input and outputs a message stating whether the line is properly formatted.
B. Write a program that inputs an entire proof, identifies the relevant fields of each line using our original format (with periods and colons), and places these items into appropriate arrays (or another data structure).
C. Write a section of a program that implements the procedure CHECK-LINE-STRUC-TURE. You may assume that the proof has already been input into an appropriate data structure.
D. Write a section of a program that implements the procedure CHECK-SUBPROOF. You may assume that the proof has already been input into an appropriate data structure.
E. Assuming that a proof has already been input into an appropriate data structure, write a program to determine if the rule →ELIM has been appropriately applied.
F. Do the same for the rule &INTRO.
G. Do the same for the rule →INTRO.
H. Again assuming that a proof has already been input into an appropriate data structure, write a program that checks the application of the rules &ELIM, &INTRO, ~ELIM, and ~INTRO. (Recall that these connectives are sufficient to express all the logic of sentences and thus that CHECK-RULE is in a sense complete when these four rules have been tested for correctness.)

CHAPTER 11

SENTENTIAL LOGIC:
A Method for
Producing Proofs

We now take up the second of our two questions from Chapter 10: how to *construct* a proof of a valid argument given the premises and the conclusion. We could give an algorithm for constructing a proof, in the logic of sentences, for any premises and any conclusion validly following from them. But the resulting algorithm would be either very long or "unnatural" (in failing to follow the "natural" inferential rules we gave in Chapters 8 and 9). Consequently, we shall not aim in this chapter to give the full algorithm for constructing a derivation. We shall instead content ourselves with describing a method for constructing a proof that will work *most* of the time. That is, in some cases, some creative intervention by a human user might be required. We shall call this method PROOF-GIVER.

CHAPTER 11

General Strategies for Constructing Proofs

The task we face in constructing a derivation of a conclusion from given premises seems, at first, like nothing we have ever done before. Consequently, the beginner might feel somewhat lost when it comes to constructing a proof. But, in fact, the construction of a proof in logic is a great deal like problems we regularly solve without much difficulty. The construction of a proof also resembles tasks for which computers (and hence algorithms) are regularly employed.

Analogous Problems

One task analogous to constructing proofs is the problem of finding our way through a maze.

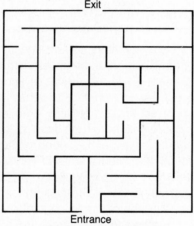

Figure 11-1   A maze.

We all quickly recognize what the goal is: to find a path through the maze, beginning at the entrance and coming out at the exit, without crossing a line (a "wall"). Finding our way through a maze might not seem at first much like constructing a proof. But the two problems have some interesting similarities. In a maze, we are always told where to begin (at the "entrance"). In constructing a proof in logic, we are also told where to begin: with our *premises*. The premises are our "entrance" to a logic puzzle. In a maze, we are also told where we are supposed to end up (at the "exit"). In constructing a proof in logic, our goal also lies clearly before us: the conclusion, which we must somehow reach.

In finding our way through a maze, certain methods of proceeding are allowed, and others are forbidden to us. We may turn left or right or go straight ahead, but we are not allowed to "jump over" or "go through" a wall. In a proof in logic, there are certain maneuvers that are allowed: these are the rules of our natural deduction system: &ELIM, →INTRO, and so on. But certain maneuvers are denied to us: we are not allowed to infer any old sentence we would like.

As it will turn out, the *strategies* we use in finding a way through a maze and in constructing a proof are quite similar. In finding our way through a maze on paper, we

PRODUCING PROOFS

might visually start at the entrance and see where we can go from there. Or we might glance ahead to our goal, the exit, and see how we might get there. That is, we might glance ahead to see what routes *lead to* the exit. In constructing a proof in logic, there are also two basic strategies. We might look at the premises and see what follows from them by the rules that are permitted to us. Or we might look ahead and see how the conclusion might come about through using the known rules.

Another analogous task is a more practical problem that a computer—in the hands of an able travel agent—is frequently used to solve. Suppose that you must fly from Chicago to New Orleans but that, unfortunately, there are no direct flights at the time, you want to make your trip. Suppose that the relevant flights have the following pattern:

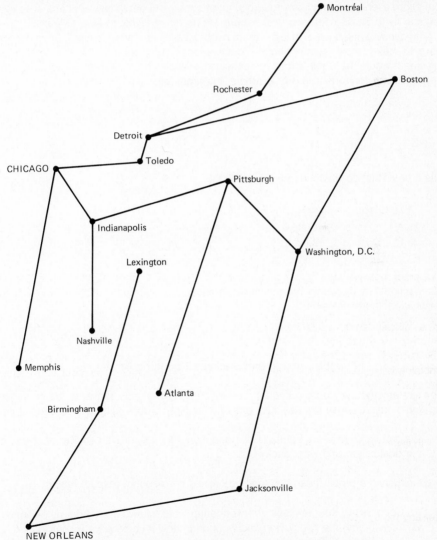

Figure 11-2 Flights with connections to Chicago and New Orleans.

Just as with the maze and with constructing a proof in logic, there are "dead ends" that will not lead to our destination, and there are sometimes *several* ways to reach our destination—some that are shorter and some that are longer. The strategies we might use to solve this flight problem are like the strategies we might use to find our way through a maze. For example, we might use a finger to trace a path beginning with Chicago, or we might use a finger to trace a path backward from New Orleans. We might even combine the two strategies to see where they meet.

The flight problem has some features that make it more like a logic problem than the maze. In order to fly from Chicago to New Orleans, we might first have to fly to other cities—Atlanta, for example. In the jargon of a travel agent, these are our "connections." We might even have to go considerably out of our way to get to New Orleans: we might have to fly to Seattle, for example, if there are no direct flights to New Orleans.

In constructing a proof in logic, there might also be no "direct flights." We might first have to make "trips" to intermediate "destinations." A "direct flight" in the proof of an argument would be one in which the conclusion follows from the premises through the application of only one rule. For example, the argument

$$(A \rightarrow B)$$
$$A$$
$$\therefore \ B$$

has a proof that corresponds to a direct flight:

1. $(A \rightarrow B)$:PREMISE
2. A   :PREMISE
3. B   :$\rightarrow$ELIM,1,2

In a proof, however, we do not often have the luxury of a "direct flight"; we must make "connections" by deducing intermediate sentences that eventually allow us to reach our destination: the conclusion.

Forward-Looking and Backward-Looking Strategies

The strategy used in constructing a proof will be so remarkably similar to the strategies we would ordinarily use to solve the maze and the flight problems that it bears repeating.

We can begin with our starting point and work forward, or we can glance ahead to our destination and work backward.

In constructing a proof, these two methods would correspond, respectively, to

1. Considering the premises and wondering what follows from them by our rules.
2. Considering the conclusion and wondering how it could arise by our rules.

PRODUCING PROOFS

For several reasons, method 2—looking ahead to the destination (our conclusion) and working backward—will turn out to be especially fruitful in logic.

There is one big difference between the logical problem of constructing a proof and the maze and flight problems. This difference will make approaching the construction of a proof with a strategy all the more important. The difference is that the *ways* we get from our point of departure to our destination in the maze and flight problems are few in number. In the maze problem, we move in any direction we wish, so long as we don't cross a line; in the flight problem, we move along connecting lines. But in the logical problem of "departing from" the premises and "arriving at" the conclusion, there are at any point *many* different rules we could use. Still worse, there are in the construction of a proof many more "intermediate destinations" than in the case of the flight from Chicago to New Orleans. There are in fact an infinite number (so we could not even chart the options, as we did in the Chicago–New Orleans case). And most of these intermediate destinations are blind alleys: they do not get us any closer to our destination—the conclusion. We must then plan our proof very carefully. And to plan our proof, we must have a *method* for creating the plan—a plan for making plans, if you wish. This method for creating plans for a proof is the purpose of PROOF-GIVER.

Consider the following argument:

A

$(A \rightarrow (B \rightarrow C))$

∴ $(B \rightarrow C)$

The argument is valid. But how do we produce a proof? We first begin by examining the premises, the conclusion, and their connection. We see that the conclusion is a conditional, '$(B \rightarrow C)$'. Furthermore, we should observe that this very same conditional is part of one of the premises: $(A \rightarrow (B \rightarrow C))$, the second premise. Reflecting briefly on this premise and its main connective, $\rightarrow$, we see that if we could somehow *eliminate* this connective (and the antecedent 'A') from the premise, we would be left with the desired result: $(B \rightarrow C)$. But, of course, to eliminate $\rightarrow$, we just apply the $\rightarrow$ELIM rule. To apply it, we need the antecedent 'A', which, conveniently, is the first premise.

The proof resulting from these observations is:

1. A   :PREMISE
2. $(A \rightarrow (B \rightarrow C))$:PREMISE
3. $(B \rightarrow C)$:$\rightarrow$ELIM,2,1

This proof resulted from our observation that the desired conclusion is a *subformula* of one of the premises. We then reasoned how this subformula could be derived by itself on a line. Obtaining a subformula by itself will typically involve the use of an ELIM rule.

But consider the following argument:

B

∴ $((A \rightarrow C) \rightarrow B)$

Here, the conclusion is not a subformula of a premise. The lengthy conclusion is not embedded anywhere in the simple premise. What information *do* we have to go on in determining our strategy for the proof? Even though we cannot see the relationship of the conclusion to the premises (as we did in the previous example), we can examine the structure of the conclusion itself. It is, again, a conditional. How could a conditional arise in a proof? It might well come from an application of →INTRO. (In fact, it is difficult in this example to see how a conditional could be arrived at other than through → INTRO.)

So we might guess that one step in the proof uses →INTRO. But what previous lines could produce '((A → C) → B)' by →INTRO? The answer is this. If '(A → C)' were an ASSUMPTION and 'B' were a later line in the same subproof, then '((A → C) → B)' could be inferred by →INTRO. A good guess, then, is that the proof proceeds as follows:

```
1.  B                      :PREMISE
*2.  (A → C)               :ASSUMPTION
       .                      .
       .                      .
       .                      .
*?.  B                     :?
*?.  ((A → C) → B)         :→INTRO,?,?
?.  ((A → C) → B)          :RETURN,?
```

The dots and question marks indicate parts of the proof yet to be filled in. The only mystery is how to derive 'B'. That, however, is easy to guess in this example: it was "sent" into the subproof from the premise, 'B'. The resulting proof, with comment lines inserted, is:

```
1. B                       :PREMISE
       /BEGIN: →INTRO to derive ((A → C) → B)/
*2.  (A → C)               :ASSUMPTION
*3.  B                     :SEND,1
*4.  ((A → C) → B)         :→INTRO,2,3
       /END:   →INTRO to derive ((A → C) → B)/
5.  ((A → C) → B)          :RETURN,4
```

These two examples give us the basis of a *strategy* for creating proofs. An overall view of the method we have just seen applied in devising a strategy is:

1. If the conclusion is a subformula in a previous line, then use the appropriate ELIM rule to isolate this subformula on its own line.

2. If the conclusion is not a subformula of a previous line, then examine the structure of this conclusion, and use the appropriate INTRO rule to reconstruct the conclusion.

These two suggestions are the basic elements in PROOF-GIVER.

In building up a derivation, we shall need two items. The first is simply the ongoing derivation. It will be composed of the steps of the proof, as far as we have gotten. The second item is what we shall call the *task list*. The task list will be our list of the steps yet needed to complete the proof. The task list is best thought of as our notes to ourselves on how to complete the proof. In this respect, the task list is little more than what we have been calling "comments."

This task list can be written immediately following any portion of the proof we have completed (or it can be kept in a separate place) and constitutes instructions on our "plan of attack" for how best to complete the proof. When we are first given the premises and the conclusion that validly follows from them, the first instruction is to *derive* that conclusion. We would write:

PROOF
   1. A   :PREMISE
   2. $(A \rightarrow (B \rightarrow C))$:PREMISE

TASK LIST
   Derive $(B \rightarrow C)$

The last line, 'Derive $(B \rightarrow C)$', is our first task and so is the sole item in our task list at the beginning of our attempt to create a proof.

The rest of the method consists of replacing 'Derive <the conclusion>' with more helpful advice; accordingly, the task list grows. Furthermore, as some of these tasks become precise enough to be turned into lines of a proof, the proof itself also grows.

Tree-Searching Strategies

One of the main areas of research in artificial intelligence concerns the topic of a "search": how to program computers to find solutions or reach goals by guided, or "intelligent," methods (including trial and error), rather than by "exhaustively" searching all possibilities. The possession of such methods seems to be essential for anything claiming to employ "intelligence."

We have already drawn some parallels between the problem of constructing a proof and other problems that require a search. Let us now display with more precision what our search looks like when we are attempting to construct a proof.

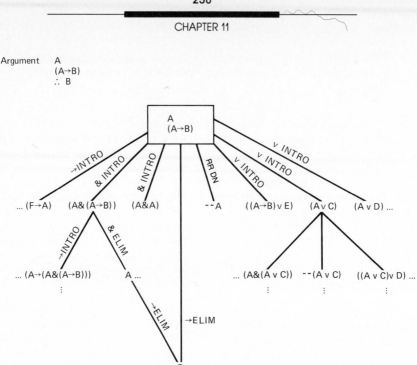

Figure 11-3 Search tree for the argument A, (A → B), ∴ B.

Such diagrams are called "trees." Our starting point is the set of our premises. Our goal is the conclusion. After correctly applying a rule, we call the point that we have reached a *node* of the tree. At this node, we write the new sentence that the rule allowed us to derive. We also have available at this node any of the previous sentences—the sentences we have derived *above* this node. We can apply any of the rules to these available sentences. (Another way of thinking about the proof-search tree is that at each node there is a *set* of "available" sentences. This set "grows" each time a rule is applied, and we can stop when the conclusion is included in the new set.) Such a display is called a *search tree,* and what it displays is called the *search space* of the problem.

Acceptable means of "traveling" from the premises to the conclusion are restricted by the available rules. Let us now introduce some terminology. We can measure the *distance* of a sentence from the premises (or the conclusion) by the number of rules used on the shortest path between the premises and the sentence. For example, all the sentences on the first row below the premises have a distance of one unit from the premises.

We can now make some observations about the above display of a rather typical proof problem.

1. The number of sentences in the tree whose distance is one unit from the premises is *infinite*—no matter what the premises are. The rules vINTRO and →INTRO can be used to add indefinitely many new nodes.

2. If there is one path through the tree from the premises to the conclusion, then there are an infinite number of such paths.
3. If there is a path of length *n* from the premises to the conclusion, then there is also a path of still greater length.
4. There are an infinite number of sentences whose distances are one unit from the conclusion.
5. The tree branches endlessly into directions that are not especially close to the premises or conclusion.

The job of PROOF-GIVER is to find a reasonably short path from the premises to the conclusion. Two strategies for searching a tree for a particular node are the "breadth-first" search and the "depth-first" search, illustrated in Figure 11-4.

A *breadth-first search* considers, first, all the nodes that are one unit distant from the starting node. Then it considers all the nodes that are one unit distant from *those* nodes, and so on until the goal is reached. It is a search which seeks its goal by first checking out all the nearest nodes from the starting node, then the next-nearest nodes, and so on.

Consider this analogy. In conducting a breadth-first search for a lost dollar, I might begin by visiting *all* the places where I might have lost it and only then turn to more "distant" options—for example, that I dropped it on the sidewalk, but it then blew away.

A breadth-first search of our proof tree would not be a reasonable way of discovering a proof. The number of sentences one unit distant from our premises is infinite (as we observed above). So we would first have to consider *all* of these sentences before going further with the search. But this first step would itself take forever. In short, a breadth-first search is not reasonable when our search tree has "unlimited branching," which rules such as vINTRO and →INTRO permit.

Although an "all-out" breadth-first search would not be feasible in our case, we might consider a limited breadth-first search. For example, we might ignore certain of the branches. (Carrying on the "tree" metaphor, researchers in artificial intelligence speak of this technique as "pruning" the tree.) The branches we might ignore would be:

1. Branches that use vINTRO or →INTRO and result in a sentence containing an atomic sentence that is contained in neither the premises nor the conclusion
2. Branches that use &INTRO and result in a sentence that is not contained as a subformula in any of the premises or in the conclusion
3. Branches that use &ELIM and result in a sentence that is neither a subformula of any premise or conclusion nor are the premises or conclusion a subformula of the sentence.

The result of this limited breadth-first search would be a much-pruned search tree that would usually reach the conclusion. But the tree would still often be quite large.

The second major search strategy is a *depth-first search*. In depth-first search, we make a single, deep plunge into the search tree, hoping to catch our quarry, the goal, in one quick thrust. This strategy contrasts with the many, equally shallow plunges (or "guesses") of breadth-first search. The depth-first strategy might also be described as pursuing our "best guesses" as far as we can take them.

CHAPTER 11

The Breadth—first Strategy

First Stage

Starting point

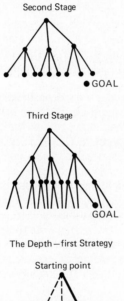

● GOAL

Second Stage

● GOAL

Third Stage

GOAL

The Depth—first Strategy

Starting point

GOAL

Figure 11-4 Breadth-first and depth-first search strategies.

The Method: PROOF-GIVER

Several concepts will be useful in our presentation of PROOF-GIVER. First, recall the notion of subproof depth from Chapter 10. A subproof of any depth may be said to *contain* itself. A subproof S of depth n may be said to *contain* a subproof S' of a depth greater than n iff there is no line with fewer than n stars between the last line of S and

PRODUCING PROOFS

the first line of S'. In particular, the main proof (which is a subproof of depth 0) contains itself and all subproofs of any depth.

Intuitively, proofs can be pictured as "nested boxes," as in Figure 11-5.

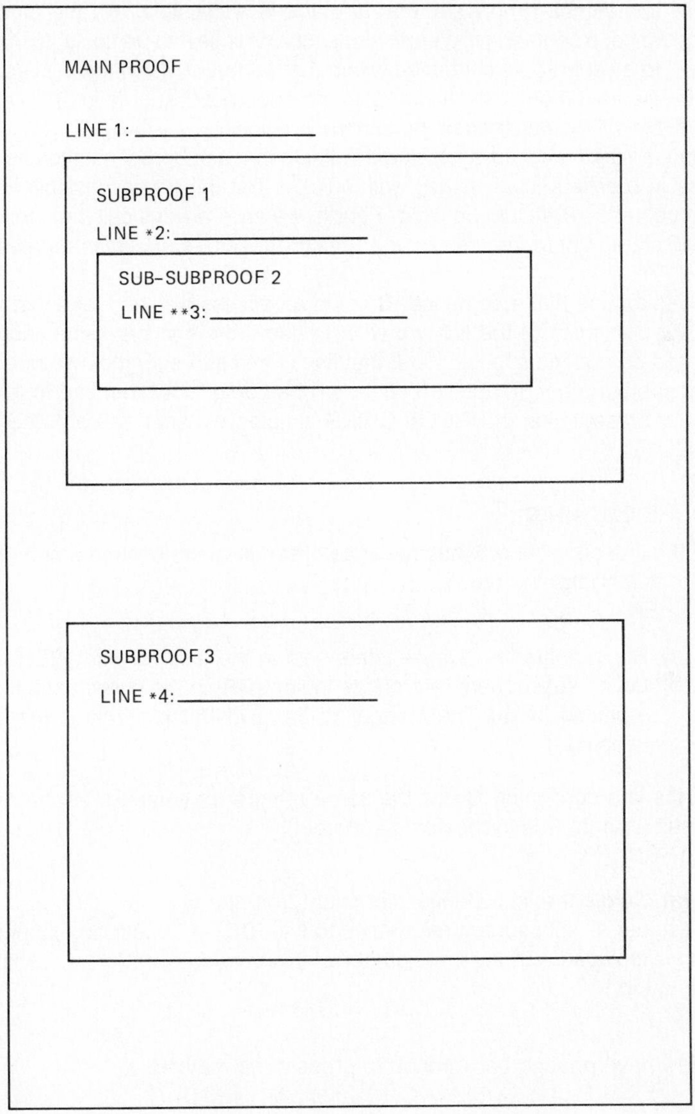

MAIN PROOF

LINE 1: _____

> SUBPROOF 1
> LINE *2: _____
>
> > SUB–SUBPROOF 2
> > LINE **3: _____

> SUBPROOF 3
> LINE *4: _____

Figure 11-5 Diagram of a proof.

In Figure 11-5, the main proof contains itself and all three subproofs. The first subproof contains only itself and subproof 2. The second and third subproofs contain only themselves.

We can now say that a line L is *accessible* to a later line L' iff the subproof that L is in contains the subproof that L' is in. For instance, in Figure 11-5, line 1 is accessible to lines in all subproofs, line 2 is only accessible to lines in subproofs 1 and 2, line 3 is only accessible to lines in subproof 2, and line 4 is only accessible to lines in subproof 3. We shall sometimes simply say that "the line is accessible." (In the terminology of computer science, a sentence in a particular subproof is said to be "local" to that subproof and "global" to all subproofs contained within that subproof. Thus line L is accessible to line L' iff the sentence on line L is global to the subproof that L' is in or L and L' are in the same subproof, in which case the sentence is local.)

Second, an asterisk before a task will indicate that a subproof must be begun. Third, a sentence in brackets, such as [**P**], will indicate that the first accessible line number containing sentence **P** should be cited. Fourth, we shall always call the sentence in the first 'Derive' statement in the task list the "desired result," sometimes representing it as '**DR**'.

Finally, suppose that a sentence, **Q**, is on an accessible line L and that we wish to use **Q** in our derivation. If the line we wish to use it on is in the same subproof as L, then we need do nothing special. But if that line is in a sub-subproof, we need to SEND **Q** into that sub-subproof. In addition, there will be some "bookkeeping" to take care of. To make our presentation of PROOF-GIVER simpler, we shall use a procedure called 'OBTAIN **Q**':

PROCEDURE OBTAIN **Q**

1. IF the line containing **Q** has fewer asterisks than the desired result (that is, **Q** is in a containing proof)
   THEN

   (a) Replace the first 'Derive' statement in the task list with: SEND,[**Q**].
   (b) Let all subsequent references to line [**DR**] in the current subproof be replaced by the line number of this SEND line. (This is the "book-keeping.")

2. IF the line containing **Q** has the same number of asterisks as the desired result (that is, **Q** is in the same subproof)
   THEN

   (a) Delete the first 'Derive' statement from the task list
   (b) Let all subsequent references to line [**DR**] in the current subproof be replaced with the line number of this previous line (more "bookkeeping").

We now have enough background to present the method.

METHOD PROOF-GIVER:

1. INPUT the premises, with the justification 'PREMISE', in the standard format for proofs.
2. Add 'Derive ⟨conclusion⟩' to the task list.

3. WHILE the task list is not empty and there is a 'Derive' statement in the task list, keep repeating (a) to (c):

   (a) IF **DR** = a subformula of a sentence, **Q,** on an accessible line THEN

   (i) OBTAIN **Q.**
   (ii) IF **DR** = **Q**
        THEN GO TO step 3(c).
   (iii) IF **DR** is a proper subformula of **Q**
         THEN

         (1) IF **Q** is a conditional
             and the desired result is a subformula of **Q**'s consequent
                THEN replace the first 'Derive' statement in the task list
                with:
                Derive ⟨antecedent of **Q**⟩
                Apply →ELIM,[**Q**],[⟨antecedent of **Q**⟩]
                Derive **DR** (if **DR** ≠ ⟨consequent of **Q**⟩)
             and GO TO step 3(c).

         (2) IF **Q** is a conjunction
             and the desired result is a subformula of one of its conjuncts
                THEN replace the first 'Derive' statement in the task list
                with:
                Apply &ELIM,[**Q**] (to obtain conjunct containing **DR**)
                Derive **DR** (if **DR** ≠ the inferred conjunct)
             and GO TO step 3(c).

         (3) IF **Q** is a disjunction, (**P** v **R**),
             and the desired result is a subformula of one of its disjuncts,
             say **R**
                THEN replace the first 'Derive' statement in the task list
                with:
                Derive ~**P**
                Apply vELIM, [**Q**],[~**P**]
                Derive **DR** (if **DR** ≠ **R**)
             and GO TO step 3(c).

         (4) IF **Q** is a negation, say ~**P**, and **DR** is a subformula of **P**, say
             R
                THEN replace the first 'Derive' statement in the task list
                with:
                *Assume ~**R**
                *OBTAIN **Q**
                *Derive **P**
                *Apply ~ELIM,[~**R**],[**P**],[**Q**]
                RETURN,[**R**]
             and GO TO step 3(c).

(b) IF **DR** is not a subformula of a sentence on an accessible line meeting the above conditions
   THEN

   (i) IF the desired result has the form (**P** → **Q**)
       THEN replace the first 'Derive (**P** → **Q**)' in the task list with:
       *Assume **P**
       *Derive **Q**
       *Apply →INTRO,[**P**],[**Q**]
       Apply RETURN,[**P** → **Q**]
       and GO TO step 3(c).

   (ii) IF the desired result has the form (**P** & **Q**)
       THEN replace the first 'Derive (**P** & **Q**)' in the task list with:
       Derive **P**
       Derive **Q**
       Apply &INTRO,[**P**],[**Q**]
       and GO TO step 3(c).

   (iii) IF the desired result has the form (**P** v **Q**)
       THEN replace the first 'Derive' statement in the task list either with:
       (1) *Assume ~(**P** v **Q**)
           *Derive **R**
           *Derive ~**R**
           *Apply ~ELIM,[~(**P** v **Q**)],[**R**],[~**R**]
           RETURN,[(**P** v **Q**)]
       or with:
       (2) Derive **P**
           Apply vINTRO,[**P**] to obtain (**P** v **Q**)
       or with:
       (3) Derive **Q**
           Apply vINTRO,[**Q**] to obtain (**P** v **Q**)
       and GO TO step 3(c).

   (iv) IF the desired result has the form ~**P**
       THEN replace the first 'Derive ~**P**' in the task list with:
       *Assume **P**
       *Derive **R**
       *Derive ~**R**
       *Apply ~INTRO,[**P**],[**R**],[~**R**]
       RETURN,[~**P**]
       and GO TO step 3(c).

   (v) IF none of the previous steps have been applied
       THEN replace the first 'Derive **P**' in the task list with:
       *Assume ~**P**
       *Derive **R**

      *Derive ~**R**
      *Apply ~ELIM,[~**P**], [**R**], [~**R**]
      RETURN,[**P**]
    and GO TO step 3(c).

   (c) Convert all statements in the task list that precede the first 'Derive' statement into lines of proof, removing them from the task list.

4. STOP.

Applications of PROOF-GIVER

Let us now apply the method to an argument:

   A
   B
   D
∴ ((A & B) & (C → D))

Following steps 1 and 2 of PROOF-GIVER, we obtain:

   PROOF
     1. A   :PREMISE
     2. B   :PREMISE
     3. D   :PREMISE

   TASK LIST
     Derive ((A & B) & (C → D))

The desired result is '((A & B) & (C → D))'. At step 3(a) we can see that it does *not* appear in the previous lines (the premises), so we pass on to step 3(b).

    Since the desired result is a *conjunction,* step 3(b)(ii) applies, and we replace the original 'Derive ((A & B) & (C → D))' in our task list with:

   Derive (A & B)
   Derive (C → D)
   Apply &INTRO,[(A & B)],[(C → D)]

obtaining:

   PROOF
     1. A   :PREMISE
     2. B   :PREMISE
     3. D   :PREMISE

TASK LIST
  Derive (A & B)
  Derive (C → D)
  Apply &INTRO,[(A & B)],[(C → D)]

We now go to step 3(c), which returns us to step 3(a).

At this point, '(A & B)' becomes our "desired result." It is a conjunction, so again step 3(b)(ii) is applied, resulting in:

PROOF
  1. A   :PREMISE
  2. B   :PREMISE
  3. D   :PREMISE

TASK LIST
  Derive A
  Derive B
  Apply &INTRO,[A],[B]
  Derive (C → D)
  Apply &INTRO,[(A & B)],[(C → D)]

After step 3(c), we again return to step 3(a). Now, however, the desired result is simply 'A', and it *is* contained in a previous line—namely, it is identical to the first premise. So, step 3(a)(i) requires us to *delete* the first 'Derive' statement and replace references to [A] with 1. Looking at the task list only, we see that the result is:

Derive B
Apply &INTRO,1,[B]
Derive (C → D)
Apply &INTRO,[(A & B)],[(C → D)]

Since there is a 'Derive' statement at the top of the task list, step 3(c) again returns us to step 3(a).

Now the desired result is 'B', which is identical to the second premise. After following the directions in the appropriate clause of step 3(a), we find that our task list looks like this:

Apply &INTRO,1,2
Derive (C → D)
Apply &INTRO,[(A & B)],[(C → D)]

We again drop down to step 3(c), but this time we do not simply return to step 3(a). It tells us to convert the first line in the task list, 'Apply &INTRO,1,2', into a line of proof. The result is:

PROOF
  1. A   :PREMISE
  2. B   :PREMISE
  3. D   :PREMISE
  4. (A & B)   :&INTRO,1,2

TASK LIST
  Derive $(C \rightarrow D)$
  Apply &INTRO,4,$[(C \rightarrow D)]$

Returning to step 3(a), we see that our desired result is now, $(C \rightarrow D)$'. It is *not* contained in a previous line, including our newly acquired line 4, so we proceed to step 3(b). The desired result is a *conditional,* so, applying 3(b) (i), we find that our task list becomes:

  *Assume C
  *Derive D
  *Apply $\rightarrow$INTRO,[C],[D]
  Apply RETURN,$[(C \rightarrow D)]$
  Apply &INTRO,4,$[(C \rightarrow D)]$

Dropping down to step 3(c), we must convert every statement that occurs in the task files before the first 'Derive' statement into a new line of proof. We obtain:

PROOF
  1. A   :PREMISE
  2. B   :PREMISE
  3. D   :PREMISE
  4. (A & B)   :&INTRO,1,2
  *5. C   :ASSUMPTION

TASK LIST
  *Derive D
  *Apply $\rightarrow$INTRO,5,[D]
  Apply RETURN,$[(C \rightarrow D)]$
  Apply &INTRO,4,$[(C \rightarrow D)]$

Returning to step 3(a), we see that 'D' is now the desired result. It is part of a previous sentence, so step 3(a)(i) applies. Following those directions, we have in the task list:

  *SEND,3
  *Apply $\rightarrow$INTRO,5,[D]
  Apply RETURN,$[(C \rightarrow D)]$
  Apply &INTRO,4,$[(C \rightarrow D)]$

Dropping down to step 3(c), we now see that there are *no* 'Derive' statements left in the task list. This means that all instructions in the task list must be converted into lines of proof. Applying the instructions in the task list line by line, we obtain the following result:

```
 1.  A                          :PREMISE
 2.  B                          :PREMISE
 3.  D                          :PREMISE
 4.  (A & B)                    :&INTRO,1,2
*5.  C                          :ASSUMPTION
*6.  D                          :SEND,3
*7.  (C → D)                    :→INTRO,5,6
 8.  (C → D)                    :RETURN,7
 9.  ((A & B) & (C → D))        :&INTRO,4,8
```

Limitations of PROOF-GIVER

PROOF-GIVER, as we have described it, falls short of being a true algorithm. The construction of proofs for *some* arguments requires imagination or inspiration. The short-comings of PROOF-GIVER fall into three major areas.

First, the application of several rules requires the user of the procedure to make additional "guesses." Chief among these are arguments that take us to steps 3(b)(iii), 3(b)(iv), and 3(b)(v). Although many steps in PROOF-GIVER could be straightforwardly translated into algorithms, these steps are not among them. Step 3(b)(iii) requires us to *choose* among three ways of introducing a disjunction. Steps 3(b)(iv) and 3(b)(v) require us to derive a contradiction: some sentence, **R,** on one line and its negation, ~**R,** on another. But *which* sentence and its negation should be derived? This is left to our own invention.

The second and third parts of step 3(b)(iii) apply the rule vINTRO. There is no ambiguity concerning what to derive. But this technique will not always work; where it does work, it works easily. So we find ourselves in a dilemma: the first technique, of indirect proof, always works (and so is listed first) but requires "creativity" to find a contradiction. The second method does not always work, but when it does, it requires no creativity.

The kinds of cases where the two different techniques of 3(b)(iii) are appropriate can be illustrated by two examples.

Consider:

(A & B)
∴ (A v C)

Using the first technique, we start with:

PROOF
  1. (A & B)   :PREMISE

TASK LIST
    Derive (A v C)

Then we have (by step 3(b)(iii)(2)):

PROOF
    1. (A & B)   :PREMISE

TASK LIST
    Derive A
    Apply vINTRO,[A] to obtain (A v C)

Going back to step 3(a), we arrive at step 3(a)(iii)(2), which results in:

PROOF
    1. (A & B)   :PREMISE

TASK LIST
    Apply &ELIM,1 to obtain A
    Apply vINTRO,[A] to obtain (A v C)

And finally, after step 3(c) is performed, we have:

PROOF
1. (A & B)   :PREMISE
2. A   :&ELIM,1
3. (A v C)   :vINTRO,2

    Step 3(b)(iii)(1) could also be applied—since it *always* works. Its application might result in:

PROOF
1. (A & B)   :PREMISE
*2. ~(A v C)   :ASSUMPTION
*3. (A & B)   :SEND,1
*4. A   :&ELIM,3
*5. (A v C)   :vINTRO,4
*6. (A v C)   :~ELIM,2,5,2
7. (A v C)   :RETURN,6

In this proof, '(A v C)' functions as the **R**. This choice of **R** results in citing line 2 *twice:* once as the assumption of the ~ELIM, and again as part of the contradiction. The unusual appearance of line 6 of this proof is in fact a symptom that there is an easier way to construct a proof of '(A v C)'—namely, using the vINTRO strategy.

    Sometimes, however, the vINTRO option in 3(b)(iii) cannot be applied successfully at all. In these cases, we *must* resort to the longer, indirect method of proof. This unfortunate circumstance will arise when neither disjunct of the desired disjunction is derivable *by itself.* Consider, for example, the following argument:

(A v B)
(A → C)
(B → D)
∴ (C v D)

The "natural" strategy might be to derive '(C v D)' by first deriving 'C' or 'D' and then applying vINTRO. But in this example, the sad fact is that 'C' alone cannot be derived, and neither can 'D'. So we would find ourselves blocked if we tried to use step 3(b)(iii)(2) on this argument:

PROOF
   1. (A v B)   :PREMISE
   2. (A → C)   :PREMISE
   3. (B → D)   :PREMISE

TASK LIST
   Derive C   [You should note that 'Derive D' is just as bad.]
   Apply vINTRO,[C] to obtain (C v D)

We could *never* derive C from these premises—a fact that could be shown by using truth tables—and so the task list would never be emptied. Hence, we could never complete the proof with these instructions.

A successful proof, using step 3(b)(iii)(1), would be:

   1. (A v B)   :PREMISE
   2. (A → C)   :PREMISE
   3. (B → D)   :PREMISE
*4.   ~(C v D)   :ASSUMPTION
*5.   (~C & ~D)   :RR DM,4
*6.   (A → C)   :SEND,2
*7.   (B → D)   :SEND,3
*8.   (A v B)   :SEND,1
*9.   ~C   :&ELIM,5
*10. ~A   :MT,9,6
*11. B   :vELIM,8,10
*12. ~D   :&ELIM,5
*13. ~B   :MT,7,12
*14. (C v D)   :~ELIM,4,11,13
   15. (C v D)   :RETURN,14

In this proof, the contradiction derived involved the sentences 'B' and '~B'. This was, however, a matter of choice (and discovery): contradictions *could* be derived involving the sentences 'A' and '~A', or 'C' and '~C', or even '(A v B)' and '~(A v B)'. PROOF-GIVER can help get us to line 4; after that, we're on our own.

Step 3(b)(iv) also cannot easily be transformed into a mechanical procedure, for it requires us to derive contradictory sentences **R** and ~**R**, but we are not told which sentences this might involve.

A second difficulty with PROOF-GIVER is that it builds a task list based on whether a sentence is *identical* to a previous sentence or subformula in the derivation. Sometimes, however, a sentence might not be exactly identical to a previous sentence but might be *logically equivalent* to it. Consider this argument:

(~A & ~B)
(~(A v B) → C)
∴ C

Our task list would at first contain only:

Derive C

Since sentence 'C' is contained in the second premise, PROOF-GIVER would then direct us to step 3(a)(iii)(1), at which point the task list would become:

Derive ~(A v B)
Apply →ELIM,2,[~(A v B)]

But how do we derive '~(A v B)'? Glancing at our list of logical equivalences, we might see that '~(A v B)' is logically equivalent to '(~A & ~B)' and so can be derived in one step using the rule RR DM. But PROOF-GIVER does not see this and notices only that the two are not *identical*. PROOF-GIVER directs us to step 3(b)(iv).

PROOF-GIVER could be corrected to allow it to "see" logical equivalences as identities and then use RR. In other words, every time PROOF-GIVER refers to "identical" sentences, we could replace this with "identical or logically equivalent" sentences. But then, unfortunately, *testing* to see whether a sentence might be logically equivalent to a previous sentence or subformula would consume almost all the time used in applying PROOF-GIVER. Consequently, the astute user of PROOF-GIVER should keep a sharp eye out for when a rule of replacement might be used. But such equivalences will not be built into PROOF-GIVER.

A still worse problem is that we can occasionally be "hung up" at step 3(a), when we should go to step 3(b). Consider the following argument:

(A → (B & C))
B
C
∴ (B & C)

After performing steps 1 and 2 of PROOF-GIVER, we have:

PROOF
   1. (A → (B & C))   :PREMISE
   2. B   :PREMISE
   3. C   :PREMISE

TASK LIST
    Derive (B & C)

We now go to step 3(a), because the desired result, '(B & C)', is contained in an earlier line (the first premise). After step 3(a)(iii)(1) we have:

PROOF
    1. (A → (B & C))   :PREMISE
    2. B   :PREMISE
    3. C   :PREMISE

TASK LIST
    Derive A
    Apply →ELIM,1,[A]

But it is easy to see—and could be shown by a truth table—that 'A' does not validly follow from the premises. Consequently, we would never be able to derive 'A' on a line by itself. (More precisely, we would never be able to eliminate all the 'Derive' statements from the task list for this argument, once it is begun in this way.)

The problem lies with step 3(a). Whenever the desired result is a subformula of an accessible line, step 3(a) applies. But *sometimes* the desired result can *only* be derived by using parts of step 3(b). As an example, if we went to step 3(b)(ii) instead of step 3(a), we would have in the task list

Derive B
Derive C
Apply &INTRO,[B],[C]

which would eventually result in this proof:

    1. (A → (B & C))   :PREMISE
    2. B   :PREMISE
    3. C   :PREMISE
    4. (B & C)   :&INTRO,2,3

The problem is not easy to correct. About the only symptom that we are hung up is if we *feel* that our proof is not going anywhere. Another symptom is that our task list grows and grows, with no end in sight. In these cases, we should retrace our steps to find where our task list seems to have gone wrong. That will be a step where PROOF-GIVER placed us at step 3(a) when it would have been more fruitful to be at step 3(b)(i). Once we have found where the difficulty seems to lie, we should rebuild the task list, this time going to step 3(b)(i) instead of step 3(a).

In our discussion of the method PROOF-GIVER, we may have become too immersed in the details of constructing proofs. Let us rise above the sometimes dreary details for a moment and review the general significance of the steps in PROOF-GIVER.

As we mentioned earlier, certain features of the construction of proofs—notably the infinitely many possible connections between the premises and the conclusion using our

PRODUCING PROOFS

rules—require that we "work backward" from the conclusion. We must first somehow determine how the conclusion *might* have arisen.

There are essentially two ways that a conclusion can be derived: It can be "part of" an earlier line of the proof (such as a premise), or it can be "reconstituted" from information contained somewhere in the premises.

It is the purpose of steps 3(a) and 3(b) to deal with these possibilities. If the conclusion is contained in some part of a previous line, we are at step 3(a), which then tells us how to extract the conclusion from the previous line. If the conclusion is *not* contained in a previous line, we are at step 3(b). There, there are numerous recipes for building up the conclusion from other bits of information that might somehow be contained in the premises.

PROOF-GIVER, as we have described it, is primarily a depth-first search strategy: It guides us on a single path through the search tree. The main flaw with PROOF-GIVER, as with other depth-first strategies, is that if we are wrong—that is, if we do not reach our goal easily—we must back up and reconsider one of the branches we earlier ignored. In other words, depth-first strategies will often require us to "backtrack."

Summary

In this chapter, we presented a method PROOF-GIVER, for constructing proofs of arguments known to be valid. PROOF-GIVER is not an algorithm, since it will not always work and, at certain points, requires human intervention. Nevertheless, it can be useful and illustrates some important techniques. PROOF-GIVER uses a *depth-first search strategy* to search a *tree* of possible lines of a proof; that is, it follows a "best guess" as to how the proof should proceed rather than trying all possibilities at once. You should find it helpful in constructing proofs of arguments.

Exercises

A. 1. Using PROOF-GIVER, determine what the next change of the proof or task list should be.

 a. PROOF
1.	(A → B)	:PREMISE
2.	(C & A)	:PREMISE

   TASK LIST
   Derive (B & C)

 b. PROOF
1.	((A → ~B) → D)	:PREMISE
2.	~B	:PREMISE
3.	(D → (E v B))	:PREMISE

   TASK LIST
   Derive D
   Apply →ELIM,3,[D]

c. PROOF
  1. (A & (B v D))   :PREMISE
  2. ((B v D) → (A → ~E))   :PREMISE
  3. A   :&ELIM,1

TASK LIST
  Apply &ELIM,1
  Apply →ELIM, [(B v D)],2
  Apply →ELIM, [(A → ~E)],3

2. From an inspection of the proof and task list of (c), what is the desired conclusion of the argument?

B. Using PROOF-GIVER, construct proofs of the following arguments:

1.   (A & (A → (B → C)))
     ∴ (B → C)

2.   ((A → B) & (B → C))
      (C → D)
     ∴ (A → D)

3.   (A & (~B & C))
     ∴ ~B

4.   (A → B)
      (A → ~E)
     ∴ ~A

5.   (A → B)
      (A & D)
     ∴ B

6.   ~A
      (A v ~B)
      (B → ~C)
     ∴ (~ B & (B → ~ C))

7.   (A → ~C)
      (B → C)
     ∴ (~ A v ~ B)

8.   (~B ↔ (A & D))
      (~B & (A ↔ E))
     ∴ E

9.   (A → (B → (~C → D)))
      (A & B)
     ∴ (~C → D)

C. Add a step to PROOF-GIVER that will enable it to handle 'Derive (P ↔ Q)' in a task list.

D. For programmers:
  1. Why doesn't "Apply &INTRO,*n,m*" in a task list *require* a goal sentence? That is, why is the goal sentence optional?
  2. Assume that premises and the conclusion contain only atomic-sentence letters and the symbol &. Write a program to input such an argument and construct a proof of it.
  3. Assume that premises and the conclusion contain only atomic-sentence letters, parentheses, and the symbol →. Write a program to input such an argument and construct a proof of it.

Suggestions for Computer Implementation

The full implementation of PROOF-GIVER should be supremely gratifying to any ambitious "hacker." As in PROOF-CHECKER, an appropriate data structure (such as an array) is necessary for storing the ongoing proof. Initially, of course, only the premises would be stored; the conclusion—with its justifying rule left blank—might be stored temporarily in some arbitrarily high line number of the final proof, sure to exceed the other lines of the proof (say, 100).

PRODUCING PROOFS

A separate data structure is also needed to store the distinct elements of the task list. Furthermore, since the contents of the task list are constantly changing, we frequently need to "sort" these elements into their order of priority.

We have not been as rigid in the text with the format of each record in the task list as we would have to be if we wished to implement PROOF-GIVER. We can impose the required rigidity here. The 'Derive' statement should have four fields:

1. A RANK: a number to indicate the priority of a task in the task list
2. A TASK: the task to be done—"DERIVE" (or "APPLY")
3. A sentence to be derived (our "goal")
4. The subproof-depth of the task

For example, consider the following argument:

A
B
∴ (A & B)

Our task list might at first contain

RANK(1) = 1
TASK(1) = DERIVE
TSEN(1) = (A & B)
TSUB(1) = 0

indicating, respectively, that the first element in the task list is *first* in order of priority, that the task is to *derive* a sentence, that the goal is to derive the sentence '(A & B)', and that it is not in a subproof. The names TSEN and TSUB indicate *task-list* sentences and subproof depths.

The other kind of statement in the task list is the 'APPLY' statement, which could have the following fields:

1. A RANK
2. The TASK: Here, 'APPLY'
3. The goal sentence (optional, except in the case of rules, ASSUMPTION, &ELIM, vINTRO)
4. The TRULE to be applied
5. The line(s) to which the rule is to be applied—expressed either as a line number or as a sentence
6. The subproof depth of the apply line

Thus we might have

RANK(2)   = 3
TASK(2)   = APPLY
TSEN(2)   = (A v B)
TRULE(2) = vINTRO
TCIT1(2) = 1

TCIT2(2) = 0
TCIT3(2) = 0
TSUB(2)   = 1

indicating that the priority of task-list line 2 is 3, that the task is to APPLY, that the goal sentence is '(A v B)', that the rule is to be applied to line 1, and that the APPLY is in a subproof of depth 1.

Note that the task can be stored in numerical fashion, since there are only two possible tasks. For example, 1 = DERIVE, and 2 = APPLY. Similarly, TRULE can also be stored numerically: 1 for &INTRO, 2 for &ELIM, 3 for vELIM, and so on. Using numbers where possible might spare us some nasty string operations. A sentence, however, such as '(A & (B v C))' cannot (easily!) be converted into numerical information.

Once the stage is set in this fashion, it is relatively straightforward to convert METHOD PROOF-GIVER into a computer program. Several features of the problem might, however, threaten this conversion.

1. Sometimes a line in a task list might be replaced by *two* (or more) lines. These new lines are always inserted at the beginning, and so they disturb the order of items in the task list. The clue to their priority in the task list is their RANK. If a task of rank 1 is to be replaced by two tasks, we might let these two tasks have ranks 1.1 and 1.2. We would first delete the original task, and we would know that the task with rank 1.1 is to be performed before the task with rank 1.2 and that both are to be performed before a task of rank 2.

    Similarly, a task of rank 2.1 might be replaced by tasks of ranks 2.11, 2.12, and 2.13. Including the RANK of a task performs an automatic sort or ordering of the elements in our task list.

2. As we have noted, sometimes PROOF-GIVER is misled or tricked, and the task list grows prodigiously—never getting closer to the conclusion. Since computers work so quickly, it might be a matter of mere microseconds before the task list is full of hundreds of tasks which will never allow PROOF-GIVER to reach the conclusion.

    There are two solutions to this problem—one a "quick fix," the other more elegant.

    We could write our program so that any time the task list grows to a certain size (say, twenty or thirty lines), then the program stops and alerts the user to the problem. (This is a so-called "disaster cutoff.")

    Another solution is to display to the user each revision of the task list and ask the user if he or she wishes to:
    a. Go on.
    b. Stop.
    c. Back up to an earlier stage of the proof and task list.
    d. Override step 3(a).
    e. Intervene and make a "human" suggestion on what to do: what contradiction to aim for, what step to follow, or what goal sentence to have.

3. The mention of "backing up" alerts us to the fact that we also need to store information about *past* proofs and task lists, as well as about the current, ongoing ones. We thus need to have the proof and task list of every previous step available

PRODUCING PROOFS

to us if we are going to be able to "back up." The easiest way to implement this suggestion is to store the proofs and task lists in some data structure (such as two-dimensional arrays). For example, TRULE(3,2) might be the TRULE in the second element of a task-list array on the third step of applying PROOF-GIVER.

4. It is possible to program other "hunches" and strategies into PROOF-GIVER beyond the ones given in this chapter. Strategies for choosing the contradictions to be aimed for with ~ELIM and ~INTRO could be given, as well as tips for keeping proofs shorter. If the arguments PROOF-GIVER is attempting to prove are all being created by a single person, we might also program strategies to deal with what seem to be this person's habits. The user might, for example, use vINTRO frequently or →INTRO rarely.

PREDICATE LOGIC:
Quantification

The procedures and techniques that we have studied so far for showing the validity of arguments are perfectly fine as far as they go. But they are limited to some extent, for there are many valid arguments whose validity cannot be shown by the methods we have studied in the previous chapters. Take, as an example, an argument found in logic texts for many years:

All Greeks are mortal.
Socrates is a Greek.
∴ Socrates is mortal.

Since all the sentences in this argument are different atomic sentences, this argument would be symbolized by three distinct sentence letters:

G
C
∴ A

This argument has the following form:

P
Q
∴ **R**

But no argument of this form can be shown to be valid in sentential logic when **R** is a different atomic sentence from atomic sentences **P** and **Q**. Yet the argument does appear to be valid: It seems impossible for the conclusion to be FALSE while the premises are TRUE.

CHAPTER 12

Individuals and Properties

If we look at our sample argument more carefully, we see that its validity rests on the fact that all individuals of a certain sort have a special property and that some particular individual, Socrates, is an individual of that sort. Therefore, the argument concludes, this particular individual (Socrates) has the special property. This observation suggests that we should extend our symbolic language to include devices for referring to individuals and for indicating properties that individuals have. In the logic of sentences, we looked only at whole sentences, either atomic or molecular. Now, in predicate logic, we are going to look at what some sentences say about certain individuals.

Individual Constants

An *individual* is a specific single thing, such as a person, a number, a horse, and so on. To be able to refer to individuals, we shall change the way we have been using various letters. From now on, we shall let lower-case letters from the front of the alphabet:

$a, b, c, \ldots, h$

be the names of (or "refer to," or "denote") individuals. These letters will be called *individual constants*. They are called "constants" because they do not change their reference within any one argument. (If we need more individual constants, we shall place numerals to the right of the letters. Thus '$a1$', '$b12$', and '$c567$' are also individual constants.) In the argument concluding that Socrates is mortal, we can let 'c' play the role of 'Socrates'. That is, let 'c' name, or refer to, Socrates.

Individuals have *properties*, such as being mortal, being evenly divisible by 2, being brown, being upholstered, and so forth. We shall now let upper-case letters from the front of the alphabet:

$A, B, \ldots, O$

indicate properties of individuals, as well as simple atomic sentences. So, 'G' might be a good choice to indicate the property of being Greek. Such property indicators are called *predicate letters*. If we need more predicate letters (or atomic sentences), we shall place numerals to the right of the letters, as above.

We shall indicate that a certain individual has a specific property by writing the predicate letter indicating that property and, immediately following, an individual constant referring to that individual. Thus 'Socrates is a Greek' would be written as

Gc

If 'E' is the predicate letter for the property of being wise, then 'Socrates is wise' would be

Ec

If '*a*' is the individual constant denoting Aristotle, then

(G*a* & E*a*)

is our way of stating that Aristotle is Greek and Aristotle is wise.

Variables

Many times, however, we make statements that are not about any particular individual. For instance, the first premise of our initial argument is about all Greeks. Or, to take another example, if we want to say

1. Someone received an A on the midterm.

we are not referring explicitly to any specific individual. We may not know exactly which individual, or we may know but prefer not to say exactly which one. In order to express such statements in our symbolic language, we need to take the procedure for forming sentences that we now have and modify it to form "incomplete" sentences, which we will then use to create new sentences.

Take the following sentence:

Bob received an A on the midterm.

Where it is possible, we choose letters that remind us of the English names of individuals and properties. So, with an obvious choice of letters for the individual constant and the predicate letter, we would write the sentence

2. A*b*

To produce sentence (1), we first need to eliminate the specific reference to Bob in sentence (2). As we suggested above, we may not want to identify who received the A, but we do want to say that someone (unspecified) did. However, if we simply erased the '*b*', it would not be evident that some symbol belongs there. So, we are going to establish some symbols as placeholders in sentences. These placeholders will be called *individual variables*. They will be lower-case letters taken from the end of the alphabet:

u, v, w, x, y, z

Notice, individual variables do not denote any particular individual; they will serve only as placeholders for reference to any nonspecified individual. (As in the case of individual constants, if we need more individual variables, we shall place numerals to the right of the letters: *x*3, *y*8, *z*52.)

The first step in constructing a sentence that does not name a specific individual is to make an "incomplete sentence" by replacing the individual constants with individual variables. Thus, to produce sentence (1) from sentence (2), we can begin by replacing the individual constant '*b*' with, say, the individual variable '*x*'. The result is:

Ax

This could be read as

x received an A on the midterm.

But this is an incomplete sentence, and it is neither TRUE nor FALSE. We shall call such incomplete sentences "formulas." (This differs from the notion of formula in Chapter 5.)

Quantifiers

We now develop the idea of a *quantifier*—an expression that states *how many* individuals, but not which ones, have the property indicated in an incomplete sentence. A quantifier placed before an incomplete sentence makes it complete; that is, it makes it into a sentence that is either TRUE or FALSE. Although there are several different ones, we shall use only two quantifiers. The *universal* quantifier is used to assert that all individuals have the indicated property, and the *existential* quantifier is used to assert that some (at least one) individual has the property.

What do these quantifier expressions look like? The universal quantifier consists of a rotated A to the left of a variable: ∀x, ∀w, ∀z. For the existential quantifier, we shall use a rotated E to the left of a variable: ∃x, ∃y, ∃w. Finally, we construct the sentence we desire by placing the appropriate quantifier to the left of the relevant formula. An "appropriate" quantifier is a quantifier that contains the same variable as does the formula. Thus sentence (1), 'Someone received an A on the midterm', looks like this:

∃xAx

And

Everyone received an A on the midterm.

looks like this:

∀xAx

These are usually read, respectively, as

There is an individual *x* such that *x* received an A on the midterm.

and

For every individual *x*, *x* received an A on the midterm.

Well-Formed Formulas

We must become quite precise about the forms of sentences. In order to do this, we define a *well-formed formula,* or *wff* for short. A string, you recall, is any sequence of characters. A formula, in Chapter 5, was a string that mixed numerals, parentheses, and connective symbols in a definite way.

We now define a well-formed formula:

1. A string consisting of a single sentence letter is a wff.
2. A string consisting of a predicate letter followed by either a constant or a variable is a wff.
3. If **P** and **Q** are wffs, so are
   ~**P**
   (**P** & **Q**)
   (**P** v **Q**)
   (**P** → **Q**)
   (**P** ↔ **Q**)
   (The list of allowable connectives can be extended.)
4. If **P** is a wff, then ∀**vP** and ∃**vP** (where **v** is any variable: *x, y, z, w, . . .*) are wffs.

Thus, the following strings are all well-formed formulas:

∀xFx	(A → ~B)
(∀xFx & Ga)	(Fx v Gy)
∀x(Fx & Ga)	∀x(Fx → Hz)
∃x~(Gx v B)	∀x(Fx → A)
(∀yHy → ∃yGy)	(∃xGx & Hx)

Later, we shall expand the notion of a well-formed formula to include relations: predicate letters followed by strings of more than one constant or variable.

Scope

To assist us in our discussion of both quantified sentences and formulas, we need some additional terminology. Every quantifier will have a *scope;* intuitively, the scope is the formula covered by the quantifier. The *scope* of a quantifier is defined precisely as *the well-formed formula immediately to its right.* Thus

The Scope of	in Sentence	is Formula
∀x	∀x(Ax → Bx)	(Ax → Bx)
∃x	(∃xAx & C)	Ax
∀y	∃x∀y(Ax & (By → Cy))	(Ax & (By → Cy))
∃x	∃x∀y(Ax & (By → Cy))	∀y(Ax & (By → Cy))
∀z	∀z~(Az v Bz)	~(Az v Bz)

CHAPTER 12

Free and Bound Variables

In each of the above sentences, the same variable appears in several different places. Each appearance of a variable is called an *occurrence* of the variable. An occurrence of a variable is *bound* if the variable occurs in a quantifier or in the scope of a quantifier using that variable. If an occurrence of a variable is not bound, it is a *free occurrence* of the variable. In a given formula, a variable could have both free and bound occurrences.

In the Formula	the Variable	Occurs
∀x∀y(Fy → Gx)	y	bound
∀x(Fx → Gy)	y	free
(Fx & ∀xGx)	x	first free, then bound

Two remarks are in order at this point. First, the rules for wffs allow what is called "vacuous quantification." That is, one may place a quantifier in front of a wff, even if the variable in the quantifier does not occur, or does not occur free, in the wff. Here are some examples of wffs that are vacuously quantified:

∀xFy
∃yA
∀z(∃zHz & Gx)

Second, a *sentence* is any wff with no free occurrences of variables. Well-formed formulas containing free occurrences of variables do not have truth values. (They are incomplete sentences.) But those wffs with no free occurrences of variables are sentences, and they do have truth values.

An Algorithm for Sentences

The algorithm in Chapter 5 that determines whether a string is a (well-formed) sentence has to be modified, since we have new possibilities. There, after replacing every atomic sentence with a truth value and changing '~0' to '1' and '~1' to '0', we found every formula from then on to be of the form

<truth value>

or else

(<truth value 1> ☆ <truth value 2>)

We now have two new possibilities: Sentences may begin with one of two quantifiers. Let us call a wff whose first two symbols are a quantifier and a variable a *quantified formula*. Hence, in the original algorithm from Chapter 5, after replacing atomic sentences with their truth values, we might have

<quantified formula>
(<quantified formula> ☆ <truth value>)
(<truth value> ☆ <quantified formula>)

or

(<quantified formula 1> ☆ <quantified formula 2>)

These strange possibilities can be avoided, however, if we perform the following operations *before* replacing atomic sentences with truth values:

Step 0. FOR every quantified formula in the string, working from left to right

  a. Delete the first two symbols.
  b. Replace all now free occurrences of the deleted variable with an individual constant not previously used.
  c. Replace all predicate formulas containing only individual constants with an atomic-sentence letter not previously used.

For example, applying these operations to the sentence

  (A & ∀xFx)

results in:

  (A & Fx)
  (A & Fa)
  (A & B)

At this point, we can continue with TRUTH-VALUE CALCULATOR, replacing the newly introduced atomic sentences with truth values. If at any point in TRUTH-VALUE CALCULATOR we do not have either a single truth value or a pair of truth values surrounding a connective, then the original string was not a sentence. Observe, however, that the truth-value result of the above algorithm is not a useful value and so *cannot* be used in VALIDITY/INVALIDITY DETERMINER.

One step in our new algorithm needs refinement. How do we mechanically identify the "now free occurrences," which were bound occurrences before we deleted the quantifier? In order to do that, we need to identify the next wff. The next symbol following the quantifier variable can only be (1) a predicate letter, (2) a negation sign, (3) a left parenthesis, or (4) a quantifier symbol. (We are excluding vacuous quantification of a sentence letter.) Each of these cases can easily be handled. Note that when the scope includes a formula with parentheses, procedure "First Counter" will find the matching right parenthesis.

Finally, let us work through a more complicated example:

$\forall x(\exists y(Fx \lor Ly) \rightarrow (Gx \& \forall yHy))$
   $(\exists y(Fx \lor Ly) \rightarrow (Gx \& \forall yHy))$
   $(\exists y(Fa \lor Ly) \rightarrow (Ga \& \forall yHy))$
   $(\exists y(A \lor Ly) \rightarrow (B \& \forall yHy))$
    $((A \lor Lb) \rightarrow (B \& \forall yHy))$
    $((A \lor C) \;\; \rightarrow (B \& \forall yHy))$
    $((A \lor C) \;\; \rightarrow (B \& Hc))$
    $((A \lor C) \;\; \rightarrow (B \& D))$

Truth Values of Quantified Sentences

Before we learn inference rules for correctly introducing and eliminating quantifiers in the course of a derivation, we must be perfectly clear about the truth values of sentences with quantifiers. Sentences like 'Aristotle is Greek', that is, 'Ga', present no problem. 'Ga' is TRUE if the individual denoted by 'a' (namely, Aristotle) has the property indicated by 'G' (namely, being Greek), and similarly for all sentences containing *only* individual constants and predicate letters. In any other situation, 'Ga' is FALSE—that is, when the individual denoted by 'a' does *not* have the property denoted by 'G'. An *instance* of a wff is a sentence that results from replacing all free occurrences of individual variables with individual constants.

Using the valuation function, V, introduced earlier, we now claim that

   $V(\forall xGx)$ = TRUE if and only if the value of every instance of 'Gx' is TRUE.
   $V(\exists xGx)$ = TRUE if and only if the value of at least one instance of 'Gx' is TRUE.

(You should remember that if the value of a sentence is not TRUE, it is FALSE.)

The set of individuals we are talking about is frequently referred to as the *universe of discourse*. Thus if the universe of discourse contains individuals denoted by 'a', 'b', and 'c', then 'Fa', 'Fb', and 'Fc' are all the instances of 'Fx'. So, $V(\forall xFx)$ = TRUE iff $V(Fa)$ and $V(Fb)$ and $V(Fc)$ are TRUE, and $V(\exists xFx)$ = TRUE iff $V(Fa)$ or $V(Fb)$ or $V(Fc)$ is TRUE.

Quantifying Molecular Formulas

Recall our earlier example that stated that Aristotle is Greek and that he is wise. This is the conjunction of the two sentences 'Aristotle is Greek' and 'Aristotle is wise', so we used our symbol for conjunction to write:

   $(Ga \& Ea)$

From this sentence we can construct a wff by replacing all occurrences of the individual constant '*a*' with the variable '*x*', obtaining

(G*x* & E*x*)

Existential Quantifiers

If we prefix the expression above with an existential quantifier using '*x*', we obtain a new sentence:

∃*x*(G*x* & E*x*)

which can be read as

There is something that is Greek and wise.

or, more naturally, as

Some Greek is wise.

We now have a general pattern for English sentences of the following forms:

Some **S** is **T**.
Some **S** are **T**.

These should all be symbolized as

∃*x*(**S***x* & **T***x*)

This can be read literally as "There is an *x* such that *x* is **S** and *x* is **T**."

This pattern, then, is proper for all the following sentences:

Some baby is cute.
Some babies are cute.
Some students are musicians.
Some musicians are students.
Some students played all night.
    (That is, some students are all-night players.)

Similarly, sentences of the forms

Some **S** is not **T**.
Some **S** are not **T**.

will be symbolized as

$\exists x(\mathbf{S}x \mathbin{\&} \sim\mathbf{T}x)$

This can be read literally as "There is an x such that x is $\mathbf{S}$ and x is not $\mathbf{T}$."

Universal Quantifiers

Placing the appropriate universal quantifier before the well-formed formula

$(\mathbf{G}x \mathbin{\&} \mathbf{E}x)$

results in

$\forall x(\mathbf{G}x \mathbin{\&} \mathbf{E}x)$

which can be read as

Everything is both Greek and wise.

We would seldom make such a claim. More likely, we would want to assert that all Greeks are wise. How can we express a statement of the form

All **S** are **T**.

In this case, we are claiming that the property **T** holds for all the **S** sort of individuals. We will now show that the conditional can be used to make this kind of claim. In particular, we symbolize

All **S** are **T**.

as

$\forall x(\mathbf{S}x \rightarrow \mathbf{T}x)$

This says that for every x, *if x is* $\mathbf{S}$, *then x is* $\mathbf{T}$. This sentence is TRUE, according to the evaluation rule, if every instance of '$(\mathbf{S}x \rightarrow \mathbf{T}x)$' is TRUE. A few of these instances are:

$(\mathbf{S}a \rightarrow \mathbf{T}a)$
$(\mathbf{S}b \rightarrow \mathbf{T}b)$
$(\mathbf{S}c \rightarrow \mathbf{T}c)$
$(\mathbf{S}d \rightarrow \mathbf{T}d)$

These instances are sentences, but what do they assert? The first states that if a has the property **S**, then it has the property **T** (for instance, if a is Greek, then a is wise).

When is this sentence TRUE? Clearly, if '**S**a' is TRUE and also '**T**a' is TRUE, then the conditional sentence '(**S**a → **T**a)' is TRUE. Indeed, for each instance, the ordinary truth table for a conditional will tell us when it is TRUE and when it is FALSE. As you know, the conditional is FALSE *just when* the antecedent is TRUE and the consequent FALSE. Again referring to the example, an instance is FALSE only when, for some individual constant, the individual denoted *is* Greek but *is not* wise. A Greek who is not wise is precisely the situation that falsifies the original sentence: All Greeks are wise.

It is important to understand how the conditional form for universally quantified sentences works. The truth value of

All hamburgers are delicious.

is TRUE if and only if each and every hamburger is delicious. So, as we go through the universe of discourse, examining individuals one at a time, we must be sure that if an individual is a hamburger, then it is delicious. If the individual is not a hamburger, then the instance is not FALSE, that is, it is TRUE. Notice that the antecedent in this instance is FALSE. Only when we find an individual that is a hamburger but is not delicious is the instance FALSE. With one instance FALSE, the universally quantified sentence is also FALSE. For example:

$\forall x(Hx \rightarrow Dx)$

Universe of discourse:

	denoted by
a hamburger that is delicious	a
an apple that is delicious	b
a rotten apple	c
Julius Caesar	d

Instances:

$(Ha \rightarrow Da)$	TRUE
$(Hb \rightarrow Db)$	TRUE
$(Hc \rightarrow Dc)$	TRUE
$(Hd \rightarrow Dd)$	TRUE

Thus, in this universe of discourse, '$\forall x(Hx \rightarrow Dx)$' is TRUE. But in a universe of discourse such as

	denoted by
a hamburger that is delicious	a
an apple that is delicious	b
a stale hamburger	c
Julius Caesar	d

Instances:

$(Ha \to Da)$	TRUE
$(Hb \to Db)$	TRUE
$(Hc \to Dc)$	FALSE
$(Hd \to Dd)$	TRUE

the universally quantified sentence is FALSE, because one instance is FALSE.
    We now have a general way of representing sentences of the form

All **S** are **T**.

We write

$\forall x(\textbf{S}x \to \textbf{T}x)$

for sentences such as

All drivers are careful.
All joggers are healthy.
All fish swim.
    (That is, all fish are swimmers.)

A sentence of the form

No **S** are **T**.

meaning that every single individual that is **S** is not **T**, can be rewritten in the more suggestive form:

All **S** are not **T**.

We write

$\forall x(\textbf{S}x \to \sim\textbf{T}x)$

for sentences like

No cobras are pets.
No Australian is sad.
No vegetarian eats meat.
    (That is, no vegetarian is a meat eater.)

You are cautioned that this type of sentence does not mean the same thing as

Not all **S** are **T**.

This should be symbolized as

$\sim\forall x(\mathbf{S}x \rightarrow \mathbf{T}x)$

'Not all Australians are sad' is quite different from 'No Australians are sad'. In the first case, it is still possible for some Australians to be sad while the given sentence is TRUE. This is not possible in the second case.

Dossiers and Models

In our discussions of sentential logic, we introduced the concept of a "situation." This is a possible case or scenario in which some sentences are TRUE and all others are FALSE. The real world is just one such situation. For our purposes in sentential logic, the most useful way to describe a situation is simply as a list of atomic sentences together with their truth values in that situation. We saw how to apply TRUTH-VALUE CALCU-LATOR to use this information to calculate the truth value of any molecular sentence.

Our purpose in considering such situations in predicate logic is the same as it was in the earlier chapters—namely, to allow ourselves to determine when an argument is valid. The basic definition of validity applies whether we are working in sentential logic or in predicate logic: An argument is valid iff in all situations in which the premises are TRUE, the conclusion is also TRUE. But in predicate logic, our descriptions of situations must refer not only to the truth values of atomic sentences but also to individuals and their properties.

In order to develop a systematic way of evaluating the truth values of sentences containing quantifiers, let us first consider the case of just one predicate letter, 'F'. We shall say that an individual j *satisfies* the predicate 'F' in a situation iff $V(Fj)$ = TRUE in that situation. This is little more than another way of saying that an individual "has" a property in a situation.

Representative Individuals

If we consider only one predicate, either each individual will satisfy that predicate or it won't. If the predicate 'F' is 'is a tomato', then each individual either is or is not a tomato. There are only two distinguishable kinds of individuals if we consider only this one predicate: An individual is either of the kind that satisfies 'F' or of the kind that does not satisfy it. Hence, we can simplify matters by dealing with only two *representative* indi-viduals, a and b, where individual a does not satisfy predicate 'F', but individual b does. The individual a is representative of all the individuals that do not satisfy 'F', and the individual b is representative of all the individuals that do satisfy 'F'. We can picture this case with a table:

	F
a	0
b	1

Let us a call a row of such a table a *dossier* on the individual named in the left column. The dossier on an individual indicates which predicates it does (= 1) or does not (= 0) satisfy. Each column of the table, on the other hand, indicates which individuals do or do not satisfy the predicate listed at the top of the column.

If we consider two predicates, 'F' and 'G', we can see that there are four distinct representative individuals that are possible:

	F	G
a	0	0
b	0	1
c	1	0
d	1	1

It should be easy to see that when there are *n* distinct predicates, there will be 2 ∗∗ *n* representative individuals needed to cover every possibility. In the table above, it is unnecessary to consider a fifth individual, since that individual will be similar to one of the four representative individuals with respect to the predicates 'F' and 'G'.

Models

A *model situation* (or simply a *model*) for a sentence consists of a set of individuals and their dossiers. We require that every model contain at least one individual and that the dossier on each individual in the model specify for every predicate in the sentence whether the individual satisfies the predicate or not. When we consider the models for several sentences simultaneously—for instance, when we are trying to show an argument to be invalid—the dossiers on individuals must include every predicate in every sentence.

For the two sentences in this argument:

$\forall x(Fx \rightarrow Gx)$
$\therefore \ \forall y(Gy \rightarrow Fy)$

one model would be:

1. Individuals: *a, b*
2. Dossiers:

	F	G
a	0	0
b	0	1

Observe that the dossiers on the individuals in a model can be listed together, forming a table that looks much like a truth table. We shall frequently characterize a model by simply giving such a table. The individuals in the model will then be indicated in the left column of the table.

The model given above meets the two requirements we have specified: It contains at least one individual, and the dossiers include information about each predicate in the original two sentences.

A model can contain any number of individuals. This means that for any sentence there are an infinite number of possible models. Some have one individual, some have two, some have three, and so on. In this section, however, we need only consider what we shall call "minimal models." A *minimal model* contains only representative individuals. The model we have just described is a minimal model, but the following model:

	F	G
a	0	0
b	0	1
f	0	1

is not a minimal model, since individual f satisfies exactly the same predicates as does individual b. Either b or f is a representative individual, but not both of them.

A complete listing of all the minimal models for the two sentences above, which contain only the predicates 'F' and 'G', is:

I.
	F	G
a	0	0

II.
	F	G
b	0	1

III.
	F	G
c	1	0

IV.
	F	G
d	1	1

V.
	F	G
a	0	0
b	0	1

VI.
	F	G
a	0	0
c	1	0

VII.
	F	G
a	0	0
d	1	1

VIII.
	F	G
b	0	1
c	1	0

IX.
	F	G
b	0	1
d	1	1

X.
	F	G
c	1	0
d	1	1

XI.
	F	G
a	0	0
b	0	1
c	1	0

XII.
	F	G
a	0	0
b	0	1
d	1	1

XIII.
	F	G
a	0	0
c	1	0
d	1	1

XIV.
	F	G
b	0	1
c	1	0
d	1	1

XV.
	F	G
a	0	0
b	0	1
c	1	0
d	1	1

Although the number of possible models is infinite, the number of minimal models is $(2 ** m) - 1$, where m is the number of representative individuals. In this case, there are just four representative individuals, and so the number of minimal models is $(2 ** 4) - 1 = 15$.

We now have the basic notions of models, representative individuals, and minimal models. We need now to develop a procedure for determining when a sentence is TRUE in a model.

Determining whether a Sentence is TRUE in a Model

The determination of whether a sentence containing quantifiers is TRUE in a model is not as simple as the earlier task of truth-value determination in sentential logic. We shall extend and modify the techniques we developed in Chapter 6 in connection with WANG'S ALGORITHM. Recall that there we constructed a pair of lists, the left list of the pair containing sentences we tried to make TRUE, and the right list containing sentences we tried to make FALSE. Let us apply this idea to the problem of determining if a single sentence containing a quantifier is TRUE.

Consider, as an example, this sentence:

$\forall x(Fx \vee Gx)$

in the model:

	F	G
a	1	0
b	0	0

We begin, as in WANG'S ALGORITHM, by trying to make the given sentence TRUE. When we wish to make a sentence TRUE, we place it on the *left* list of a list-pair:

$\forall x(Fx \vee Gx)|$

Now when is such a universally quantified sentence TRUE in a model? Only when all the instances of the nonquantified formula are TRUE. In this model, the instances are '(Fa v Ga)' and '(Fb v Gb)'—obtained by deleting the initial quantifier and then replacing the now free occurrences of the variable first with 'a' and next with 'b'. Putting both of these instances on the left list, we have:

$(Fa \vee Ga)\ |$
$(Fb \vee Gb)\ |$

Neither of the sentences on the left list contains a quantifier, so we can now proceed with the earlier rules from WANG'S ALGORITHM. The first sentence is a disjunction on the left, which requires us to branch:

```
    Fa       |      Ga       |
  (Fb v Gb)  |    (Fb v Gb)  |
```

The second sentence on both lists is again a disjunction on the left, so we branch again on both list-pairs:

$$\left.\begin{matrix} Fa \\ Fb \end{matrix}\right| \qquad \left.\begin{matrix} Fa \\ Gb \end{matrix}\right| \qquad \left.\begin{matrix} Ga \\ Fb \end{matrix}\right| \qquad \left.\begin{matrix} Ga \\ Gb \end{matrix}\right|$$

Observe that the right list of each of these four list-pairs is empty. We cannot apply WANG'S ALGORITHM any further, since at this point, every sentence in the lists is a simple predicate formula, containing neither a quantifier nor a connective. Sentences on the left list, we recall, are to be made TRUE. Are the two sentences in the first list-pair satisfied in the model? To answer this question we turn to the dossiers. 'Fa' is indeed TRUE in this model situation, but 'Fb' is not, so this branch fails. We can indicate this failure by placing a '0' under the branch and then proceed to the next branch. Here, 'Fa' is TRUE, but 'Gb' is not, and this branch also fails. Continuing on to the third and fourth branches, we finally obtain:

$$\left.\begin{matrix} Fa \\ Fb \end{matrix}\right| \qquad \left.\begin{matrix} Fa \\ Gb \end{matrix}\right| \qquad \left.\begin{matrix} Ga \\ Fb \end{matrix}\right| \qquad \left.\begin{matrix} Ga \\ Gb \end{matrix}\right|$$
$$\quad 0 \qquad\qquad 0 \qquad\qquad 0 \qquad\qquad 0$$

All branches originating from the sentence '∀x(Fx ∨ Gx)' fail. From the failure of all branches, we conclude that the original sentence is not TRUE in the model.

We now formulate a principle for evaluating list-pairs relative to a model:

The original sentence is TRUE in a model if one of the branches leading from it is successful.

This can also be formulated alternatively as:

The original sentence is FALSE in a model if all branches leading from it fail.

A branch succeeds when nothing but simple predicate formulas occurs on both lists, and all the sentences on the left list are satisfied in the model, and all the sentences on the right list are not satisfied in the model. When this condition is met, we can write a '1' under the branch to indicate that it is successful. We may also stop at this point, since one successful branch is sufficient to show that the original sentence is TRUE in the model.

A branch fails when either of the following conditions occurs:

1. The same sentence occurs on both the left list and the right list of a list-pair.
2. Nothing but simple predicate formulas occurs on both lists, but either a formula on the left list is not satisfied in the model or a formula on the right list is satisfied in the model.

In the case where a branch fails, we shall write a '0' below it and go on to the next branch. If there are no more branches to examine, and if all previous branches failed, then we conclude that the original sentence is not TRUE in this model.

CHAPTER 12

To the previous seven substeps in step 3 of WANG'S ALGORITHM we now add four more:

- (viii) If a sentence is universally quantified and on the left list, then delete the sentence and add to the left list all the instances of the formula without its initial quantifier.
- (ix) If a sentence is universally quantified and on the right list, then branch and replace the sentence in each branch with one instance.
- (x) If a sentence is existentially quantified and on the left list, then branch and replace the sentence in each branch with one instance.
- (xi) If a sentence is existentially quantified and on the right list, then delete this sentence and add to the right list all the instances of the formula without its initial quantifier.

The number of instances added in steps viii and xi, as well as the number of branches required in steps ix and x, is exactly the number of individuals in the model. It goes without saying that different instances should be used on different branches. In the example we have been working with, there are only two individuals, a and b.

Using this same model situation, let us consider a slightly more difficult sentence:

$$\exists x \exists y (Gx \vee {\sim}Fy)|$$

$\exists y(Ga \vee {\sim}Fy)|$		$\exists y(Gb \vee {\sim}Fy)|$	
$(Ga \vee {\sim}Fa)|$ $(Ga \vee {\sim}Fb)|$		$(Gb \vee {\sim}Fa)|$ $(Gb \vee {\sim}Fb)|$	

$Ga|$ ${\sim}Fa|$ $Ga|$ ${\sim}Fb|$ $Gb|$ ${\sim}Fa|$ $Gb|$ ${\sim}Fb|$
0   0   0   0

    $|Fa$ $|Fb$ $|Fa$ $|Fb$
    0   1   0   1

The original sentence is TRUE in this model because we found a branch that succeeds: 'Fb' is not satisfied in the model.

It should be kept in mind that we are only using part of WANG'S ALGORITHM here. We are simply trying to determine whether a sentence is TRUE in a given model. It is quite clear that the above use of list-pairs and branches is convenient only when the number of individuals in the model is relatively small, or when the original sentence contains only a few quantifiers.

Finally, let us take up the question of whether the premise and conclusion of a simple argument are TRUE or FALSE in a model. A simple argument is:

$$\forall x (Fx \rightarrow Gx)$$
$$\therefore \ \forall y (Gy \rightarrow Fy)$$

QUANTIFICATION

Consider minimal model I:

	F	G
a	0	0

Applying the list-pair method to the premise, we have:

$$\forall x\ (Fx \rightarrow Gx)|$$

$$(Fa \rightarrow Ga)|$$

~Fa| Ga |
                              0

|Fa
1

Since one of the branches concludes with a '1', the premise is TRUE in this model. Applying the same method to the conclusion, we discover that it, too, is TRUE in this model. But we cannot yet conclude that the argument is valid, since we have to consider *all* minimal models. We must not have any model where the premises are TRUE and the conclusion FALSE, or else the argument is invalid. Consider, then, this argument relative to minimal model II:

	F	G
b	0	1

After applying the list-pair method, we would find that in this model the premise is TRUE but the conclusion is FALSE. Hence, this model shows the argument to be invalid.

Here is a sketch of a procedure to determine whether an argument containing quantifiers is valid:

1. INPUT the sentences of the argument.
2. Determine the representative individuals from the number of distinct predicates contained in the premises and conclusion.
3. Construct all the possible minimal models.
4. FOR each minimal model:
   a. Apply the list-pair method to determine whether the premises and conclusion are TRUE or FALSE in the model.
   b. IF all the premises are TRUE in the model and the conclusion is FALSE
      THEN OUTPUT "Argument invalid" and STOP.
5. OUTPUT "Argument valid" and STOP.

This procedure is not an algorithm because, in many cases, steps 2 and 3 cannot be completed.

There are two additional special circumstances we should mention. A sentence with a quantifier might also contain a single atomic-sentence letter, such as '(A & ∃xFx)'.

CHAPTER 12

Whenever a sentence contains sentence letters, then the model must also specify the truth value of those atomic sentences. Second, we have been identifying individuals in the model with lower-case letters. This usage could become confused with the occurrence of individual constants in sentences. Let us agree, then, to identify the individuals in the model with lower-case letters different from any individual constants occurring in the sentences under examination. Furthermore, whenever a sentence occurs on a list-pair and contains an individual constant that is not within the scope of *any* quantifier, we treat the sentence as if it were an instance of an *existentially* quantified sentence. That is, if such a sentence occurs on the left, branch and replace all occurrences of the individual constant with names of the individuals in the model. If such a sentence occurs on the right, delete the sentence and add all instances resulting from replacement of the individual constant with names of individuals in the model. For instance,

$$(Ga \rightarrow \forall xFx)|$$

$$(Gb \rightarrow \forall xFx)| \qquad (Gc \rightarrow \forall xFx)|$$

where the model contains two individuals, *b* and *c*.

Limitations of Models

It can be quite time-consuming to determine whether an argument is valid or invalid by examining its models. In some cases, we might find a model in which the premises are TRUE but the conclusion FALSE rather quickly. In other cases, we might have to examine many models. We must examine *all* models, although we have simplified this task by restricting ourselves to minimal models. Yet even after we restrict ourselves to minimal models, the task of determining validity can be huge. For example, in an argument containing only three predicates, there will be eight representative individuals, and thus 255 minimal models. The task of determining the truth values for each premise and the conclusion would be very time-consuming, unless, of course, we had programmed a computer to do it.

Furthermore, as we shall soon see, even a modest extension of predicate logic to include relations between individuals, or to include the special logical relation of identity (symbolized by '='), renders the notion of a minimal model almost useless. In these cases, we shall be forced, in general, to consider infinitely many minimal models.

Examining all minimal models is not the most efficient way to determine truth values. There are numerous shortcuts, too sophisticated for this book, by which one can transform sentences into a normal form and then quickly determine if the normal form is TRUE in a minimal model. We shall return to this topic briefly in Chapter 14.

Relations

Before we turn to the delicate task of representing more complicated English sentences using the device of quantification symbols, it is important to note that not all the arguments we are interested in involve individuals and their properties. Some arguments depend on *relations* between individuals. For example, consider:

Tom is older than Jane.
Jane is older than Sam.
∴ Tom is older than Sam.

In this argument, it is the relations between the individuals Tom, Jane, and Sam, and not just the properties they have, that underlie the validity of the argument. This argument makes sense to us, and is apparently valid, because of our understanding of the relation *being older than,* which relates two individuals.

To deal with relations between two or more individuals, we will simply extend the use of predicate letters. Let 'L' indicate the relation of being older than. We write the names of the individuals to the right of the predicate letter *in the proper order.* So, if

a = Tom
b = Jane
c = Sam

we now write

Lab for: Tom is older than Jane.
Lbc for: Jane is older than Sam.
Lac for: Tom is older than Sam.

The order of the individual constants is important, for 'Lba' represents 'Jane is older than Tom', a quite different sentence from 'Tom is older than Jane'.

We can handle well-formed formulas and quantifications involving relations as we did before. Relation letters are simply more-than-one-place predicates, taking more than one constant or variable after them in order to result in a well-formed formula. It is a simple matter to revise the definition of a wff to deal with n-place predicates. We must, however, pay close attention to the location of the variable. The wff 'Lxb' (x is older than Jane) can be existentially quantified as

∃xLxb Someone is older than Jane.

Notice that

∃xLbx Jane is older than someone.

is a very different sentence.

In order to keep straight what is related to what in a completely quantified sentence, we use different variables for possibly different (unspecified) individuals:

∃x∃yLxy Someone is older than someone.

If we used just one variable, we would have

∃xLxx Someone is older than himself (or herself).

which is, of course, a sentence whose truth value is FALSE.

The universal quantifier is handled in a similar fashion:

∀xLxb   Everyone is older than Jane.

'Everyone' is understood in logic quite literally; it does not mean "everyone else." This sentence is evidently FALSE, since Jane is not older than herself. Likewise,

∀xLbx   Jane is older than everyone.

is FALSE, since Jane is not older than herself. And, finally, mixing quantifiers we can get:

∃x∀yLxy   Someone is older than everyone.
∀x∃zLxz   Everyone is older than someone.

Both of these, of course, are FALSE in the real world (because no one is older than himself or herself, and there are only a finite number of individuals.)

We must extend our earlier notion of a dossier on an individual in order to construct models for sentences containing relational predicates. Consider, first, just one two-place predicate 'R' and, for simplicity, three individuals a, b, and c. There are *nine* relationships that might exist between a, b, and c with respect to the relation R. That is, there are nine sentences whose truth values we must specify. An orderly array of these sentences is:

Raa	Rba	Rca
Rab	Rbb	Rcb
Rac	Rbc	Rcc

The format above does not lend itself easily to the notion of a dossier, but with some redundancy we can construct a dossier for each of the individuals. The dossier on a should show which two-place predicates are satisfied with 'a' as the first term and which ones are satisfied with 'a' as the second term. After all, with regard to, say, individual a, we want to know which instances of 'Rax' are TRUE *and* which instances of 'Rxa' are TRUE. We proceed, then, to construct, for our simple example, *six* columns, first fixing the first individual to a, b, and c and then similarly fixing the second individual:

	Ra_	Rb_	Rc_	R_a	R_b	R_c
a						
b						
c						

The top row of cells contains the truth values for the sentences resulting from placing 'a' in the blanks at the top. The second row uses 'b' in the blank spaces, and the bottom row uses 'c'. If 'Raa' is TRUE, then the cell at the top left will contain '1' (and so will the fourth cell over). If 'Raa' is not TRUE, then the cell will contain '0' (and likewise for the fourth cell). For V(Raa) = 1, we have:

	Ra_	Rb_	Rc_	R_a	R_b	R_c
a	1			1		
b						
c						

Simply stated, to construct the dossier on a, move across the top of the table inserting 'a' in each of the blank spaces, ensuring that when the *same* expression results at the tops of the different columns, the *same* value occurs in the corresponding cells in the appropriate row.

The proviso in the final clause of the previous sentence must be observed. Note that in the construction of the dossier on a, the second entry evaluates 'Rba'. But 'Rba' will also occur in the construction of the dossier on b. In particular, this will be the fourth entry to the right on the row for b. Whatever value for 'Rba' is in the dossier on a must also be the value for 'Rba' in the dossier on b.

	Ra_	Rb_	Rc_	R_a	R_b	R_c
a		0				
b				0		
c						

Once dossiers are specified, models can be constructed as we did earlier, and various quantified sentences can be evaluated for truth or falsity in different models.

In general, the interesting two-place relations require a large number of individuals for the construction of appropriate minimal models. When more than a handful of individuals are in a universe of discourse, dossiers and tables are quite difficult to exhibit and work with. The idea of a dossier, nevertheless, helps us to see how to evaluate a quantified sentence, even if the dossier cannot easily be displayed.

Symbolizing

The art of symbolizing English sentences depends on a clear understanding of the truth conditions of the original sentence. For instance, if we were to state

Only students are fun-loving.

we should first clearly understand the conditions under which this sentence is TRUE, and also the conditions under which it is FALSE. Notice that if some nonstudent, say, a teacher, were found to be fun-loving, then the sentence would be FALSE. In other words, the basic claim amounts to saying that all fun-loving (persons) are students. This is easily symbolized as

$\forall x(Fx \rightarrow Dx)$

A sentence such as

Voters are either Democrats or Republicans.

can be symbolized quite simply as

$\forall x(Ex \rightarrow (Dx \lor Bx))$

That is, for any individual x, if x is a voter, then x is a Democrat or x is a Republican. More care must be taken with

Bats and cats are mammals.

This is correctly symbolized as

$(\forall x(Bx \rightarrow Mx) \,\&\, \forall x(Cx \rightarrow Mx))$

or as

$\forall x((Bx \lor Cx) \rightarrow Mx)$

If one were to neglect the truth conditions of the original English sentence, one might incorrectly symbolize the sentence with a formula that begins:

For any x, if x is a bat *and* x is a cat. . .

But nothing is both a bat and a cat, and surely the original sentence was not talking about bat-cats.

Not only can English sentences appear in greater and greater grammatical complexity once quantifiers and predicates are permitted, but they are also frequently ambiguous. When one exclaims:

God helps those who help themselves.

the claim could be

1. God helps (only) those who help themselves.

Or it could be

    2. God helps (all) those who help themselves.

Or possibly the claim could be both (1) and (2)!
    Using 'Hxx' for 'x helps x' (that is, x helps himself or herself), we have two different claims:

    1'. $\forall x(Hgx \rightarrow Hxx)$

and

    2'. $\forall x(Hxx \rightarrow Hgx)$

In this symbolization, it should be evident that g = God and that 'Hgx' means that God helps x.
    You will frequently find it helpful to symbolize more complicated statements in stages starting at the beginning of the sentence. Consider this example:

    3. All students like some professor or other.

Since this is a universal claim about all students, the first stage of symbolizing is to represent the universal form:

    $\forall x$(if x is a student, then x likes some professor)

We now symbolize 'x is a student' as 'Dx' and get:

    $\forall x(Dx \rightarrow x$ likes some professor)

How do we symbolize 'x likes some professor'? Using 'Lxy' for 'x likes y' and 'Fy' for 'y is a professor', we write:

    $\exists y(Fy \,\&\, Lxy)$

We now place this clause in the consequent of the conditional, in place of 'x likes some professor'.

    3. $\forall x(Dx \rightarrow \exists y(Fy \,\&\, Lxy))$

In this example, we used 'Fy' for 'y is a professor'. It is important to recognize that the variable could be different in both places:

Fy: y is a professor
Fz: z is a professor

Had we chosen 'z', we would have had this equally correct symbolization:

3a. $\forall x(Dx \rightarrow \exists z(Fz \ \& \ Lxz))$

Let us look at a related example:

4. Professors admire any professor who is liked by students.

Here we have a universal claim about professors. Our first stage might look like this:

$\forall x(Fx \rightarrow x$ admires any professor who is liked by students)

We need to characterize a professor, any one, who is liked by students. Then we shall state that x admires such a professor. So, this last clause will be written as

For any y, if y is a professor who is liked by students, then x admires y.

Now 'y is a professor who is liked by students' can be written (with the understanding that we mean *some* students) as follows:

$(Fy \ \& \ \exists z(Dz \ \& \ Lzy))$

Putting all the clauses together, we get:

4. $\forall x(Fx \rightarrow \forall y((Fy \ \& \ \exists z(Dz \ \& \ Lzy)) \rightarrow Axy))$

Summary

Predicate logic takes us beyond assigning truth values to sentences and requires us to consider individuals and their properties, relations between individuals, and quantification. Individuals are denoted by lower-case letters from the beginning of the alphabet, while individual variables are lower-case letters from the end of the alphabet. Predicate letters are upper-case letters from the beginning of the alphabet. A single-place predicate followed by an individual constant is a sentence. An n-place predicate followed by n constants is a sentence.

Among the possible strings (sequences of symbols), we carefully distinguished well-formed formulas (wffs). A wff preceded by a quantifier is also a wff. Quantifiers are either universal or existential. They have a scope, and any occurrence of the quantifier variable in the scope of the quantifier is bound. A wff with no free occurrences of variables is a sentence.

The truth conditions for a quantified sentence are:

$V(\forall xSx)$ = TRUE iff the value of every instance of 'Sx' is TRUE.
$V(\exists xSx)$ = TRUE iff the value of at least one instance of 'Sx' is TRUE.

Finally, the notions of a model, a minimal model, and dossiers on individuals were introduced, and some suggestions for symbolizing were put forward.

Exercises

A. Using the individual constants and predicate letters in the table below, symbolize the sentences that follow.

a = Socrates   F = is (or was) a philosopher
b = Plato   G = is (or was) a logician

1. Socrates is a logician.
2. Plato was a logician.
3. Socrates was a philosopher and Plato was a logician.
4. Plato was not a logician but Socrates was a philosopher.
5. If Plato was a philosopher, then so was Socrates.

B. Using the table from Exercise A, translate the following formulas into English:
1. Fa
2. Fb
3. (Ga v Fb)
4. (Gb & ~Fa)
5. (Ga ↔ Gb)

C. Let C = is a computer programmer
   D = is a philosopher
   E = is a mathematician
Symbolize the following sentences:
1. Everyone is a philosopher.
2. Someone is a mathematician.
3. Nobody is a computer programmer.
4. Not everyone is a mathematician.
5. All mathematicians are philosophers.
6. Some philosophers are computer programmers.
7. Every computer programmer is not a philosopher.
8. Some philosophers are not computer programmers.
9. Not all mathematicians are philosophers.
10. Everyone is either a mathematician or a philosopher.
11. Everyone is a mathematician and a philosopher.
12. No mathematician programs computers.

D. Using the same interpretations for the symbols as in C, translate the following formulas into English:
1. ∀xCx
2. ∀yCy
3. ∃uDu
4. ~∃xDx

    5. ∃x~Dx
    6. ∀x~Ex
    7. ∀x(Cx → Dx)
    8. ∃x(Cx → Dx)
    9. ∃x(Cx & Ex)
   10. ∀x(Cx & Ex)

E. In which of the fifteen minimal models mentioned in the chapter are the following sentences TRUE, and in which are they FALSE?
    1. ∀xFx
    2. ∀x(Fx → Gx)
    3. ∀x(Fx v Gx)
    4. ∀x(Fx & Gx)
    5. ∀x~Gx
    6. ∃xFx
    7. ~∃x~Gx
    8. ∃x~Gx
    9. ~∀xGx
   10. ∃x(Fx v Gx)
   11. ∃x(Fx & Gx)
   12. ∃x(Fx → Gx)
   13. ∀x(Fx v Fx)
   14. ∀x(Fx → Fx)
   15. ∃x(Fx & Fx)

F. Let L = is taller than
        a = Alfred
        b = Betty
Symbolize the following sentences:
    1. Alfred is taller than Betty.
    2. Betty is taller than Alfred.
    3. Alfred is not taller than himself.
    4. Someone is taller than Betty.
    5. Alfred is taller than everyone.
    6. Everyone is taller than someone. (*Hint:* Be careful!)
    7. Someone is taller than everyone.

G. Using the same interpretations of the symbols as in F, translate the following formulas into English:
    1. Lba
    2. ~Lab
    3. ~Lbb
    4. ∀xLax
    5. ∀xLxa
    6. ∃xLbx
    7. ∃xLxb
    8. ∃x∀yLxy
    9. ∃x∀yLyx
   10. ∀x∃yLxy

11. $\forall x \exists y Lyx$
12. $\forall x Lxx$
13. $\exists y Lyy$

H. Symbolize the following sentences:
1. If Sam really loves Mary, then no one loves Sam.
2. All owners of handguns are in violation of some law. (Where $Oxy = x$ owns y, $Hx = x$ is a handgun, $Vxy = x$ violates y, and $Lx = x$ is a law.)
3. All lovers of lovers love themselves. (Use only the predicate $Lxy = x$ loves y.)
4. Every doctor who treats himself has a fool for a client. (Where $Dx = x$ is a doctor, $Txy = x$ treats y, $Fx = x$ is a fool, $Cx = x$ is a client.)
5. Some business people have their fingers in every business. (Where $Bx = x$ is a business person, $Hxyz = x$ has y in z, $Fxy = x$ is the finger of y and $Ox = x$ is a business.)
6. All those who admire themselves and who love no one other than their mothers are going to get elected in every country. (Where $Axy = x$ admires y, $Lxy = x$ loves y, $Mxy = x$ is the mother or y, $Exy = x$ is going to get elected in y, $Cx = x$ is a country.)
7. No one who despises Napolean loves a dirty joke.
8. No one admires anyone who tries to do everything.
9. Everyone has some problems but no one has every problem.
10. Everyone either admires or despises Franklin D. Roosevelt.
11. If anyone gives me a stupid gift on my birthday, I won't send him a thank-you card. (Where $Gxyzw = x$ gave y to z on w, $Gx = x$ is a stupid gift, $Bx = x$ is my birthday, $m = $ I/me, $Sxyz = x$ will send y a z, $Tx = x$ is a thank-you card.)

Suggestions for Computer Implementation

It is not especially difficult to convert into a computer program the algorithm for deciding when a string that might include quantifiers, variables, or constants is a well-formed sentence. We only need to modify the algorithm given in Chapter 5. Since few computer terminals have the symbols '$\forall$' and '$\exists$', you might wish to reserve the letters 'A' and 'E' to serve in their place and then avoid using these letters for sentences or predicates. Or, you could use the words 'ALL' and 'SOME'.

If we restrict ourselves to sentences containing one-place predicates, a program could also be written that determines whether an argument is valid or invalid. We gave a sketch of the underlying algorithm in this chapter. When the corresponding program is written, one of the first steps must be to provide some data structure to hold a model or many models. As we have hinted, a model can be stored as an array (a table) whose rows (dossiers) indicate the predicates satisfied by distinct individuals. One early step also must be to count the total number of distinct predicates contained in the sentences of the argument. We then need to generate all the representative individuals. (For inspiration on a method for doing so, you might recall how we generated all the possible combinations for truth values in Chapter 6. Additionally, if the representative individuals are "named" by numbers, they can carry their dossiers with them.) We next need to produce all the minimal models. This task amounts to producing all the various combinations of representative individuals.

Once the minimal models have been produced, we need to devise a procedure for determining the truth values of the premises and conclusion in a given model. As we have seen, this can be accomplished by borrowing the main technique from WANG'S ALGORITHM (step 3 in Chapter 6) and by adding the conditions whose "main connective" is in fact a quantifier. For suggestions on programming these steps, consult the implementation suggestions at the end of Chapter 6. Note that we also need a slightly different TEST procedure than that given in Chapter 6 for WANG'S ALGORITHM.

Exercises

1. Write an algorithm (or program) that inputs the sentences of an argument and determines the total number of distinct predicates in them.
2. Write an algorithm (or program) that takes a list of distinct predicates (either as input or produced by another procedure in the same program) and generates all the representative individuals.
3. Modify the algorithm MAIN-CONNECTIVE in Chapter 6 so that if a formula is universally or existentially quantified, the quantifier whose scope covers the rest of the formula is identified as the "main connective" of the formula. (The initial quantifier is not really a connective, since it does not connect sentences. It is a "connective" much like negation is a connective.)
4. Write an algorithm (or program) that takes as input a universally or existentially quantified formula and a list of individuals and then does the following: (a) deletes the initial quantifier and (b) outputs all the *instances* of the resulting formula.
5. Write an algorithm (or program) to determine when a formula is a simple predicate formula—a formula containing only a predicate and individual constants.

PREDICATE LOGIC:
Quantifier Inference
Rules

A valid argument, we recall, is an argument where it is impossible for the premises to be TRUE and the conclusion FALSE. In the logic of sentences, there are several ways to determine if an argument is valid or invalid. We can, in the logic of sentences, construct a truth table and examine every situation to see if it is possible for the premises to be TRUE and the conclusion FALSE. In predicate logic, however, it is not possible, in general, to construct or to inspect all models, including those models in which the premises are TRUE or the conclusion FALSE. Consequently, other ways of showing an argument to be valid must be found. One of the simplest ways is to derive the conclusion from the premises in a formal deduction system with truth-preserving rules of inference. (The system should also be complete, in the sense that every conclusion of a valid argument can be derived in the system.)

We turn now to the problem of deriving conclusions with sentences containing quantifiers and variables. The whole point of symbolizing the structure of sentences with quantifiers and variables is to enable ourselves to derive conclusions that we could not prove by the methods of sentential logic alone.

We feel sure that

1. All Greeks are mortal.
2. Socrates is a Greek.
∴ 3. Socrates is mortal.

is a valid argument. We need to see why it is valid, and also we need to develop rules that will allow us to derive the conclusion from the premises.

When the above argument is symbolized, we get something like

1. $\forall x(Gx \rightarrow Mx)$
2. Gc
∴ 3. Mc

Sentence (1) "says" that for every individual x, '$(Gx \rightarrow Mx)$' is satisfied by that individual. Hence, an instance using 'c', the name of Socrates, for 'x' is TRUE. That is, if (1) has the truth value TRUE, so does

1a. $(Gc \rightarrow Mc)$

But now we can use →ELIM on (1a) and (2) to obtain (3).

The earlier rules for introducing and eliminating connectives in a sentential derivation remain unchanged. We need only to add some rules for introducing and eliminating quantifiers. Our general strategy will be to eliminate quantifiers somehow, manipulate and transform the results using the earlier sentential rules, and, finally, introduce appropriate quantifiers, if needed, to obtain the desired conclusion. These new rules for quantifier INTRO and ELIM are very precisely stated, and careful attention must be paid not only to the sentence on the line to which the rule is applied but also to other sentences in the proof or subproof.

Universal Quantifier Rules

Our earlier rules of inference from Chapters 8 and 9 apply to quantified sentences considered as atomic sentences. Thus &ELIM will apply to a line with the sentence '$(\forall xFx \ \& \ \forall yGy)$' on it. We take '$\forall xFx$' as a single sentence **P** and '$\forall yGy$' as **Q**. That is, we take '$(\forall xFx \ \& \ \forall yGy)$' as having the form (**P** & **Q**). Now, however, we are going to extend our deduction system in order to make additional derivations to and from quantified sentences.

Universal Elimination

Reflecting on the truth conditions for a universally quantified sentence, say '∀xFx', we note that it has the value TRUE only if all instances of 'Fx' also have the value TRUE. Hence, if we infer an instance, any instance, from '∀xFx', we shall never move from a true sentence to a false one. This provides a justification for the rule:

∀ELIM RULE: From a sentence of the form
                 ∀vP
               you may derive
                 P[c/v]

In the statement of the rule, '**v**' is used for any variable at all (*w, x, y, z, . . .*) and '**c**' for any constant at all (*a, b, c, d, . . .*). We use the notation **P[c/v]** for the result of replacing all free occurrences of the variable **v** in formula **P** with the constant **c**.

For example, if **P** is '∃x(Fx ∨ Gy)', then **P**[a/y] is '∃x(Fx ∨ Ga)', but **P**[a/x] is still '∃x(Fx ∨ Gy)', since 'x' is not free in **P**.

In a derivation, the use of ∀ELIM would look like this:

   10. ∀x(Fx → Hx)   :<PREMISE or Rule>
     ·
     ·
     ·
   15. (Fd → Hd)   :∀ELIM,10

The sentence on line 10 is universally quantified, and the sentence on line 15 results from the one on line 10 by deleting the initial quantifier and replacing all now free occurrences of the quantifier variable 'x' with the individual constant 'd'.

It is essential to note that this rule and all the other quantifier rules require the scope of the initial quantifier to stretch to the end of the sentence on that line. Here is an example of a sentence where ∀ELIM cannot be used, because the scope of the universal quantifier expression '∀x' is not the entire sentence:

   (∀xFx ∨ ∀yGy)

From this sentence, one cannot get '(Fa ∨ ∀yGy)' by ∀ELIM.

One can use ∀ELIM several times over, citing the same line:

   10. ∀x(Fx → Hx)
     ·
     ·
     ·
   15. (Fd → Hd)   :∀ELIM,10
   16. (Fe → He)   :∀ELIM,10

CHAPTER 13

Universal Introduction

Next, we would like to be able to generalize, that is, to introduce a universal quantifier. A clue to justifying this move can be found in elementary geometry classes, where the teacher draws a triangle on the board and then uses this specific triangle to prove theorems about *all* triangles. This works as long as no appeal is made to any special properties of the example triangle. That is, if we can prove something about an *arbitrarily* selected individual, we have proved it for *any* individual. We need only to ensure that special properties of the selected individual play no role in the proof. The following rule is qualified to ensure just that.

∀INTRO RULE: From a sentence
                P
you may derive
∀**v**P[**v**/**c**]
Provided that:
1. **c** does not occur in any premise.
2. If **P** occurs in a subproof, no constant in **P** occurs in an ASSUMPTION still in force.
3. All new occurrences of the variable **v** in **P** are free after the replacement in P[**v**/**c**].

In proviso (2), an ASSUMPTION is "still in force" during the subproof following it and during any sub-subproofs within that. Finally, the notation **P[v/c]** means that all occurrences of the constant **c** are replaced by the variable **v.** So, proviso (3) means that when **v** replaces **c,** it should not fall within the scope of a quantifier already present that uses **v.** The new occurrence of the variable should not, so to speak, be "captured" by a quantifier already present in the wff **P.**

Examples of the correct use of ∀INTRO are given below. Assume throughout that the restrictions on the constant on line 5 are all met.

Example 1.
  5. $(Fa \rightarrow Ga)$:<Rule>
    .

    .

    .

  9. $\forall x(Fx \rightarrow Gx)$:∀INTRO,5

Example 2.
    5. $(Fb \lor \exists yGy)$:<Rule>
      .

      .

      .

  12. $\forall x(Fx \lor \exists yGy)$:∀INTRO,5

Here is a complete derivation for the following argument:

$\forall x(Fx \rightarrow Gx)$
$\therefore (\forall yFy \rightarrow \forall zGz)$

   1. $\forall x(Fx \rightarrow Gx)$:PREMISE
      /BEGIN: $(\forall yFy \rightarrow \forall zGz)$ by $\rightarrow$INTRO/
  *2. $\forall yFy$:ASSUMPTION
  *3. Fa :$\forall$ELIM,2
  *4. $\forall x(Fx \rightarrow Gx)$:SEND,1
  *5. $(Fa \rightarrow Ga)$:$\forall$ELIM,4
  *6. Ga :$\rightarrow$ELIM,5,3
  *7. $\forall zGz$:$\forall$INTRO,6
  *8. $(\forall yFy \rightarrow \forall zGz)$:$\rightarrow$INTRO,2,7
      /END: $(\forall yFy \rightarrow \forall zGz)$/
   9. $(\forall yFy \rightarrow \forall zGz)$:RETURN,8

Here is an incorrect use of $\forall$INTRO:

Example 3.
   5. $(Fa \rightarrow Ga)$:<Rule>
     .
     .
     .

   9. $\forall x(Fx \rightarrow Ga)$:$\forall$INTRO,5   [INCORRECT—Not all occurrences of 'a'
                                   replaced.]

Another incorrect use of $\forall$INTRO is:

Example 4.
   5. $(Fa \rightarrow \exists x(Ga \ \& \ Hx))$:<Rule>
     .
     .
     .

   9. $\forall x(Fx \rightarrow \exists x(Gx \ \& \ Hx))$:$\forall$INTRO,5   [INCORRECT—the 'x' in 'Gx'
                                   was captured.]

Observe that the replacement of 'a' in 'Ga' by 'x' in line 5 led to its being captured by the existential quantifier already there. Instead of 'x', we could use another variable, say 'y', and correctly infer:

   9. $\forall y(Fy \rightarrow \exists x(Gy \ \& \ Hx))$:$\forall$INTRO,5

With these two rules we can derive the conclusions of some arguments traditionally studied since the time of Aristotle. One, for instance, is the ancient syllogistic argument:

All humans are mortal.
All Greeks are humans.
∴ All Greeks are mortal.

The first step, of course, is to symbolize the English sentences:

∀x(Hx → Mx)
∀x(Gx → Hx)
∴ ∀x(Gx → Mx)

A proof of the conclusion using our two quantification rules goes as follows:

1. ∀x(Hx → Mx)   :PREMISE
2. ∀x(Gx → Hx)   :PREMISE
3. (Ha → Ma)   :∀ELIM,1
4. (Ga → Ha)   :∀ELIM,2
5. (Ga → Ma)   :HS,2,1
6. ∀x(Gx → Mx)   :∀INTRO,5

The restrictions on the rule ∀INTRO prevent the following attempted derivation:

1. ∀x(Gx → Mx)   :PREMISE
2. Gf   :PREMISE
3. (Gf → Mf)   :∀ELIM,1
4. Mf   :→ELIM,2,3
5. ∀xMx   :∀INTRO,4 [INCORRECT]

Here, 'f' occurs in PREMISE 2 and cannot be generalized on.

Existential Quantifier Rules

Having a pair of rules for introducing and eliminating universal quantifiers, we need now to develop a pair of rules of inference to introduce and eliminate existential quantifiers.

Existential Introduction

The next rule is again easy to justify. If something is true of a particular individual, then there is some individual for which it is true. Schematically,

Fa
∴ ∃xFx

The correct statement of the rule is:

∃INTRO   From a sentence of the form
          P[c/v]
          you may derive
          ∃vP

In this rule, the constant **c** replaces all *free* occurrences of the variable **v** in well-formed formula **P.**

You may find the statement of this rule to be odd, because as you move down the lines of a derivation, you encounter the sentence **P[c/v]** before you come to the sentence with the variable **v,** namely, ∃vP. But to use the rule correctly, you need only to ensure that the earlier sentence and the wff you are about to existentially quantify are properly related: The earlier one can be obtained from **P** by replacing all free occurrences of **v** with **c.** In addition, if you are following a modified version of PROOF-GIVER, then you will, in fact, encounter ∃vP first in your task file before you get to **P[c/v].** This is because the task file begins at the end of the derivation and works up to the premises.

These are all correct uses of the rule ∃INTRO:

n.	Faa	Faa	Faa	Faa	:\<PREMISE or Rule\>
	·	·	·	·	
	·	·	·	·	
	·	·	·	·	
n + k.	∃xFxx	∃xFxa	∃xFax	∃xFaa	:∃INTRO,*n*

Each of these is a truth-preserving inference allowed by the rule. Any argument with line *n* as premise and line (*n* + *k*) as conclusion is a valid argument. Each of the four simple inferences above is allowable by the rule ∃INTRO. Moreover, in our previous example, although we could not derive '∀xMx' ('Everything is mortal'), we could at line 5 derive '∃xMx' ('Something is mortal').

1. ∀x(Gx → Mx)   :PREMISE
2. Gf   :PREMISE
3. (Gf → Mf)   :∀ELIM,1
4. Mf   :→ELIM,3,2
5. ∃xMx   :∃INTRO,4

Existential Elimination

The final rule, ∃ELIM, deals with the sorts of inferences one can validly make from an existentially quantified sentence. Here we take a cue from legal practice. Frequently, in legal situations, we know that *someone* committed the crime, but we don't know who specifically it was. A warrant is issued for someone, John Doe or Jane Doe. We then reason about, say, John Doe, although we don't know exactly who he is. Whatever conclusion we reach that does not refer to John Doe *by that name* is, in general, a correct conclusion.

Our strategy with an existentially quantified sentence is to name someone as John Doe and see what follows. If we reach a conclusion that does not depend on someone's actually being named John Doe, then that is a valid conclusion from the original statement referring, nonspecifically, to someone or other. Let us look at the rule and practice using it.

∃ELIM   If a sentence on a previous line has the form
           ∃vP
         and there is a subproof beginning with ASSUMPTION
           P[c/v]
         where constant **c** is new to the proof, and ending with a sentence
           Q
         not containing **c**,
         then **Q** may be RETURNed from that subproof.

To say that a constant is "new to the proof" means, simply, that it has not been used before. Note that the RETURN rule has now been slightly, but significantly, expanded.

Rule ∃ELIM is different from any of the other elimination rules because it is not a rule for eliminating an existential quantifier from a line. It is more like a strategy for constructing subproofs to derive conclusions from existentially quantified sentences.

Let us work a few examples, again drawn from traditional Aristotelian logic.

All circus animals are tame animals.
Some lions are circus animals.
∴ Some lions are tame animals.

1. $\forall x(Cx \rightarrow Ax)$:PREMISE
2. $\exists x(Lx \& Cx)$:PREMISE
     /BEGIN: ∃ELIM/

*3. $(La \& Ca)$:ASSUMPTION for ∃ELIM,2
*4. $\forall x(Cx \rightarrow Ax)$:SEND,1
*5. $(Ca \rightarrow Aa)$:∀ELIM,4
*6. Ca :&ELIM,3
*7. Aa :→ELIM,5,6
*8. La :&ELIM,3
*9. $(La \& Aa)$:&INTRO,8,7
*10. $\exists x(Lx \& Ax)$:∃INTRO,9
     /END: ∃ELIM/

11. $\exists x(Lx \& Ax)$:RETURN,10

In line 3, we assumed that a is a lion who is a circus animal. The subproof concludes on line 10 with a sentence that does not mention a and thus does not depend on the assumption that '*a*' is a name of a circus lion. So, the information on line 10 may be returned to the main proof.*

Some Examples

When using the quantifier introduction and elimination rules, one must take care that the scope of the quantifier (introduced or eliminated) is the entire sentence on the line. We shall examine some ways of dealing with sentences having quantifiers whose scope is only a proper part of the sentence. For instance, in

($\forall x$Fx & A)

the scope of '$\forall x$' is just the left conjunct. The inner structure of the right conjunct, 'A', is of no concern here; it can be any sentence whatever, with one caution to be explained shortly. We cannot use $\forall$ELIM on this sentence as it stands, but we can derive another sentence from it to which $\forall$ELIM can apply:

1. ($\forall x$Fx & A)   :PREMISE
2. $\forall x$Fx :&ELIM,1
3. A   :&ELIM,1
4. Fa :$\forall$ELIM,2
5. (Fa & A)   :&INTRO,4,3
6. $\forall x$(Fx & A)   :$\forall$INTRO,5

The derivation assumes that the sentence A does not contain the constant '*a*'. If there are constants in sentence A, then the constant introduced at line 4 should be different from any of them.

Here is another simple derivation that moves a quantifier to the beginning of the sentence:

1. (A $\rightarrow \forall x$Fx)   :PREMISE
     /BEGIN: $\rightarrow$ INTRO for (A $\rightarrow$ Fa)/

Historical note: The argument above was stated as a correct Aristotelian syllogistic argument. The noun phrase "tame animals" must be used, although to a modern ear, the sentence sounds stilted. With our symbolism, we could deal directly with the more naturally sounding argument:

All circus animals are tame.
Some lions are circus animals.
∴ Some lions are tame.

The symbolic form remains the same. The difference is that earlier, 'Ax' symbolized 'x is a tame animal', while now it symbolizes 'x is tame'.

```
*2.   A                  :ASSUMPTION
*3.   (A → ∀xFx)         :SEND,1
*4.   ∀xFx               :→ELIM,3,2
*5.   Fa                 :∀ELIM,4
*6.   (A → Fa)           :→INTRO,2,5
      /END: →INTRO/

7. (A → Fa)             :RETURN,6
8. ∀x(A → Fx)           :∀INTRO,7
```

Quantifier Negation Rule

Before we work on the next examples, it will be helpful to consider the cases where a negation sign precedes a quantifier whose scope is the rest of the sentence. There are two kinds of cases:

$\sim\forall xFx \qquad \sim\exists xFx$

We propose to show that

'$\sim\exists xFx$' is logically equivalent to '$\forall x\sim Fx$'.

The equivalence between the other two, '$\sim\forall xFx$' and '$\exists x\sim Fx$', is shown similarly; it is an exercise at the end of the chapter. The results are of some importance, since these logical equivalences open the way to using the rule of replacement on wffs with quantifiers flanked by negation signs.

One way to show the equivalence is by way of a *semantic* discussion of the truth conditions for the pair of sentences. Thus we would begin by pointing out that

'$\sim\exists xFx$' is TRUE if and only if '$\exists xFx$' is FALSE

and that

'$\exists xFx$' is FALSE if and only if every instance of 'Fx' is FALSE.

But this is so if and only if every instance of '$\sim Fx$' is TRUE, and that is the condition if and only if '$\forall x\sim Fx$' is TRUE.

A second way of showing equivalence is to prove that the biconditional of the two is a theorem. Thus we shall prove '$(\sim\exists xFx \leftrightarrow \forall x\sim Fx)$' beginning with no premises. There is a problem of strategy during the derivation, and we shall interrupt the derivation at that point to discuss the problem and a solution.

QUANTIFIER RULES

```
 *1.   ~∃xFx                          :ASSUMPTION
       /BEGIN: ~INTRO to derive ~Fa/
**2.     Fa                           :ASSUMPTION
**3.     ∃xFx                         :∃INTRO,2
**4.     ~∃xFx                        :SEND,1
**5.     ~Fa                          :~INTRO,2,3,4
       /END: ~INTRO/
 *6.   ~Fa                            :RETURN,5
 *7.   ∀x~Fx                          :∀INTRO,6
 *8.   (~∃xFx → ∀x~Fx)                :→INTRO,1,7
       /END: →INTRO/
  9.   (~∃xFx → ∀x~Fx)                :RETURN,8
*10.   ∀X~Fx                          :ASSUMPTION
       /BEGIN: ~INTRO to derive ~∃xFx/
**11.    ∃xFx                         :ASSUMPTION
         /BEGIN: ∃ELIM/
***12.     Fb                         :ASSUMPTION for ∃ELIM,2
***13.     ∀x~Fx                      :SEND,10
***14.     ~Fb                        :∀ELIM,13
```

We now have a problem: A contradiction can be seen on lines 12 and 14, but since they contain 'b'—the constant in the assumption at 12—they cannot be returned out of the subproof. But given a contradiction, any sentence can be proved—in particular, a contradiction without the constant 'b'. Letting 'A' be an atomic sentence (say, 'Grass is green'), we continue the proof.

```
***15.     (Fb v (A & ~A))           :vINTRO,12
***16.     (A & ~A)                  :vELIM,15,14
         /END: ∃ELIM/
**17.    (A & ~A)                    :RETURN,16
**18.    A                           :&ELIM,17
**19.    ~A                          :&ELIM,17
**20.    ~∃xFx                       :~INTRO,11,18,19
       /END: ~INTRO/
*21.   ~∃xFx                         :RETURN,20
*22.   (∀x~Fx → ~∃xFx)              :→INTRO,10,21
       /END: →INTRO/
 23.   (∀x~Fx → ~∃xFx)              :RETURN,22
 24.   (~∃xFx ↔ ∀x~Fx)              :↔INTRO,9,23
```

Since 'Fx' played no significant role in the above proof, this result holds for any wff in place of 'Fx'. We can now adopt a quantifier negation rule:

QUANTIFIER NEGATION (QN)   ~∃vS is derivable iff ∀v~S is derivable.
                              ~∀vS is derivable iff ∃v~S is derivable.

This rule enables us, at any time in a proof, to "move the negation sign through a quantifier" if we change the *quantity* of the quantifier. This derived rule is very useful, as the following proof shows:

To prove that '∀x(Fx → A)' is logically equivalent to '(∃xFx → A)'

A proof, using no premises, of the biconditional:

*1.	∀x(Fx → A)	:ASSUMPTION
	/BEGIN: → INTRO for (∃xFx → A)/	
**2.	∃xFx	:ASSUMPTION
	/BEGIN: ∃ELIM/	
***3.	Fa	:ASSUMPTION for ∃ELIM,2
***4.	∀x(Fx → A)	:SEND,1
***5.	(Fa → A)	:∀ELIM,4
***6.	A	: → ELIM,3,5
	/END: ∃ELIM/	
**7.	A	:RETURN,6
**8.	(∃xFx → A)	: → INTRO,2,7
	/END: → INTRO/	
*9.	(∃xFx → A)	:RETURN,8
*10.	(∀x(Fx → A) → (∃xFx → A))	: → INTRO,1,9
	/END: → INTRO/	
11.	(∀x(Fx → A) → (∃xFx → A))	:RETURN,10
*12.	(∃xFx → A)	:ASSUMPTION
	/BEGIN: ~ELIM to derive ∀x(Fx → A)/	
**13.	~∀x(Fx → A)	:ASSUMPTION
**14.	∃x ~(Fx → A)	:QN,13
	/BEGIN: ∃ELIM/	
***15.	~(Fb → A)	:ASSUMPTION for ∃ELIM,14
***16.	~~(Fb & ~A)	:RR EQ,15
***17.	(Fb & ~A)	:RR DN,16
***18.	Fb	:&ELIM,17
***19.	∃xFx	:∃INTRO,18
***20.	~A	:&ELIM,17
***21.	(∃xFx & ~A)	:&INTRO,20,19
	/END: ∃ELIM/	
**22.	(∃xFx & ~A)	:RETURN,21
**23.	∃xFx	:&ELIM,22
**24.	(∃xFx → A)	:SEND,12
**25.	A	: → ELIM,24,23

**26.	~A	:&ELIM,22
**27.	∀x(Fx → A)	:~ELIM,13,25,26
	/END: ~ELIM/	
*28.	∀x(Fx → A)	:RETURN,27
*29.	((∃xFx → A) → ∀x(Fx → A))	:→ INTRO,12,28
	/END: → INTRO/	
30.	((∃xFx → A) → ∀x(Fx → A))	:RETURN,29
31.	(∀x(Fx → A) ↔ (∃xFx → A))	:↔INTRO,11,30

Let us apply our expanded set of rules to a few examples in order to become more familiar with proofs. The first example has some historical interest. The British logician and logic-machine builder W. S. Jevons, modifying an example from Augustus De Morgan, accused traditional Aristotelian logic of being unable to validate this argument:

Horses are animals.
Therefore, every head of a horse is a head of an animal.

Using 'Dyx' for 'y is a head of x', we can symbolize these sentences as:

∀x(Hx → Ax)
∴∀y(∃x(Hx & Dyx) → ∃z(Az & Dyz))

Now working back from the conclusion, we can devise a simple proof.

1.	∀x(Hx → Ax)	:PREMISE
	/BEGIN: → INTRO for (∃x(Hx & Dax) → ∃z(Az & Daz))/	
*2.	∃x(Hx & Dax)	:ASSUMPTION
	/BEGIN: ∃z(Az & Daz)/	
**3.	(Hb & Dab)	:ASSUMPTION for ∃ELIM,2
**4.	∀x(Hx → Ax)	:SEND,1
**5.	(Hb → Ab)	:∀ELIM,4
**6.	Hb	: & ELIM,3
**7.	Ab	: → ELIM,6,5
**8.	Dab	:&ELIM,3
**9.	(Ab & Dab)	: & INTRO,7,8
**10.	∃z(Az & Daz)	:∃INTRO,9
	/END: ∃ELIM/	
*11.	∃z(Az & Daz)	:RETURN,10
*12.	(∃x(Hx & Dax) → ∃z(Az & Daz))	: → INTRO,2,11
	/END: → INTRO/	
13.	(∃x(Hx & Dax) → ∃z(Az & Daz))	:RETURN,12
14.	∀y(∃x(Hx & Dyx) → ∃z(Az & Dyz))	:∀INTRO,13

This concludes the proof. Notice that line 13 contains 'a' with no restrictions on ∀INTRO, since the assumptions at lines 2 and 3 are no longer in force.

The next example illustrates how we can handle the identity relation with our present notation. [We could, by the way, extend our present system to treat the identity relation in a special way, with special rules of inference for formulas with an identity sign (=).] Consider this argument:

If one event causes another event, the first event begins before the second. When one event begins before another, the events are not identical. Every event is identical to itself. Hence, no event is its own cause.

Our dictionary for symbolizing is:

Cxy: x causes y
Bxy: x begins before y
Ixy: x is identical to y

We symbolize this argument as follows:

1. $\forall x \forall y (Cxy \rightarrow Bxy)$
2. $\forall x \forall y (Bxy \rightarrow \sim Ixy)$
3. $\forall x Ixx$
∴ 4. $\forall x \sim Cxx$

Observe that the conclusion is a universally quantified sentence. This suggests that in the last step in the derivation, the rule ∀INTRO is applied. As usual, our strategy will be to eliminate quantifiers first, perform sentence transformations, and then introduce quantifiers where needed.

1.	$\forall x \forall y (Cxy \rightarrow Bxy)$	:PREMISE
2.	$\forall x \forall y (Bxy \rightarrow \sim Ixy)$	:PREMISE
3.	$\forall x Ixx$	:PREMISE
4.	Iaa	:∀ELIM,3
5.	$\forall y (Bay \rightarrow \sim Iay)$	:∀ELIM,2
6.	$(Baa \rightarrow \sim Iaa)$	:∀ELIM,5
7.	$\forall y (Cay \rightarrow Bay)$	:∀ELIM,1
8.	$(Caa \rightarrow Baa)$	:∀ELIM,7
9.	$\sim\sim Iaa$	:RR DN,4
10.	$\sim Baa$	:MT,6,9
11.	$\sim Caa$	:MT,8,10
12.	$\forall x \sim Cxx$	:∀INTRO,11

Our final example will give us some practice with the quantifier negation rule:

Not all successful people are rich. But all successful people are either happy or rich. So, there are some people who are not rich and yet who are happy.

Symbolizing this with some care, we get:

1. $\sim\forall x(Sx \rightarrow Rx)$
2. $\forall x(Sx \rightarrow (Rx \lor Hx))$
∴ 3. $\exists x(\sim Rx \,\&\, Hx)$

One proof of this argument is:

1.	$\sim\forall x(Sx \rightarrow Rx)$	:PREMISE
2.	$\forall x(Sx \rightarrow (Rx \lor Hx))$	:PREMISE
3.	$\exists x\sim(Sx \rightarrow Rx)$	:QN,1
	/BEGIN: $\exists$ELIM to derive $\exists x(\sim Rx \,\&\, Hx)$/	
*4.	$\sim(Sa \rightarrow Ra)$	:ASSUMPTION for $\exists$ELIM,3
*5.	$\forall x(Sx \rightarrow (Rx \lor Hx))$	:SEND,2
*6.	$(Sa \rightarrow (Ra \lor Ha))$	:$\forall$ELIM,5
*7.	$\sim\sim(Sa \,\&\, \sim Ra)$	:RR EQ,4
*8.	$(Sa \,\&\, \sim Ra)$	:RR DN,7
*9.	Sa	:&ELIM,8
*10.	$(Ra \lor Ha)$	:$\rightarrow$ELIM,9,6
*11.	$\sim Ra$	:&ELIM,8
*12.	Ha	:$\lor$ELIM,11,10
*13.	$(\sim Ra \,\&\, Ha)$	:&INTRO,11,12
*14.	$\exists x(\sim Rx \,\&\, Hx)$	:$\exists$INTRO,13
	/END: $\exists$ELIM/	
15.	$\exists x(\sim Rx \,\&\, Hx)$	:RETURN,14

This concludes the proof. It will be very helpful for you to review these examples and to work some of the related exercises at the end of the chapter.

Invalid Arguments

We have been deriving conclusions of valid arguments. But what if an argument is invalid? How would we show that an argument is invalid? Consider this argument:

All circus animals are tame.
Some lions are not circus animals.
∴ Some lions are not tame.

$\forall x(Cx \rightarrow Ax)$
$\exists x(Lx \,\&\, \sim Cx)$
∴ $\exists x(Lx \,\&\, \sim Ax)$

Try as we might, we would not be able to produce the indicated conclusion using our rules. And it is well that we cannot, for the conclusion is not a logical consequence of the premises. But how do we show that it is not?

To show an argument to be *invalid,* we must provide a model in which the premises are true sentences but the conclusion is a false one. That is, we must describe a model where inspection of the dossiers on individuals in the model reveals that the premises are TRUE but the conclusion is FALSE. There are many such models for the argument we are now considering; here is one with just two individuals:

	C	A	L
a	1	1	0
b	0	1	1

We can see that both '$(Ca \rightarrow Aa)$' and '$(Cb \rightarrow Ab)$' are TRUE in this model. Thus

'$\forall x(Cx \rightarrow Ax)$' is TRUE in the model.

Furthermore, $V(Lb \ \& \sim Cb) =$ TRUE, so

'$\exists x(Lx \ \& \sim Cb)$' is TRUE in the model.

But $V(La \ \& \sim Aa) =$ FALSE, and $V(Lb \ \& \sim Ab) =$ FALSE also. Since there are no other individuals,

'$\exists x(Lx \ \& \sim Ax)$' is FALSE in the model.

There is no algorithm for finding models that invalidate an argument. However, some procedures and rules of thumb can be devised for this search task, as we shall see in the next chapter.

Summary

Two universal quantification rules were discussed: universal elimination ($\forall$ELIM) and universal introduction ($\forall$INTRO).

$\forall$ELIM—From a sentence of the form $\forall v\mathbf{P}$, you may derive $\mathbf{P}[c/v]$.
$\forall$INTRO—From a sentence $\mathbf{P}$, you may derive $\forall v\mathbf{P}[v/c]$, *provided that:*
   1. $\mathbf{c}$ does not occur in any premise.
   2. If $\mathbf{P}$ is in a subproof, no constant in $\mathbf{P}$ occurs in an ASSUMPTION still in force.
   3. All new occurrences of $\mathbf{v}$ in $\mathbf{P}$ are free after the replacement in $\mathbf{P}[v/c]$.

The notation $\mathbf{P}[c/v]$ means that the constant $\mathbf{c}$ replaces all free occurrences of the variable $\mathbf{v}$ in $\mathbf{P}$. Similarly, $\mathbf{P}[v/c]$ means that the variable $\mathbf{v}$ replaces all occurrences of the constant $\mathbf{c}$ in $\mathbf{P}$ and is free after replacement.

Two existential quantification rules were also discussed: existential introduction ($\exists$INTRO) and existential elimination ($\exists$ELIM).

∃INTRO—From a sentence **P[c/v]**, you may derive **∃vP**.
∃ELIM—If a sentence has the form **∃vP**, and there is a subproof with ASSUMPTION **P[c/v]**, where **c** is new to the whole proof, and the subproof ends with sentence **Q** not containing **c**, then **Q** may be RETURNed from the subproof.

A quantifier negation rule was (partially) proved:

~∃**vS** is derivable iff ∀**v**~**S** is derivable.
~∀**vS** is derivable iff ∃**v**~**S** is derivable.

This rule enables us to move negation signs back and forth through quantifiers, if we change the quantity of the quantifiers.

Some examples were worked, and then the problem of showing an argument to be invalid was introduced.

Exercises

A. Construct derivations for the following arguments:

1. ∀x(Fx → Gx)
   ∃x(Fx & Hx)
   ∴∃x(Gx & Hx)

2. ~∀x(Fx → Gx)
   ∴∃x(Fx & ~Gx)

3. ~∃x(Fx & ~Gx)
   ∴∀x(Fx → Gx)

4. ∀x(Fx → ∃yRxy)
   ∀x∀y(Rxy → Gx)
   ∃xFx
   ∴∃xGx

5. ∀x(Fx → Gx)
   (∃xGx → ∃x(Hx & Dx))
   ∴(∃xFx → ∃xHx)

6. ~∃xFx
   ∴∀x(Fx → Gx)

7. ~∀x(Fx → ~Gx)
   ∴∃x(Fx & Gx)

8. ~∃x(Fx & Gx)
   ∴∀x(Fx → ~Gx)

9. ∀x~Gx
   ∀x∀y(Rxy → Fx)
   ∀x(Fx → Gx)
   ∴∃x∃y~Rxy

10. ∀x((Fx v Gx) → Hx)
    ∀x((Hx v Dx) → ~Fx)
    ∴∀x~Fx

B. Prove that the following pairs of sentences are logically equivalent as was done on pages 290 to 293 in this chapter.

1. ∀x(Fx & Gx)   (∀xFx & ∀xGx)
2. ∀x(Fx & A)   (∀xFx & A)
3. ∃x(Fx v Gx)   (∃xFx v ∃xGx)
4. ∀x(Fx v A)   (∀xFx v A)
5. ∀x(A → Fx)   (A → ∀xFx)
6. ∃x(Fx → A)   (∀xFx → A)
7. ∀x∀yFxy   ∀y∀xFxy
8. ∃x∃yFxy   ∃y∃xFxy
9. ~∀x∃yFxy   ∃x∀y~Fxy
10. ∀x((Fx v Gx) → Hx)   ∀x((Fx → Hx) & (Gx→ Hx))

CHAPTER 13

C. Some sentences are derivable from no premises at all. These sentences are called theorems of logic, and if our rules are correctly chosen, they will be universally valid sentences. Let us prove a theorem of logic.

To prove: $(\exists y \forall x Fxy \rightarrow \forall x \exists y Fxy)$

$\quad$ /BEGIN: $\rightarrow$ INTRO to derive conclusion/

*1.	$\exists y \forall x Fxy$	:ASSUMPTION
	/BEGIN: $\exists$ELIM/	
**2.	$\forall x Fxa$	:ASSUMPTION for $\exists$ELIM,1
**3.	Fba	:$\forall$ELIM,2
**4.	$\exists y Fby$	:$\exists$INTRO,3
	/END: $\exists$ELIM/	
*5.	$\exists y Fby$	:RETURN,4
*6.	$\forall x \exists y Fxy$	:$\forall$INTRO,5
*7.	$(\exists y \forall x Fxy \rightarrow \forall x \exists y Fxy)$	:$\rightarrow$ INTRO,1,6
	/END: $\rightarrow$ INTRO/	
8.	$(\exists y \forall x Fxy \rightarrow \forall x \exists y Fxy)$	:RETURN,7

Notice that in the proof of a theorem of logic, the last line is not starred. Prove the following theorems of logic:

1. $\exists x(Fx \rightarrow \forall x Fx)$
2. $((\exists x Fx \rightarrow \forall x Fx) \rightarrow (\forall x Fx \vee \forall x \sim Fx))$
3. $(\forall x(Fx \rightarrow Gx) \rightarrow (\exists x \sim Gx \rightarrow \exists x \sim Fx))$
4. $(\exists x(\exists y Fy \rightarrow Gx(\exists x Fx \rightarrow \exists y Gy))$
5. $\sim \exists y \forall x(Fxy \leftrightarrow \sim Fxx)$

D. Symbolize and then construct derivations for these arguments.
1. All phenomenalists deny the reality of matter, but no materialist does. Hence, no materialist is a phenomenalist.
2. No capitalists are socialists. Only socialists are egalitarians. Therefore, no capitalist is an egalitarian.
3. All politicians are good communicators. Some women are politicians. Thus, some women are good communicators.
4. All students take either logic or mathematics. Some students do not take mathematics. Therefore, some students take logic.
5. Anyone who helps a criminal is guilty. Therefore, any criminal who helps himself is guilty.
6. If Adam graduates, then everyone does. Adam graduates only if Betty does also. But Betty graduates only if everyone does. So, if someone doesn't graduate, neither Adam nor Betty graduates.
7. No one who thinks for himself or herself supports every position of the party. One is totally loyal only if one supports every position of the party. Hence, those who are totally loyal do not think for themselves.
8. Some teachers are admired by all those students who admire any teacher at all. Every student admires some teacher or other. Therefore, there are teachers who are admired by all students.

9. People like anything liked by anyone they like. Not everybody dislikes everybody. People like those who like them. Consequently, somebody likes himself.
10. Whenever there is a problem at the college, all the faculty blame the dean for it. Now, if someone blames someone for something, then he (or she) must think that person has control over what he (or she) is being blamed for. The dean is a person. Hence, there is a person whom the faculty thinks has control over all the problems at the college.

CHAPTER 14

PREDICATE LOGIC:
Determining Validity
and Proving Theorems

As we mentioned in Chapter 2, a part of the field known as Artificial Intelligence is concerned with instructing computers to perform the activities we associate with an ability to reason. These activities include determining whether or not arguments are valid, deducing valid consequences from sentences, and producing proofs for valid arguments.

Chapter 6 gave us an algorithm for determining whether or not an argument in sentential logic is valid. As we observed, this method is perfectly "mechanical" and can, for any argument, determine in a finite amount of time whether the argument is valid or invalid. This method thus qualifies as an algorithm.

In Chapter 11, we gave a method for producing a proof of a valid argument in the logic of sentences. Although this method is mechanical (or can easily be made so), it will not always produce a correct proof of any valid argument in a finite amount of time. So this method is not a real algorithm. It so happens, however, that an algorithm to produce proofs in the logic of sentences *can* be given—although the resulting PROOF-GIVER will be larger and less convenient to use than the method we gave.

CHAPTER 14

In Chapters 12 and 13 we introduced the concepts of predicate logic, which go far beyond those used in the logic of sentences. While the logic of sentences treats arguments with no examination of the inner structure of atomic sentences, predicate logic examines how even "atomic" sentences are constructed.

Decidability

There are two important questions that can be posed for any system of logic. These questions are:

1. Is it possible to devise an algorithm for classifying any argument in the system of logic as being valid or invalid?
2. Is there a mechanical procedure that always produces a proof of any valid argument in the system of logic?

The first question is usually described as the question of whether the system of logic is *decidable*—whether there exists a decision procedure (an algorithm) that "decides" whether an argument is valid or invalid. We did not explicitly pose this question with regard to the logic of sentences, because it is easy to see, once truth tables are introduced (as in Chapter 6), that sentential logic *is* decidable.

The surprising answer to question 1 for predicate logic is that it is undecidable. There is no algorithm that can classify every argument according to whether it is valid or invalid. It is important to realize the full force of this claim. We are *not* saying merely that such an algorithm is difficult to find or that it hasn't yet been found. Nor are we saying that the algorithm is long and hard to describe. We are saying that it is *impossible* to find such an algorithm. This far-reaching result is known as *Church's theorem,* after its discoverer, the American logician Alonzo Church, who proved it in 1936.

Church's theorem implies that no chapter like Chapter 6 is possible for predicate logic. There is nothing like a "truth table" that can be generated by an algorithm and applied to an argument in predicate logic in order to determine whether it is valid or invalid. Explaining the incontrovertible reasoning behind Church's theorem is beyond the scope of this book. In a sentence, the difficulties that Church's theorem identifies creep into logic when both quantifiers and relations are admitted.

Models

There are some types of arguments that escape the force of Church's theorem and for which an algorithm *can* be constructed that classifies them as valid or invalid. One type of argument that escapes the force of Church's theorem is, as we have already remarked, sentential logic.

Let us call the logic in which formulas may contain quantifiers, relations, sentence connectives, and the other symbols of logic we have discussed the *full predicate logic.* Church's theorem asserts that the full predicate logic is undecidable.

Are there certain kinds of arguments in predicate logic that are decidable, even though there is no decision procedure for all arguments? Not surprisingly, the answer to this question is affirmative, but a detailed discussion *and proof* of this answer is beyond the scope of this book.

The question of whether such an argument is valid or invalid is the same as this question:

Is there a model in which the premises are satisfied (TRUE) but in which the conclusion is not satisfied (FALSE)?

If so, the argument is invalid; if not, then the argument is valid. This observation can be put in the form of an algorithm:

1. INPUT an argument.
2. FOR every possible model of this argument:
    (a) IF the premises are satisfied and the conclusion is not satisfied in this model, THEN OUTPUT "Invalid" and STOP.
3. OUTPUT "Valid" and STOP.

In order to use this algorithm, we need to refine step 2. In particular, we need a procedure for constructing every possible model of an argument and a way to order the models so that we can be sure that each one is examined in the FOR-loop. We also need to be sure that there are only a finite number of models so that we can be sure that we shall eventually exit the FOR-loop [either by running through all the models without finding one in which the premises are satisfied but in which the conclusion is not, thus moving to step 3, or else by finding such a model, thus exiting the loop early, at step 2(a)].

Arguments with no quantifiers are decidable. One simply treats 'Fa' or 'Gb' or 'Hbc' as atomic sentences, each of which is either TRUE or FALSE in a given model. The number of models, in this case, is clearly finite. Indeed, WANG'S ALGORITHM can be applied directly. In the terminology of Chapter 6, if the same sentence occurs on both the left and right sides, the attempt fails. If all attempts fail, the argument is valid.

Arguments having only one-place predicates (and possibly other atomic sentences) are also decidable. If there are n distinct one-place predicate letters in the argument, then at most $2 ** n$ distinct types of individuals need to be considered to determine validity or invalidity. Whenever only a finite number of individuals are involved, a decision procedure can be devised. In this case, universally quantified sentences reduce to a finite conjunction of instances, and existentially quantified sentences reduce to a finite disjunction of instances. Then, truth tables or WANG'S ALGORITHM can be used.

The trouble arises when we have quantified n-place relations, for $n > 1$. The number of distinct types of individuals—and, hence, the number of different possible models—increases quite rapidly. Consider

$\exists x F x a$

CHAPTER 14

Begin with a model with only one kind of individual, say Alfie. The letter 'a' refers to Alfie. Now 'Faa' could be TRUE (and then so would '∃xFxa'), or 'Faa' could be FALSE (and then so would '∃xFxa'). So, in order to explore all possible situations, we need two kinds of individuals: those for which 'Faa' is TRUE and those for which 'Faa' is FALSE. Let Alfie be the first kind of individual and Betty the second kind. When 'a' is the name of Alfie, V(Faa) = TRUE, and when 'a' is the name for Betty, V(Faa) = FALSE. Now we want a model containing both Alfie and Betty, whose names will be 'a' and 'b', respectively. (Of course, we could switch the names around, or even let both of them refer to one individual, say Alfie.) But what are the truth values of 'Fab' and 'Fba'? The number of possible kinds of individuals doubles, and doubles again. As we continue, the number of possible kinds of individuals quickly becomes infinite, and the number of models becomes even larger—since models are subsets of the collection of individuals.

Since the time that Church's theorem was proved, logicians have not only tried to identify types of arguments that are decidable but have also tried to identify types of arguments that are undecidable by any algorithm. Indeed, some logicians have shown that some kinds of arguments are "more undecidable" than others. The intriguing notion of "being more undecidable than" can be made quite precise. Argument type A is *more undecidable* than argument type B if, given a way of deciding type A arguments (say, an oracle), we could then decide type B arguments, but given a way (another oracle!) of deciding type B arguments, we still could not decide type A arguments. Unfortunately, the pursuit of this issue is well beyond the scope of this book.

Church's Thesis

Can a computer exist that would decide the question—for any argument—of whether the argument is valid or invalid? What we have said thus far does not quite imply that no such computer is possible. We have only asserted that:

> No algorithm for classifying arguments as valid or invalid is possible.

To claim that computers could not ever classify any argument as valid or invalid, we need an additional assumption:

> Computers can perform only what algorithms describe.

This latter assertion is widely believed to be true but cannot be conclusively shown to be true. The assertion is known as *Church's thesis,* or as the *Church-Turing thesis.* It is not to be confused with Church's *theorem,* which has been conclusively proved.

A valid argument concerning the limitations of computers would be:

1. No algorithm for classifying all arguments as valid or invalid is possible. (Church's theorem)
2. Computers can perform only what algorithms describe. (Church's thesis)

Therefore, 3. No computer could ever effectively classify all arguments as valid or invalid.

The claim that Church's thesis is true is discussed in Appendix B.

Some people have been eager to capitalize on this weakness of computers that no computer could ever effectively classify all arguments as valid or invalid, further asserting that this shows that there are some things humans can do that computers can't. It is true that Church's theorem, together with Church's thesis, implies certain limitations on the ability of computers to reason. However, it also seems that humans are subject to the same limitations. Are there *human beings* who can always, and in a finite time, state correctly whether an argument is valid or invalid? It seems that there do not exist such human beings. In fact, very few of us, and then only with a great deal of time, can determine whether relatively complicated arguments in predicate logic are valid or invalid. We do not normally say that these limitations of human beings render us altogether unable to reason. We should not say it of computers either. So computers' inability to decide, for any argument, whether it is valid or invalid does little to show the superiority of human reasoning. We are apparently subject to the same limitations.

Mechanical Theorem Proving

Church's theorem and Church's thesis are heavy doses, because they apparently show the limitations of intelligence to solve problems—regardless of whether this intelligence is "artificial" or human. In the light of these observations, we might face the second of our two original questions with some pessimism:

If we know (somehow) that an argument in predicate logic is valid, is there a mechanical procedure that always produces a proof of it?

After the blow Church's theorem delivered to our confidence, we might be tempted to answer, "Probably not!"

Contrary to these expectations, however, the answer to this question is, Yes, there is such a procedure. If an argument is valid, there exists a method that will eventually show that it is valid. Moreover, the procedure can be designed so that it will also tell us *why* the argument is valid—that is, it will give us a demonstration of the argument's validity. It is interesting to contemplate what would happen if we fed this procedure an *in*valid argument. It is in this case that Church's theorem comes into play: the method will never halt. If a computer were programmed with this method and we gave it an invalid argument, we would never know whether the computer was about to give us a proof or disproof or whether the computer might be working *forever* on the problem.

The general topic addressed by this question is called *mechanical theorem proving*. There are essentially two different ways a procedure can be constructed to give a demonstration of a valid argument. One way is along the lines of the method we gave in Chapter 11, PROOF-GIVER. There, we created an *almost* mechanical procedure that would output a proof in the deductive system in which we were working. We might call this the *proof* method of demonstrating an argument to be valid.

CHAPTER 14

The other way of creating a procedure to demonstrate that an argument is valid will not output a real proof. It will not give us a proof using our rules of deduction, but will instead demonstrate that it is impossible for the premises to be TRUE and the conclusion FALSE.

Consider the following argument:

A
B
∴ C

As we saw in Chapter 7, this argument is valid if and only if its corresponding conditional

$$((A \ \& \ B) \rightarrow C)$$

is a tautology. That is, the argument is valid if and only if this conditional is TRUE in all possible situations. But it is also true that the argument is valid if and only if the conjunction

$$((A \ \& \ B) \ \& \ {\sim}C)$$

is inconsistent, that is, if and only if a contradiction can be derived from it. That is, the argument is valid if and only if this conjunction is FALSE in all situations. (For a review of the meaning of 'tautology', 'contradiction', and 'inconsistent', you should reread the relevant sections of Chapter 7.)

Resolution

There is a technique that relies on this second observation: An argument is valid if and only if the conjunction formed by taking the conjunction of all the premises together with the negation of the conclusion is not satisfiable in any model. This technique is called *resolution.* It might not at first seem very promising to assert that an argument is valid if and only if some formula is FALSE in *every* possible situation. The determination of whether a formula is FALSE in every situation might, after all, take forever.

Let us see how resolution works in the case of the logic of sentences. The idea behind resolution is that many valid argument forms (including most rules of inference) can be seen as instances of a single, very general pattern that can be used as a solitary rule of inference: the Rule of Resolution. To see this more clearly, consider a new notation for the logic of sentences. Let us agree to write a disjunction

$$(P \lor Q)$$

as

PQ

DETERMINING VALIDITY

and a negation

$\sim$**P**

as

P′

And let's agree to write the premises of an argument separated by commas above a line, with the conclusion below the line. Now let's consider some valid argument forms, with the premises converted first to CNF and then to our new notation:

$$(P \rightarrow Q)$$
$$P$$
$$\therefore Q$$

becomes

$$\frac{P'Q, P}{Q}$$

$$(P \rightarrow Q)$$
$$\sim Q$$
$$\therefore \sim P$$

becomes

$$\frac{P'Q, Q'}{P'}$$

$$((P \ \& \ (Q \ \& \ R))$$
$$Q$$
$$\therefore ((P \ \& \ R \rightarrow S))$$

becomes

$$\frac{P'Q'R'S, Q}{P'R'S}$$

$$(P \rightarrow Q)$$
$$(Q \rightarrow R)$$
$$\therefore (P \rightarrow R)$$

becomes

$$\frac{P'Q, Q'R}{P'R}$$

$$(P \ v \ Q)$$
$$\sim P$$
$$\therefore Q$$

becomes

$$\frac{PQ, P'}{Q}$$

If we look at these valid arguments in our new notation, we see that they all have a common form:

1. Each premise is a disjunction of sentences.
2. One of the premises has some sentence **U** as a disjunct.
3. The other premise has **U′** as a disjunct.
4. The conclusion is the disjunction of all the sentences in the premises except **U** and **U′**.

That is, in general, all arguments of the form

$$\frac{U'QR \ldots, \ UST \ldots}{QRST \ldots}$$

are valid. This is the Rule of Resolution.

The following algorithm for using resolution to decide whether an argument in sentential logic is valid begins with writing the sentences in the argument in conjunctive normal form (CNF). We discussed this notation and presented an algorithm for turning a sentence into a logically equivalent CNF sentence in Chapter 7.

1. INPUT an argument.
2. Let C be a collection consisting of the premises and the negation of the conclusion of the argument.
3. FOR each sentence **S** in the collection C:
   (a) Replace **S** with its CNF equivalent.
4. Repeat the following:
   (a) Find two sentences **S₁** and **S₂** in collection C such that **S₁** contains some atomic sentence letter **P** as a disjunct and **S₂** contains its negation~**P** as a disjunct.
   (b) Let **S** be a new CNF sentence whose disjuncts are all the disjuncts of **S₁** and **S₂** except for **P** and ~**P**. (**S** is called the "resolvent of" **S₁** and **S₂**.)
   (c) Remove **S₁** and **S₂** from C.
   (d) Add **S** to C.
   Until (i)   C contains two atomic sentences **Q** and ~**Q**
   or
   (ii) no new resolvent **S** can be formed.
5. IF the repeat-loop in step 4 stopped because of case (i)
   THEN OUTPUT "Valid" and STOP.
6. IF the repeat-loop in step 4 stopped because of case (ii)
   THEN OUTPUT "Invalid" and STOP.

Recall that we are trying to derive a contradiction from the collection C. Step 4 is a loop that keeps searching for a contradiction by generating and testing successive resolvents. Each resolvent is logically derivable from the two sentences that are used to generate it, so if an inconsistency is produced, we can exit the loop knowing that the argument is valid. Some examples should help clarify this method.

Example 1.
1. $(A \rightarrow B)$
   A
∴ B

2. $C = \{(A \rightarrow B), A, \sim B\}$
3. $C = \{(\sim A \vee B), A, \sim B\}$
4. Choose $S_1 = (\sim A \vee B)$ and $S_2 = A$.
   Then $S = B$.
   So $C = \{B, \sim B\}$.

This is case (i), so the argument is valid (as you can check by a simple application of →ELIM).

    Example 2.
    1. ~(~A & ~B)
       B
  ∴ A
    2. C = {~(~A & ~B), B, ~A}
    3. C = {(A v B), B, ~A}
This is case (ii), so the argument is invalid.

    For arguments in predicate logic, it is necessary to find *instances* of quantified formulas and then to apply the above technique to them. The main problem is to find appropriate instances. In 1930, the French logician Jacques Herbrand showed that if a formula is FALSE in a certain finite number of situations (described in what is called the "Herbrand universe of clauses"), then it is FALSE in *all* situations. So according to Herbrand's theorem, we do not really have to look at *all* situations or instances to see if a formula is inconsistent. We really only need to look at whether it is FALSE in a certain finite number of situations. Then, we may reason, if it is FALSE in all of these situations, it is FALSE in absolutely all situations. That is, it is inconsistent. Herbrand showed that his theorem was true in the abstract, so to speak. He did not actually show how to go about economically applying it to various formulas. He showed only that there *exists* a mechanical procedure to show an argument to be invalid.

    No computer existed in 1930 that could have been used to apply Herbrand's result. But in the 1960's, the importance of Herbrand's theorem to mechanical theorem proving was recognized, and various computer scientists and logicians set about showing how it could be applied on a working computer. The early attempts unfortunately were not entirely successful. Some formulas could not be shown to be inconsistent (even when they were), and showing that others were sometimes consumed tremendous amounts of computer time.

    Enormous progress was made by the logicians and computer scientists who developed resolution in the early 1960s. This technique, as we have seen, is a method of showing how a formula is inconsistent. It "flushes out" an inconsistency that is lurking in the formula, somewhere. The resolution technique turned out to be a genuine mechanical procedure (if a formula is inconsistent, the method can always determine that this is so in a finite amount of time). And the resolution technique also led to computer programs that could discover these inconsistencies in a reasonably short amount of computer time.

    Even the resolution method of theorem proving has the limitation imposed by Church's theorem—namely, if it is given an invalid argument to analyze, it will work forever. If a computer is programmed with this method, it will still be working on the problem when we are forced to shut it off—at the end of the day, or after years. At the point where we shut it off, we will not know whether the argument is invalid (and the program will never halt) or whether the argument is valid (but is one of those difficult problems that takes days or years to prove). For more information on resolution, see Raphael, 1976.

The Proof Method

Let us return to the proof method of mechanical theorem proving, because it is usually more enlightening. Our question is, Can PROOF-GIVER be modified to incorporate the new rules governing quantifiers, constants, predicates, and variables? We shall call the modified method for generating proofs PROOF-GIVER*, to distinguish it from its strictly sentential predecessor.

Our investigation into the required modifications will begin with some observations about strategy in using quantifiers and constants. Suppose we have three premises—'A', 'B', and 'C' (whose internal structure will not interest us now)—and a conclusion:

$$\forall xFx$$

How can we go about deriving this conclusion? We might reason as follows. If we somehow earlier derived 'Fb', then we can infer '$\forall xFx$' from it—provided that 'Fb' arose in the "proper" manner. Once 'Fb' is derived, $\forall$INTRO is applied, resulting in the desired $\forall xFx$. But consider what our strategy should be if the third premise, 'C', is in fact

$$(B \rightarrow \forall xFx)$$

In such a situation, it does not seem necessary to derive 'Fb'. Instead, '$\forall xFx$' can be derived directly—if we can derive 'B'. These two observations give us the tips we need for part of our modifications. The two possible strategies we have just mentioned are in fact already addressed by steps 3(a) and (b) of PROOF-GIVER:

3(a) IF **DR** = a subformula of a sentence, **Q,** on an accessible line, . . .
3(b) IF **DR** is not a subformula of a sentence on an accessible line, . . .

These steps decide whether we proceed to derive the desired result from previous lines or whether we construct it by some standard strategy.

We modify PROOF-GIVER by changing the number of step 3(b)(v)to 3(b)(viii) and inserting the following:

3(b)(v) IF the desired result has the form $\forall x(\ldots x \ldots)$
THEN replace the first 'Derive $\forall x(\ldots x \ldots)$' in the task list with:
Derive $(\ldots b \ldots)$
Apply $\forall$INTRO $[(\ldots b \ldots)]$
where '$(\ldots b \ldots)$' is the earlier formula with the outermost universal quantifier deleted and all resulting free occurrences of the quantified variable replaced by some individual constant, 'b'. The constant 'b' should be the alphabetically first constant not previously appearing in an accessible line.

3(b)(vi) IF the desired result has the form $\exists x(\ldots x \ldots)$
THEN replace the first 'Derive $\exists x(\ldots x \ldots)$' in the task list with:
Derive $(\ldots b \ldots)$
Apply $\exists$INTRO $[(\ldots b \ldots)$
where b is any individual constant.

3(b)(vii) IF the desired result has the form (. . . *b* . . .)
            THEN replace the first 'Derive (. . . *b* . . .)' in the task list with:

Derive ∀*x*(. . . *x* . . .)
Apply ∀ELIM [∀*x*(. . . *x* . . .)]

where '*x*' is some variable.

No other modifications to PROOF-GIVER are necessary.

Summary

In this chapter, we discussed the *decidability* of predicate logic—the issue of whether there is an algorithm that decides whether or not an argument is valid.

Church's theorem states that the full predicate logic is *not* decidable. However, parts of predicate logic *are* decidable, and we discussed the relationship of this fact to our notion of models. *Church's thesis,* on the other hand, is the unprovable but generally accepted claim that computers can perform only what algorithms describe.

We ended with a presentation of two methods of proving theorems in predicate logic mechanically: *resolution,* which we presented in the form of a rule of inference and as an algorithm, and a proof method—an extension of the PROOF-GIVER method of Chapter 11.

APPLICATIONS OF SENTENTIAL LOGIC TO CIRCUIT DESIGN AND ARITHMETIC

In Chapter 2, we mentioned that there is a close relationship between truth values (TRUE and FALSE, or 1 and 0) and the presence or absence of an electric current flowing through a circuit. In the areas of computer architecture and computer electronics, a circuit is thought of as an electronic device that has "inputs" and "outputs." An input will be a current flowing into the device, and an output will be a current flowing out of the device. Since the output is completely determined by the input and the design of the circuit, a circuit can be thought of as a function. Moreover, if we limit the inputs and outputs to two "values"—the presence or absence of current, which we can represent by 1 and 0, respectively—then we can think of a circuit as a truth function.

APPENDIX A

Electric Circuits

Modern circuits used in computers are usually engraved on "chips" of silicon, but they can be (and were, in the early days of computers) built out of wires and such electric components as resistors, capacitors, transistors, and diodes. (You don't have to know what these are or how they work—only that they are things that can be combined to form circuits.)

Consider a circuit whose input is a source of current (such as a battery) controlled by a switch and whose output is an electric device such as a bulb, as in Figure A-1.

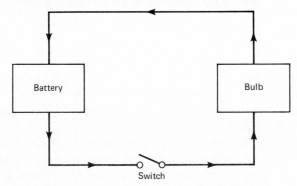

Figure A-1 A simple circuit. (The arrows indicate the direction in which the current flows.)

The switch in Figure A-1 is in the "open" position, so no current reaches the bulb. If the switch is closed, the bulb will light. The operation of this circuit can be shown in the following table:

Input (Switch)	Output (Bulb)
Closed	On
Open	Off

Now consider a similar circuit with one more device: an *inverter*. An inverter is actually another circuit, with its own wires and electric components (usually a resistor and a transistor). We shall be concerned not with its actual structure but only with its behavior: When an electric current enters an inverter, the inverter acts as an open switch, preventing the current from leaving; and when no current (or a very low current) enters, the inverter acts as a source of electricity, allowing a current to leave it. It thus behaves very much like an emergency light with its own battery, which only lights when there has been a power failure. The new circuit, with both bulb and inverter, is diagrammed in Figure A-2.

Now, when the switch is closed, electricity flows from the battery to the inverter, which blocks it; so the bulb doesn't light. But when the switch is open, so that no current

LOGIC AND CIRCUIT DESIGN

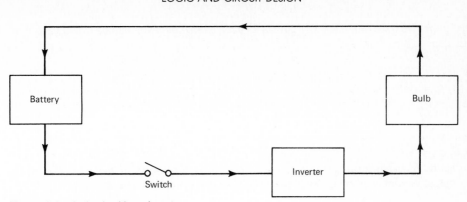

Figure A-2   A circuit with an inverter.

flows to the inverter, the inverter sends a current to the bulb, causing it to light. The operation of such a circuit can be summarized in the following table:

Input (Switch)	Output (Bulb)
Open	On
Closed	Off

Using 1 to represent the presence of current and 0 to represent its absence, the table then looks like this:

Input	Output
0	1
1	0

But this is just the truth table for FNEG; so, an inverter can be used to represent negation. In fact, an inverter is called a "NOT gate." (The term "gate" is used because such a device acts as a gate, an entranceway, that transforms the current.)

Logic Gates

In general, a *logic gate* is a circuit whose output current depends on its input currents in a way that can be described by (and therefore used as a representation of) the laws of sentential logic. In theory, there could be gates corresponding to each of the logical connectives, but in practice, the most common ones are the NOT gate, the AND gate, the OR gate, the NAND gate, and the NOR gate.

As we have seen, the NOT gate is a circuit whose behavior can be symbolized thus:

Figure A-3　A NOT gate.

Here, 'A' represents the input current. So, '~A' is a reasonable way to represent the output current. Computer engineers use a special symbol for the NOT gate:

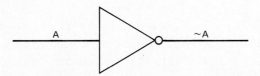

Figure A-4　Symbol for the NOT gate.

An AND gate that has two inputs (and, of course, only one output) can be represented as either

Figure A-5　An AND gate.

or

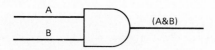

Figure A-6　Symbol for the AND gate.

The AND gate behaves by taking two low currents as input and producing a low-current output, taking one high and one low-current input and producing a low-current output, and taking two high-current inputs and producing a high-current output.

LOGIC AND CIRCUIT DESIGN

Exercises

1. Explain the relationship between an AND gate and the truth table for conjunction, as we did for the NOT gate and negation.
2. Describe the behavior of an OR gate.

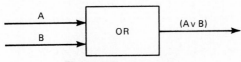

Figure A-7   An OR gate.

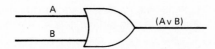

Figure A-8   Symbol for an OR gate.

Explain its relationship to disjunction.

3. A NAND gate can be constructed from an AND gate and a NOT gate:

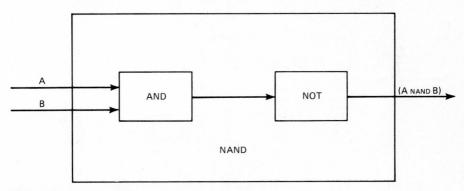

Figure A-9   A NAND gate.

    a. Describe its behavior.
    b. Explain its relationship to the *logical* connective NAND.
    c. Explain the relationship between the tautology
       ((A NAND B) ↔ ~A & B))
       and the behavior of a NAND gate.

4. a. Show how to construct a NOR gate.
    b. Describe its behavior.
    c. Explain its relationship to the logical connective NOR.

   d. Explain the relationship between the tautology
      ((A NOR B) ↔ ~ (A v B))

      and the behavior of a NOR gate.
  5. Do the same for an XOR gate. (*Suggestion:* Consider the tautology
      ((A XOR B) ↔ ((A v B) & ~ (A & B)))

Combining Logic Gates

These logic gates can be combined so that they can represent any truth-functional formula (as we combined a NOT gate with an AND gate to form a NAND gate, in Exercise 3).

For instance,

((A & B) v ~C)

can be represented by the following circuit:

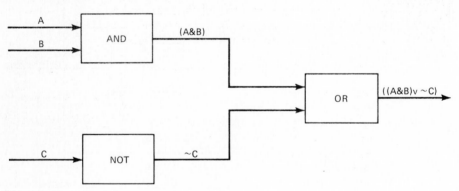

Figure A-10   A circuit that represents ((A & B) v ~C)

Similarly,

(~A v ~B)

can be represented by

LOGIC AND CIRCUIT DESIGN

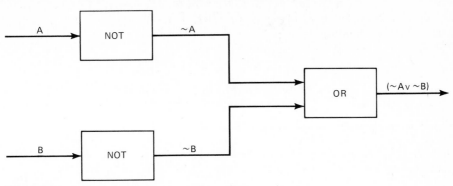

Figure A-11 A circuit that represents (~A v ~B)

But, by De Morgan's law (see Chapter 7),

((~A v ~B) ↔ ~(A & B))

there is another combination of circuits that behaves exactly the same:

Figure A-12 A circuit that represents ~(A & B) and so behaves like the circuit in Figure A-11.

(This, of course, is also a NAND circuit.)

Exercises

6. Use the other of De Morgan's laws to construct a circuit that behaves like a NOR gate.
7. Construct circuits for the following formulas:
   a. ((A v B) v C)
   b. (A v (B v C))
   c. ((A & B) v C)
   d. (A & (B v C))
   e. (~A v B)
   f. ~(A & ~B)
   g. (((~A & ~B̄) v C) & ~D)
   h. (~(A & (~A v B)) v B)

8. a. Construct an IF-THEN circuit. (*Hint:* See Exercise 7.)
   b. Using your IF-THEN circuit, construct a circuit for
      $((A \ \& \ (A \rightarrow B)) \rightarrow B)$

Translating between Logic and Circuits

We have seen that information about truth values and truth functions can be described in two ways: by using the logic of sentences and by using electric circuits. Whenever there are two ways of representing the same information, it is important to be able to translate between the representations. In the present case, it is important to be sure that any logic circuit with precisely one output can be understood as (that is, can be translated into) a sentence and that any sentence can be represented by (that is, can be translated into) a logic circuit with one output. Moreover, if a logic circuit corresponds to two different sentences, it is important that the sentences be logically equivalent; and if a sentence can be translated into two different circuits, it is important that both circuits have the same input-output behavior.

In fact, the relationship between circuits and sentences that has been described here guarantees that those criteria are satisfied. We shall not prove that they are, but you have enough information in this book to carry out the proof yourself. What we shall do in the remaining sections is give examples of how to perform the translations.

Given a logic circuit, it is rather straightforward to write down a corresponding sentence (although, of course, the more complicated the circuit, the more tedious it will be to find a sentence). Sometimes, a circuit can have more than one output. If a circuit has more than one output, then it can be viewed as a combination of separate circuits, each of which has precisely one output. Consider the following circuit:

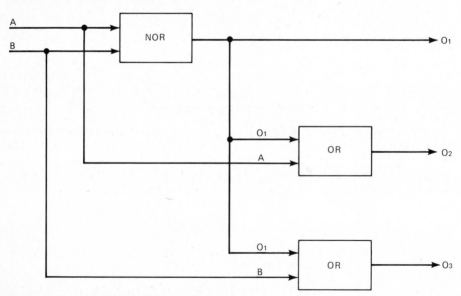

Figure A-13 A combination of three circuits.

LOGIC AND CIRCUIT DESIGN

This circuit has two inputs—A and B—and three outputs—O_1, O_2, and O_3. It can be seen as three circuits linked together: first, a NOR gate whose inputs are A and B and whose output is O_1; second, an OR gate whose inputs are A and O_1 and whose output is O_2; and third, another OR gate, whose inputs are B and O_1 and whose output is O_3.

The question is, What sentences do O_1, O_2, and O_3 represent? You should be able to see that if the currents A and B represent atomic sentences 'A' and 'B', respectively, then:

1. O_1 represents '(A NOR B)'—or, if you prefer, '$\sim$(A v B)'.
2. O_2 represents '(A v O_1)'—that is, '(A v $\sim$(A v B))', to use just the inputs.
3. O_3 represents '(B v O_1)'—that is, '(B v $\sim$(A v B))'.

But there is a much more informative way of describing O_2 and O_3. If we put O_2, that is

$$(A \lor \sim(A \lor B))$$

into disjunctive normal form (see Chapter 7), we get

$$(A \lor (\sim A \ \& \sim B))$$

which is logically equivalent to

$$((A \lor \sim A) \ \& \ (A \lor \sim B))$$

which, in turn, is logically equivalent to

$$(A \lor \sim B)$$

In a similar fashion, O_3 can be shown to represent '(B v $\sim$A)'.

You should observe that the most "straightforward" sentences represented by the circuit—the ones we simply "read off" it—were not the simplest. The converse is also the case: given our three simple sentences, if we built a circuit directly from them, we would get the circuit of Figure A-14. This has two more NOT gates than the first circuit, so it is not the simplest circuit to represent our sentences.

Simplifying Circuits

This trade-off in complexity between two different representations of the same information is a common feature of representations in general. Once we have proved that

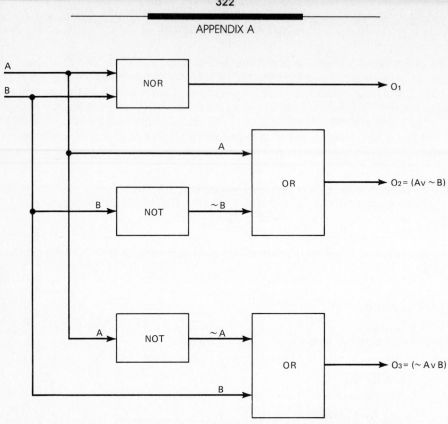

Figure A-14   A circuit whose behavior is the same as that of the circuit of Figure A-13.

representations are equivalent, we can then use whichever is simplest or best suited for our purposes.

Thus if we are building computers, we would prefer the first circuit to the second one, because it is no doubt less expensive and easier to build and repair; but if we are studying the logical behavior of the circuits, we would prefer the second set of sentences to the first one.

This trade-off can be measured. One way to do this is to say that one circuit is simpler than another if it has fewer gates (and fewer input lines); this translates into the terminology of the logic of sentences as fewer connectives (and fewer occurrences of sentence letters).

As you know from Chapter 8, all quantifier-free sentences can be expressed using only $\sim$ and &, so an engineer could get by with only NOT and AND gates. In fact, even simpler circuits can be constructed if NAND and NOR gates are used wherever possible, since they are easier to construct than sequences of AND, OR, and NOT gates. NAND and NOR gates are particularly useful, since, as you know from Exercise F of Chapter 8, all sentences can be expressed using NAND (or else NOR) as the only connective.

(There are standard algorithms for translating between circuits and sentences, using an alternative representation for truth tables called "Karnaugh maps." For further reading, see Ennes, 1978; Kasper and Feller, 1983; or Malvino, 1976.)

Circuits for Adding

In this section, we shall show how to construct a logic circuit that adds two numbers. It is hoped that you will see that it is no exaggeration to say that computers are truly based on logic.

Let us proceed "bottom-up." Consider the following circuit:

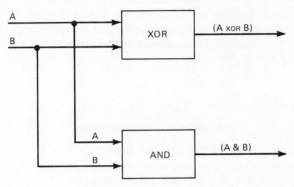

Figure A-15 A half-adder.

Two inputs, A and B, of either high or low current are sent through two circuits, an XOR gate and an AND gate. Letting 1 represent a high current and 0 represent a low current, we can tabulate the outputs of this circuit as follows:

A	B	(A & B)	(A XOR B)
0	0	0	0
0	1	0	1
1	0	0	1
1	1	1	0

Now, consider the following fragment of an addition table for binary arithmetic:

A	B	A + B
0	0	0
0	1	1
1	0	1
1	1	10

If we write the sum of two 1-bit numerals as a 2-bit numeral, using a "leading zero" as a placeholder on the left, then this table becomes:

A	B	A + B
0	0	00
0	1	01
1	0	01
1	1	10

And now, here is the link between the electronic implementation of a logic circuit and the mathematical operation of addition: When electronic inputs A and B are interpreted as numbers, then the ones column of their sum is represented by the output of the XOR gate and the twos column is represented by the output of the AND gate. Such a circuit is called a *half-adder.*

Exercises

9. A *full-adder* is a circuit that can be used to represent the addition of three 1-bit binary numerals. That is, given three binary numbers A, B, and C, a full-adder outputs A + B + C. Here is a full-adder circuit:

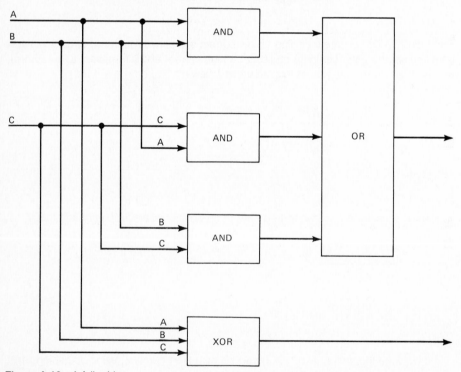

Figure A-16 A full-adder.

LOGIC AND CIRCUIT DESIGN

Explain how it works.

10. A *binary-adder* is a circuit that can be used to represent the addition of any two binary numbers.

In particular, if binary number A is a string of 4 bits, $A_1A_2A_3A_4$, and binary number B is $B_1B_2B_3B_4$, then their sum can be represented thus:

$$A_1A_2A_3A_4$$
$$+ \underline{B_1B_2B_3B_4}$$
$$S_0S_1S_2S_3S_4$$

For instance, if A = 1010 and B = 1011, then we have:

$$1010$$
$$+ \underline{1011}$$
$$10101$$

where $S_4 = 0 + 1 = 1$, $S_3 = 1 + 1 = 0$ with a "carry" of 1, $S_2 = 0 + 0 +$ the "carried" $1 = 1$, $S_1 = 1 + 1 = 0$ with a "carry" of 1, and $S_0 =$ the "carried" 1. A binary-adder that will add any two such numbers is:

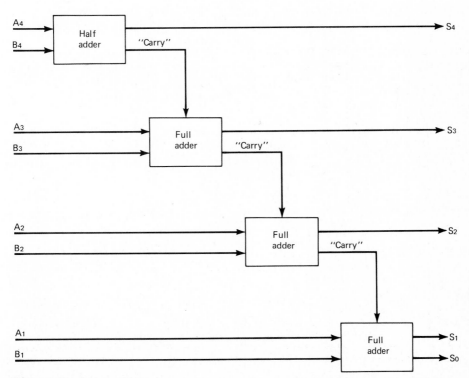

Figure A-17 A binary-adder.

a. Explain how it works.
b. Show how it can be used to add:
   (i) 1000 and 0111
   (ii) 1111 and 1111

TURING MACHINES

Throughout this book, we have relied heavily on the description of an algorithm (given in Chapter 2) as a detailed, step-by-step, finite sequence of instructions that are mechanical and unambiguous for performing a task. This is a rather informal and intuitive notion: How detailed must an algorithm be? What kinds of instructions are allowed? What does "mechanical" mean? How can ambiguity be avoided? The purpose of this appendix is to try to make the notion of "algorithm" a bit more precise by clarifying the notion of a mechanical procedure.*

---

*The presentation of Turing machines in this appendix is based on Clark and Cowell, 1976, pp. 44–49.

Turing's Analysis of Computation

We have said that an algorithm is a "mechanical procedure" for carrying out some task in a finite number of steps. If we limit ourselves to tasks that can be described in some language (either a natural language or a programming language), then we can think of such a procedure as a "computation." In 1937, the English logician Alan Turing (1912–1954) presented an analysis of this notion in an important paper, "On Computable Numbers, with an Application to the *Entscheidungsproblem*," that led, among other things, to the notion of the stored-program computer. (The English translation of the German word *Entscheidungsproblem* is "decision problem"—the question of whether a procedure for a given task will produce a definite affirmative or negative answer in a finite number of steps.)

Turing's analysis begins by considering what it means for a computation to be carried out "mechanically." At the very least, we would need:

1. A "computer"—either a person or a machine—to do the computation,
2. Some scratch paper (a memory device) to do the computation on,
3. A deterministic program for the computer to follow—that is, a finite sequence of instructions for performing the computation by manipulating symbols on the scratch paper.

We can refine this somewhat informal picture. Let us suppose that the mind of the person (or computer) can only be in a finite number of different "states." Also, let's suppose for the sake of convenience that the person (or computer) has memorized the program (so that we only have to concern ourselves with two things: the computer and the scratch-pad "memory").

As for the scratch-pad memory, let's suppose that we have lots of paper—not necessarily an actually infinite amount of paper, but enough paper so that if we need more, we can always get it. And, so that we can describe precisely what's written on the paper, let's imagine that it is crosshatched into small squares (like graph paper), each containing one symbol, so that we can systematically locate any symbol in any square on any page of the scratch pad (for instance, by starting at the square in the first row and first column of the first page and examining each square in turn until we either find the symbol or else reach the last square on the last page without having found it).

Finally, imagine that the person (or computer) doing the computing can only see a finite, bounded number of squares on the scratch pad at any one time.

As the next refinement, let us now assume the following:

1. The person (or computer) sees only one square (containing at most one symbol) of the scratch pad at a time.
2. (a) The scratch pad is a linear tape (like an adding-machine tape), divided into squares, that is potentially infinite in both directions (that is, we can always add an extra square on either end).

TURING MACHINES

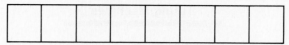

Figure B-1 A Turing-machine tape.

   (b) Each square on the tape has a '1' or a '0' printed on it at the start (this is the input).

3. The program that the person (or computer) memorized doesn't consist of complex instructions (such as "Find the word MULTIPLY on the tape"); instead, it consists of a finite sequence of instructions of the following five kinds:

   (a) START.

   (b) IF your state of mind is P
      and you are scanning symbol **S**
         THEN
           (i) Change **S** to **S**′.
           (ii) Change your state of mind to Q.

   (c) IF your state of mind is P
      and you are scanning symbol **S**
         THEN
           (i) Move 1 square to the right.
           (ii) Change your state of mind to Q.

   (d) IF your state of mind is P
      and you are scanning symbol **S**
         THEN
           (i) Move 1 square to the left.
           (ii) Change your state of mind to Q.

   (e) STOP.

Below, we shall make these instructions even more precise. The result of this is a "Turing machine," which may be imagined as a physical machine on wheels, with a unit for reading and writing on the tape and a "register" to indicate what state it is in.

Figure B-2 An imaginary, physical Turing machine.

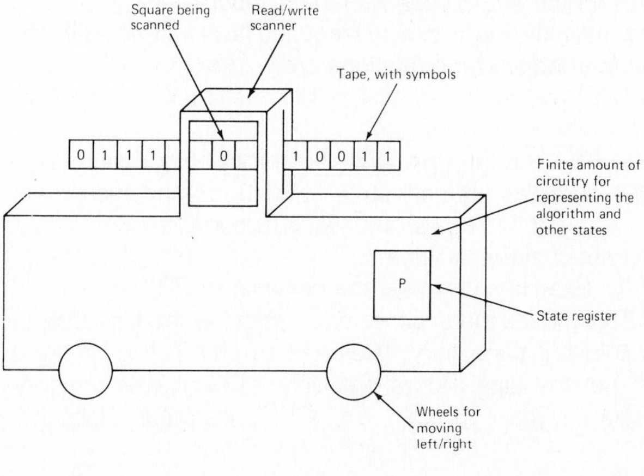

Square being
scanned

Read/write
scanner

Tape, with symbols

0 1 1 1   0   1 0 0 1 1

Finite amount of
circuitry for
representing the
algorithm and
other states

P

State register

Wheels for
moving
left/right

APPENDIX B

Turing Machines

A Turing machine can be defined as follows: It consists of a certain set, called the *memory set,* and a program constructed from elements of specified sets of *operations* and *tests.*

The memory set is the formal analog of the tape. Each element of the set consists of two items: (1) a string of '0's and '1's (representing the information stored on the tape) and (2) a positive integer (representing the symbol currently being scanned by the Turing machine). For instance,

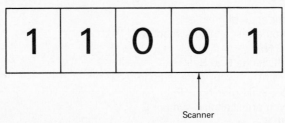

Scanner

Figure B-3   The Turing-machine tape represented by (11001, 4) or by 11001.

would be represented by the memory-set element

(11001, 4)

where the first element of this pair is the string and the second is the square being scanned, or by the symbol

11001

where the underline represents the position of the scanner. The "empty" tape—the tape with *no* little squares of paper—is represented by any element whose scanning number is 0; we'll represent the empty tape with the symbol e.

The Turing-machine programming language (TM) that we shall use consists of seven operations and four tests. The operations are:

1. START.
2. PRINT-0. This changes the symbol currently being scanned to 0. More precisely, PRINT-0 changes memory-state e to (0, 1) and memory-state $s_1 s_2 \ldots s_{i-1} s_i$ $s_{i+1} \ldots s_k$ to $s_1 s_2 \ldots s_{i-1} \underline{0} s_{i+1} \ldots s_k$. (Of course, if s_i were 0 to begin with, PRINT-0 would not change the tape.)
3. PRINT-1. (Exercise: Describe the behavior of PRINT-1.)
4. LEFT. This moves the scanner one symbol to the left, adding on a new square with a 0 in it if necessary. (*Remember:* Our Turing machine is on wheels; *it* moves, not the tape.) More precisely, LEFT leaves memory-state e alone; it changes $s_1 \ldots \underline{s_j} \ldots s_k$ to $s_1 \ldots \underline{s_{j-1}} s_j \ldots s_k$; and it changes $\underline{s_1} \ldots s_k$ to $\underline{0} s_1 \ldots s_k$.

5. RIGHT. This operation moves the scanner one symbol to the right, adding a new square with a 0 in it if necessary. That is, it leaves e alone; it changes $s_1 \ldots \underline{s_j} \ldots s_k$ to $s_1 \ldots s_j \underline{s_{j+1}} \ldots s_k$; and it changes $s_1 \ldots \underline{s_k}$ to $s_1 \ldots s_k \underline{0}$.

6. ERASE. This operation does nothing unless the scanner is at the left-hand end or the right-hand end of the tape, in which case it erases the symbol being scanned and cuts off the square. That is, ERASE leaves e and $s_1 \ldots \underline{s_j} \ldots s_k$ alone; but it changes $\underline{s_1} s_2 \ldots s_k$ to $\underline{s_2} \ldots s_k$, and it changes $s_1 \ldots s_{k-1} \underline{s_k}$ to $s_1 \ldots \underline{s_{k-1}}$; also, it causes a 1-square tape with only one symbol on it to disappear (that is, $\underline{s}$ becomes e).

7. STOP.

The tests are:

1. 0? and 1? These two test whether the symbol being scanned is 0 or 1. Formally, if the tape is e, then the result of the tests is FALSE; and if the tape is $s_1 \ldots \underline{s_j} \ldots s_k$, then the result is TRUE if $s_i = s$ and FALSE otherwise (where s is 0 or 1, depending on the test).

2. LEFTEND? Tests whether the scanner is at the left-hand end of the tape. If it is, or if the tape is empty, the test result is TRUE; otherwise, it is FALSE.

3. RIGHTEND? Tests whether the scanner is at the right-hand end of the tape. If it is, or if the tape is empty, the test result is TRUE; otherwise, it is FALSE.

Turing-Machine Programs

Let us see what some of our simple algorithms look like when translated into programs in TM.

Negation

We'll begin with the algorithm for FNEG, that is, for computing the truth value of the negation of a sentence (see Chapter 3). The first decision we need to make is how to "code" truth values so that they can be expressed on the tape. One obvious way is to represent a TRUE sentence with a 1-square tape containing a '1' and a FALSE sentence with a 1-square tape containing a '0'.

Next, we must decide what the output should look like. One possibility is to have our algorithm end with a 2-square tape whose first symbol is the original truth value and whose second symbol represents the negation of that truth value, with the scanner on the second symbol. (*Remember:* We can add new squares to our tape whenever we want.) Thus for input '1', the output would be '1$\underline{0}$', and for input '0', the output would be '0$\underline{1}$'.

So, we'll need to scan the input tape and, if there's a '$\underline{1}$', move right and print a '0', but if there's a '$\underline{0}$', we'll move right and print a '1'.

In TM we shall let the "states of mind" be represented by M_0, M_1, M_2, M_3, etc. We shall always begin (START) in the state of mind M_0. The program for computing FNEG in the manner we have just described is:

1. START.
2. IF you are in M_0 and are scanning 0,
      THEN
   (a) RIGHT.
   (b) Change state of mind to M_1.
3. IF you are in M_0 and are scanning 1,
      THEN
   (a) RIGHT.
   (b) Change state of mind to M_2.
4. IF you are in M_1 and are scanning 0,
      THEN
   (a) PRINT-1.
   (b) Change state of mind to M_2.
5. IF you are in M_2,
      THEN STOP.

Notice that you will never be in M_1 and scanning 1, so that possibility is not covered in the program.

It is easier to represent the program using a flowchart, where your position on the chart corresponds to a "state of mind":

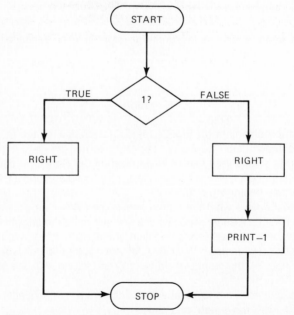

Figure B-4 TM program (in flowchart form) for computing the truth value of a negation.

The Turing machine begins by scanning the input tape. If it has '1', then the Turing machine moves right, automatically attaching a new square to the tape with a '0' already on it, and the scanner is over that square; so the output tape is '10'. On the other hand, if the input tape has '0', then the Turing machine moves right, adding on a square with '0', which is being scanned; it then prints a '1' on the scanned square, so the output tape is '01'.

Exercise

Suppose we use the same coding for the input, but we code the output as follows: If the input tape has '0', then the output tape has '1'; and if the input tape has '1', then the output tape has '0'. In other words, both input and output tapes have only one square (and so there is no record of the original truth value on the output tape). Write a Turing-machine program in flowchart form for FNEG, using this coding.

Conjunction

Now let's look at an algorithm in TM for FCNJ, that is, for computing the truth value of the conjunction of two sentences. Again, we need to decide on the input-output coding. A reasonable extension of the coding we used before would be this: The input tape has two squares, each containing a '0' or '1' to represent the truth values of two sentences, and the scanner is over the first square (that is, the leftmost square). The output tape will have three squares: the original two, unchanged, and a new one (being scanned) containing the truth value of the conjunction. Thus if the input is '01', the output will be '010'.

You should verify that the TM program in Figure B-5 does the job.

Exercises

Write TM programs in flowchart notation for each of the following problems:

1. An algorithm for FCNJ, starting with the test 1?, using the above input-output coding.
2. An algorithm for FCNJ using the "destructive" input-output coding, where, for instance, if the input tape is 01, the output will be 0.
3. An algorithm for FDSJ. Be sure to specify your input-output coding.
4. An algorithm for FCND.
5. An algorithm for FBIC.
6. An algorithm for FXOR.
7. An algorithm for FNOR.
8. An algorithm for FNAND.

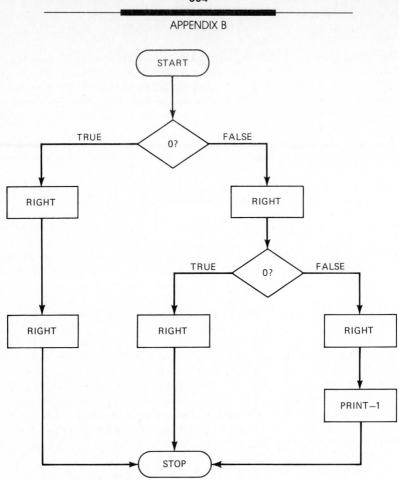

Figure B-5 TM program for computing the truth value of a conjunction.

9. An algorithm for adding two positive integers. Let the input-output coding be as follows: The addition problem $m + n$ will be representd by m '1's, followed by a '0', followed by n '1's. A nice notation for this is:

$$1^m 0 1^n$$

The output tape will consist of $m + n$ '1's, that is:

$$1^{m+n}$$

Palindromes

As a final example of TM programming, we shall sketch out a program that decides if the input tape contains a palindrome. A *palindrome* will be any string of '0's and '1's that reads the same backward and forward. For instance,

000
010
001100

are palindromes, but

01
110
0011110

are not. Clearly, a 1-square tape always contains a palindrome. It will be useful to consider the empty tape to be a palindrome too.

The input will be a tape containing the string to be tested, with the scanner on the first (leftmost) symbol. The output will be a 1-square tape with a '1' if the input is a palindrome and a '0' otherwise. Two examples are as follows:

Input	Output
101	1
100	0

The algorithm that we shall use is the following:

---

1. IF the tape is empty
   THEN OUTPUT '1' [since it is a palindrome].
2. IF the tape has only 1 square
   THEN OUTPUT '1' [since it is a palindrome].
3. IF the tape has 2 or more squares
   THEN
   (a) Compare the symbol in the leftmost square with the symbol in the rightmost square.
   (b) IF they match
       THEN
       (i) Erase both symbols.
       (ii) GO TO step 1.
   (c) IF they do not match
       THEN
       (i) Erase the tape.
       (ii) OUTPUT '0' [since it is not a palindrome].
4. STOP.

(You should try this algorithm on a few examples to convince yourself that it works.)

This time, we shall use top-down design and stepwise refinement to write the program (and we shall leave some of the details as exercises). To do this, we shall introduce a new flowchart symbol—a circle—to represent steps that will have to be refined into the basic TM operations and tests.

The top-level program is:

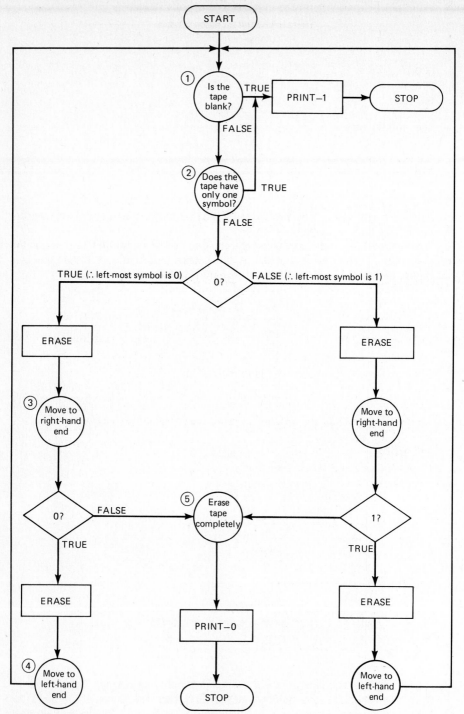

Figure B-6 TM program for the palindrome problem.

The circles labeled 1 to 5 represent procedures that must be refined. Here is the refinement of procedure 1:

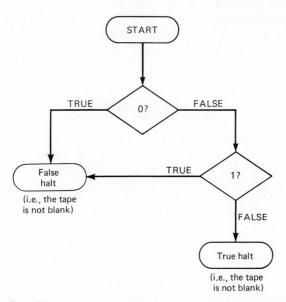

Figure B-7   TM program for procedure 1 of the palindrome program.

And here is the refinement of procedure 5:

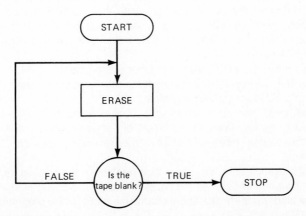

Figure B-8   TM program for procedure 5 of the palindrome program.

Exercises

10. Refine procedure 2.
11. Refine procedure 3.
12. Refine procedure 4.
13. Refine the given refinement of 5 (in Figure B-8).
14. Refine procedure 5 without using procedure 1. (*Hint:* Use LEFTEND?)

Church's Thesis

Let us consider the relationship between a Turing machine and our notion of an algorithm.

One version of *Church's thesis* (see Chapter 14), known as the *Church-Turing thesis,* says that our intuitive notion of a mechanical computation can be *defined* as any computation that can be carried out by a Turing machine. This cannot be proved (because our notion of a mechanical computation is intuitive and vague, and proofs require precise notions), but there is a substantial amount of evidence to suggest the following two points:

1. Any computation that seems intuitively "mechanical" can be carried out on a Turing machine.
2. Any computation that can be carried out on a Turing machine is intuitively "mechanical."

The main evidence for statement 2 is Turing's analysis of computation that we discussed in an earlier section. It seems, intuitively, that any computation that can be done by a Turing machine is intuitively mechanical.

We said that the thesis cannot be proved; but if it is false, then it *can* be falsified: If anyone were to deny the Church-Turing thesis, it would have to be because he or she denied statement 1, that is, claimed that there might be an intuitively mechanical procedure that a Turing machine could not carry out—that, perhaps, Turing machines, with all their limitations of size and of operations, were not powerful enough. (After all, those instructions seem rather simplistic, especially if the only symbols allowed are '0' and '1'.)

But there are two sorts of evidence in favor of statement 1. First, there is empirical evidence: All (intuitively mechanical) procedures that have been constructed so far can be translated into Turing-machine programs.

Second, all "rival" theories of what might count as being "mechanically computable" have turned out to be equivalent to the theory of Turing-machine computability.

Some of these other theories of what is "mechanically computable" are:

1. Church's lambda calculus—the notion he used in the original formulation of the thesis; it was later used as the basis for the programming language LISP.
2. Markov algorithms—which later became the basis for the programming language SNOBOL.

3. The theory of partial-recursive functions, which lies at the foundation of Gödel's incompleteness theorem, and which also can be considered to underlie much of the recent theory of "structured" programming.
4. The Herbrand-Gödel theory of recursion equations—which later became the basis for the programming language ALGOL (and thus, indirectly, its descendant Pascal).
5. The theory of register machines—which is a mathematical analogue of a "von Neumann" digital computer.

BIBLIOGRAPHY

Anderson, Alan Ross (ed.): *Minds and Machines* (Englewood Cliffs, N.J.: Prentice-Hall, 1964).

Boden, Margaret: *Artificial Intelligence and Natural Man* (New York: Basic Books, 1977).

Broad, C. D.: *The Mind and Its Place in Nature* (London: Routledge, 1962).

Church, Alonzo: *Introduction to Mathematical Logic* (Princeton, N.J.: Princeton Univ. Press, 1956).

Clark, Keith L., and Don F. Cowell: *Programs, Machines, and Computation* (London: McGraw-Hill, 1976).

Dennett, Daniel C.: *Brainstorms: Philosophical Essays on Mind and Psychology* (Montgomery, Vt.: Bradford Books, 1978).

Descartes, René: "Rules for the Direction of the Mind" (1628), in E. S. Haldane and G. R. T. Ross (trans. and eds.), *The Philosophical Works of Descartes,* Vol. I (London: Cambridge Univ. Press, 1970), pp. 1–77.

Dreyfus, Hubert: *What Computers Can't Do: The Limits of Artificial Intelligence,* rev. ed. (New York: Harper and Row, 1979).

Ennes, Harold E.: *Boolean Algebra for Computer Logic* (Indianapolis: Sams, 1978).

Gardner, Martin: *Logic Machines and Diagrams,* 2d ed. (Chicago: University of Chicago Press, 1982).

Haugeland, John (ed.): *Mind Design: Philosophy, Psychology, Artificial Intelligence* (Cambridge, Mass.: M.I.T. Press, 1981).

Hofstadter, Douglas R.: *Gödel, Escher, Bach: An Eternal Golden Braid* (New York: Basic Books, 1979).

Kasper, J., and S. Feller: *Digital Integrated Circuits: An Introduction for Students and Hobbyists* (Englewood Cliffs, N.J.: Prentice-Hall, 1983).

McCorduck, Pamela: *Machines Who Think: A Personal Inquiry into the History and Prospects of Artificial Intelligence* (San Francisco: Freeman, 1979).

Malvino, Albert Paul: *Digital Computer Electronics* (New York: McGraw-Hill, 1983).

Otto, Herbert R.: *The Linguistic Basis of Logic Translation* (Washington, D.C.: University Press of America, 1978).

BIBLIOGRAPHY

Raphael, Bertram: *The Thinking Computer: Mind Inside Matter* (San Francisco: Freeman, 1976).

Rich, Elaine: *Artificial Intelligence* (New York: McGraw-Hill, 1983).

Slagle, James R.: *Artificial Intelligence: The Heuristic Programming Approach* (New York: McGraw-Hill, 1971).

Turing, A. M.: "On Computable Numbers, with an Application to the Entscheidungsproblem," *Proceedings of the London Mathematical Society,* 42 (1937), 230–265.

———:"Computing Machinery and Intelligence" (1950), in Anderson (1964), pp. 4–30.

Weizenbaum, Joseph: *Computer Power and Human Reason: From Judgment to Calculation* (San Francisco: Freeman, 1976).

Winograd, Terry: *Language as a Cognitive Process,* Vol. I: *Syntax* (Reading, Mass: Addison-Wesley, 1983).

Winston, Patrick Henry: *Artificial Intelligence* (Reading, Mass.: Addison-Wesley, 1977).

INDEX

Absolute-value function (ABS), 77
Accessible line, 234
Ada, computer language, 15
Adders, 323–326
Addition, rule of, 185
Affirming the consequent, 112, 182
ALGOL, computer language, 339
Algorithms, 20–22, 27–31, 41–43, 48–50, 53–55, 91–98, 108–109, 112–125, 139, 146–147, 203–218, 223–229, 256–258, 302, 304, 327–339
  CNF-1, 139–141
  CNF-2, 140–141
  INFIX-TO-POLISH, 146–147
  PROOF-CHECKER, 204–218, 220–221
  PROOF-CHECKER-1, 217
  SENTENCE-CHECKER, 97–98, 208
  TRUTH-TABLE GENERATOR, xvi, 108–110, 139
  TRUTH-VALUE CALCULATOR, 91–97, 101, 103, 108, 114, 123, 257, 263
  VALIDITY/INVALIDITY DETERMINER, xvi, 112–114, 131, 257
  WANG'S ALGORITHM, xvii, 114–125, 129–131, 147, 266–268, 279, 303

Algorithms (*Cont.*):
  (*See also* Mechanical procedure)
AND (*see* Conjunction)
Antecedent, 68
Arguments, 3–7, 37, 134–136, 153–154, 158, 163–165, 251
Arithmetic, 323–326
Arithmetical functions, 43, 50, 55
Array, 105, 246
Artificial Intelligence, 16–17, 301
  (*See also* Mechanical theorem proving; Searches)
Assertion, 7
Assignment operation, 29
Associativity, 192
Assumptions, 166–168, 170
Asterisks, 166, 204
Atomic sentences, 45
Automated reasoning (*see* Mechanical reasoning)
Axiom, 157

Babbage, Charles, 15
Backtracking in a search, 245
Backward-looking strategy, 226–229
BASIC, computer language, xiii–xiv, 22, 64–65
Basic disjunctions, 138–139

BEGIN, comment, 173
Biconditional, 76–77, 84, 137, 189–191, 194
Binary adder (*see* Adders)
Boole, George, 8, 15, 65
Boolean algebra, 15, 65
Boolean operations, 64
Boolean values, 8
Boolean variables, 8
Bound occurrence of a variable, 256
Branches, 266–269
Breadth-first search, 231–232
Byron, Lord, 15

Calculus ratiocinator, 14
CHECK-LINE-STRUCTURE, procedure, 206–208, 217, 221
CHECK-RULE, procedure, 206, 208–213, 215, 217
CHECK-SENTENCE-STRUCTURE, procedure, 206, 208, 217
CHECK-SUBFORMULA, procedure, 97
CHECK-SUBPROOF, procedure, 206, 211, 213–217
Church, Alonzo, 302
Church's theorem, 302, 304–305, 309
Church's thesis, 305, 338–339
Circuit design, 313–326

Citation field, 205
Clauses, 309
CNF-1, algorithm, 139–141
CNF-2, algorithm, 140–141
Commands (*see* Instructions)
Comments in a derivation,
172–175
Commutativity, 192
Completeness, 175–178, 281
Computation, theory of,
328–329
Computational linguistics, 58
Computers:
design of, 17–20
giving instructions to, 18–20
history of, 13–16
(*See also* Turing machines)
Conclusion, 4–7, 224
Conclusion indicators, 4–5
Condition, 28
Conditional:
converse, 84
corresponding, 135–136
(*See also* Conditional
sentence)
Conditional ELIMination (*see*
ELIMination rules)
Conditional instruction, 28, 30,
68, 138
Conditional INTROduction
(*see* INTROduction rules)
Conditional sentence, 58,
68–75, 135–136, 180–185
Conjunct, 45
Conjunction, 44–52, 56–57,
82, 84, 137, 158–163,
316–317, 333
Conjunction ELIMination (*see*
ELIMination rules)
Conjunction INTROduction
(*see* INTROduction rules)
Conjunctive normal form
(CNF), 138–141, 307–308
Connectives (*see* Truth-
functional connectives)
Consequent, 68
affirming the, 112, 182
Consistency, 141–144
Constant, individual, 252–253,
258
Constructive dilemma (CD),
201
Containing proof, 232–233
Contingent sentence, 134–135
Contradiction, 134–135, 137,
141–143, 167, 306
Contrapositive, 136, 192
Control statements, 28–32

Converse conditional, 84
Converse non-conditional, 84
Correctness, logical and
factual, 6
Corresponding conditional,
135–136
Counter in algorithm TRUTH-
VALUE CALCULATOR,
92–93, 123, 257

Dagger, 81
Data structure, 204, 246–247
Data type, 29
Decidability, 302
Decision problem, 328
Deduction, 154
Deductive logic, 2–3, 6
Deductive system, 153–156
De Morgan's laws, 137, 192,
319
Denial, 38
(*See also* Negation)
Depth-first search, 231–232
Derivable rule of inference, 197
Derivation, 154, 158, 160–161,
163–165
Descartes, René, 2–3, 14
Disjunct, 52
Disjunction, 44, 52–57, 77–79,
81–82, 84, 137, 185–188,
317
basic disjunctions, 138–139
exclusive, 55–56, 77–79, 84,
86
inclusive, 55–56, 77–78,
81–82, 84
Disjunction ELIMination (*see*
ELIMination rules)
Disjunction INTROduction (*see*
INTROduction rules)
Disjunctive normal form (DNF),
138, 142, 151
Disjunctive syllogism (*see*
ELIMination rules, vELIM)
Distributivity, 192
Dossier, 263–273
Double negation, 43–44, 192
Dual of a sentence, 150

Either (*see* Disjunction)
ELIMination rules:
&ELIM, 161–163, 240–243
~ELIM, 171–172, 240–243
→ELIM, 180–185, 240–243
vELIM, 185–188, 240–243
↔ELIM, 189–191

ELIMination rules (*Cont.*):
∀ELIM, 283
∃ELIM, 287–289
ELIZA, computer program,
33
END comment, 173
Entscheidungsproblem
(decision problem), 328
Equality (*see* Identity)
Equivalence:
logical (*see* Logical
equivalence)
rule of replacement, 192
Exclusive disjunction, 55–56,
77–79, 84, 86
Existential generalization,
286–287
Existential instantiation,
287–289
Existential quantifier, 254,
259–260, 286–289
Existential quantifier
ELIMination (*see*
ELIMination rules)
Existential quantifier
INTROduction (*see*
INTROduction rules)
Exportation, 137–138, 192
Extensional characterization of
a function, 40–42, 105

Fallacy, 112, 182
FALSE, 8, 39
FBIC, 77, 84
FCND, 70–72, 84
FCNJ, 47–52, 64, 84
FDSJ, 53–55, 64, 84
Field of a derivation line, 204
First Counter (*see* Counter in
algorithm TRUTH-VALUE
CALCULATOR)
Flowchart, 22–27, 42
FNAND, 82, 84
FNEG, 40–43, 64, 84, 315
FNOR, 81–82, 84
FOR-loop, 30–31
Formula, 95–98, 254–256
hybrid, 88, 95
well-formed, 95, 255
(*See also* Well-formed
string)
Forward-looking strategy,
226–229
Free occurrence of a variable,
256, 287
Frege, Gottlob, 8
Full-adder (*see* Adders)

Functions, 40–45
  arithmetical, 43, 50, 55
  truth, 40, 44, 47–55, 105
FXOR, 78, 84

Game of stars and slashes,
  154–158, 176–177
Gate, logic, 315–320
Goal, 224–226
Gödel's theorem, 339
GOTO, 30–31, 50

Half-adder (*see* Adders)
Herbrand, Jacques, 309, 339
Higher-level language, 19–20
Hybrid formula, 88, 95
Hypothetical syllogism (HS),
  201

Idempotency, 192
Identity, 294
IF...THEN... (*see* Conditional
  instruction)
If...then... (*see* Conditional
  sentence)
Iff ("if and only if"), 76
Inclusive disjunction, 55–56,
  77–78, 81–82, 84
Inconsistency, 143, 167, 306
Indirect proof, 167
Individual, 252–254
  representative, 263–264
Individual constant, 252–253,
  258
Individual variable, 253–254,
  258
Inference (*see* Rules, of
  inference)
Infix notation, 144–145
INFIX-TO-POLISH, algorithm,
  146–147
Innermost subformula, 90–94,
  96–97, 122
INPUT, 23–24, 29
Instances, 258, 283, 287
Instructions, 18–32
Intensional characterization of
  a function, 41
INTROduction rules:
  &INTRO, 158–160, 240–243
  ~INTRO, 165–168, 170–171,
    240–243
  →INTRO, 180–185,
    240–243
  vINTRO, 185–188, 240–243

INTROduction rules (*Cont.*):
  ⟷ INTRO, 189–191
  ∀INTRO, 284–286
  ∃INTRO, 286–287
Invalidity, 6–7, 110, 112,
  295–296
Inverter, 314–315

Jevons, William Stanley, 15
Justification in a derivation line,
  160, 167

Karnaugh maps, 322

Labyrinth (*see* Maze)
Lambda calculus, 338
Language:
  higher-level, 19–20
  machine, 19
  (*See also* Symbolization of
    an English sentence)
Laws of thought, 1
Leibniz, Gottfried Wilhelm, 2,
  14–15
Limitations:
  of predicate logic, 302–305
  of PROOF-GIVER, 240
Line-number field, 160,
  204–205
LISP, computer language, 129,
  338
Lists and list-pairs in WANG'S
  ALGORITHM, 115–120,
  129–131, 266–270
Logic, 1
  mathematics and, 1–3
  of sentences, 37
Logic gate, 315–320
Logical equivalence, 136–152,
  175, 177–178, 192, 194
Logically true (*see* Tautology)
LOGO, computer language,
  129
Lovelace, Lady Ada, 15
Lull, Ramon, 14

Machine language, 19
Macros in computer
  programming, 197
Main connective, 122–123,
  129–131, 146–147
MAIN-CONNECTIVE,
  procedure, 122–123,
  129–131, 146, 279–280

Marquand, Allan, 15
Material conditional, 68–75, 84
Material non-conditional, 84
Mathematics and logic, 1–3
Matrix (*see* Array)
MAXimum function, 55
Maze, 224–227
Mechanical procedure, 20–22,
  327
Mechanical reasoning, 14–17
Mechanical theorem proving,
  305–311
Memory set, 330
Method, 227
Minimal model, 265
MINimum function, 50–51
Model, 263–273, 302–304
  (*See also* Situations)
Modular design, 28
Modus ponens, 111, 180
Modus tollens (MT), 196–197
Molecular sentence, 45

NAND, 58, 82, 84, 86, 137, 178,
  317
Natural deduction, 153–222,
  281–299
Natural deduction system,
  157–158
Necessary condition, 75–76
Negation, 38–45, 52, 56–57,
  137, 165–168, 170–172,
  331–333
  double, 43–44, 192
Negation ELIMination (*see*
  ELIMination rules)
Negation INTROduction (*see*
  INTROduction rules)
Neither...nor... (*see* NOR)
Node of a tree, 230
NOR, 58, 81–82, 84, 86, 178,
  317–318
Normal form, 138–141
  conjunctive, 138–141,
    307–308
  disjunctive, 138–141
NOT, 64, 315–316

OBTAIN Q, procedure, 234
Only if, 74
Operation, 22, 28–29, 330
Or (*see* Disjunction)
OUTPUT, 23–24, 29

Palindromes, 334–338

Parentheses, 92, 123, 257
Pascal, Blaise, 15
Pascal, computer language, xiii-xiv, 22, 64–65, 101, 220–221, 339
Peirce, Charles S., 15
PL/I, computer language, 101
Polish notation, 93, 144–147, 151–152
   reverse, 151
Postfix notation (reverse Polish notation), 151
Predicate letter, 252
Prefix notation (see Polish notation)
PREMISE, 158, 160, 168
Premise indicators, 4–5
Premises of an argument, 4–7, 166, 224
Procedure, 97, 169
Program, xiii, 22, 27
Program design language, xiv, 27–32
Proof, 114, 154, 166–167, 204, 223–249
   (See also Derivation; Subproof)
PROOF-CHECKER, algorithm, 204–218, 220–221
PROOF-CHECKER-1, algorithm, 217
PROOF-GIVER method, 223–229, 305, 310–311
Property, 252–254
Proposition, 7, 37–38
Pruning of a search tree, 231

Quantification theory, 251–299
Quantified formula, 256–257
Quantifier negation rules, 290–295
Quantifiers, 254–258
   existential, 254, 259–260, 286–289
   universal, 254, 260–263, 282–286
Queue, 130

Reasoning, 1, 16–17
   mechanical, 14–17
Recursive functions, 339
Reductio ad absurdum, 167
Register machines, 339
Relations, 270–273

Replacement, rules of, 191–196, 243–245
Representative individual, 263–264
Resolution, 306–309
Resolvant, 308
RETURN, 168–170
Reverse Polish notation (RPN), 151
Rhetoric, 3
Rule of resolution (see Resolution)
Rule field of a derivation line, 204–205
Rules:
   of inference, 154, 157–159, 179–201, 281–299
   of replacement (RR), 191–196, 243–245
   truth-preserving (see Truth-preserving rules)
   for well-formedness, 255
   (See also ELIMination rules; INTROduction rules)

Satisfaction, 263
Satisfiability, 141–144
Scope of a quantifier, 255–256
Search space, 230
Search tree, 229–232
   pruning of, 231
Searches, 229–240
   breadth-first, 231–232
   depth-first, 231–232
SEND, 168–169
SENTENCE-CHECKER, algorithm, 97–98, 208
Sentence field, 204
Sentence letters, 8–9
Sentence logic, 37
Sentences, 7–9, 37–38, 45, 52, 56, 82, 95–98, 134–135, 144, 157, 256
   atomic, 45
   conditional (see Conditional sentence)
   contingent, 134–135
   logic of, 37
   symbolization of (see Symbolization of an English sentence)
Sentential logic, 16, 37–38, 45
   (See also Sentences)
Shannon, Claude, 16
Sheffer stroke function (see NAND)
Simple sentence, 45

Simultaneously satisfiable, 142–143, 167
Situations, 105, 110
   (See also Model)
SNOBOL, computer language, 328
Soundness, 6–7
Stack, 120, 130
Stanhope, Charles, 15
Stars (see Asterisks)
Stars and slashes, game of, 154–158, 176–177
START, 22
State of a Turing machine, 328–331
Statements, 7
   control, 28–32
Stepwise refinement, 21–22
STOP, 22, 30–31
Strategies, 224, 226–232
String, 37
Stroke function (see NAND)
Structured programming, 329
Subformula, 88, 90–94, 227
   innermost, 90–94, 96–97, 122
Subprocedure, 28, 169
Subproof, 165–171, 232–234
Subproof-depth field in a derivation line, 204
Sub-subproof (see Subproof)
Sufficient condition, 75–76
Suffix notation (see Reverse Polish notation)
Switches, 16, 314
   (See also Circuit design)
Symbolization of an English sentence, 58, 72–75, 78, 254, 259–263, 270–276

Tape of a Turing machine, 328–330
Task list, 229
Tautology, 134–137, 140, 194, 306
TEST, procedure in WANG'S ALGORITHM, 121–122, 279
Theorem, 157, 177, 298, 301–311
TM, Turing machine programming language, 330–331
Top-down approach, 21, 28
Translation (see Symbolization of an English sentence)